BACTERIOLOGY RESEARCH DEVELOPMENTS

LISTERIA INFECTIONS

EPIDEMIOLOGY, PATHOGENESIS AND TREATMENT

BACTERIOLOGY RESEARCH DEVELOPMENTS

Additional books in this series can be found on Nova's website
under the Series tab.

Additional e-books in this series can be found on Nova's website
under the e-book tab.

ALLERGIES AND INFECTIOUS DISEASES

Additional books in this series can be found on Nova's website
under the Series tab.

Additional e-books in this series can be found on Nova's website
under the e-book tab.

LISTERIA INFECTIONS

EPIDEMIOLOGY, PATHOGENESIS AND TREATMENT

ANDINO ROMANO

AND

CARMINE F. GIORDANO

EDITORS

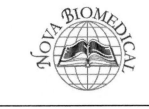

Nova Science Publishers, Inc.
New York

For permission to use material from this book please contact us:
Telephone 631-231-7269; Fax 631-231-8175
Web Site: http://www.novapublishers.com

NOTICE TO THE READER

The Publisher has taken reasonable care in the preparation of this book, but makes no expressed or implied warranty of any kind and assumes no responsibility for any errors or omissions. No liability is assumed for incidental or consequential damages in connection with or arising out of information contained in this book. The Publisher shall not be liable for any special, consequential, or exemplary damages resulting, in whole or in part, from the readers' use of, or reliance upon, this material. Any parts of this book based on government reports are so indicated and copyright is claimed for those parts to the extent applicable to compilations of such works.

Independent verification should be sought for any data, advice or recommendations contained in this book. In addition, no responsibility is assumed by the publisher for any injury and/or damage to persons or property arising from any methods, products, instructions, ideas or otherwise contained in this publication.

This publication is designed to provide accurate and authoritative information with regard to the subject matter covered herein. It is sold with the clear understanding that the Publisher is not engaged in rendering legal or any other professional services. If legal or any other expert assistance is required, the services of a competent person should be sought. FROM A DECLARATION OF PARTICIPANTS JOINTLY ADOPTED BY A COMMITTEE OF THE AMERICAN BAR ASSOCIATION AND A COMMITTEE OF PUBLISHERS.

Additional color graphics may be available in the e-book version of this book.

Library of Congress Cataloging-in-Publication Data

ISBN: 978-1-62081-639-4

Library of Congress Control Number: 2012936694

Published by Nova Science Publishers, Inc. † New York

Contents

Preface

Microbial food-borne illnesses have a great impact not only on public health but also represent high economic costs for many countries around the world. Listeria monocytogenes, is a gram-positive facultative intracellular pathogen. In this book, the authors discuss the epidemiology, pathogenesis and treatment of Listeria infections. Topics include the behavior of L. monocytogenes in Greek PDO cheeses and preventing the pathogen's proliferation; epidemic clones of Listeria monocytogenes; description of outbreaks, pathogenesis and technology for controlling Listeria; sublethal damage in Listeria monocytogenes after non-thermal treatments and implications for food safety; and Listeria monocytogenes in RTE fermented meat and smoked fish products.

Chapter I - Among the numerous traditional cheese varieties produced throughout Greece today, 21 cheeses have been granted the Protected Designation of Origin (PDO) status, whereas others are awaiting recognition. The Greek PDO cheeses include all types of cheeses (hard, semi-hard and soft cheeses). Several studies worldwide have reported the occurrence of *Listeria* spp. including *Listeria monocytogenes* in raw milk from sheep and goats. The majority of the Greek PDO cheeses are manufactured by a mixture of sheep and goat milk, which can be used raw, or after pasteurization. According to the European Commission Regulation (EC) 2073/2005 and its amendment by Regulation (EC) 1441/2007 food business operators are responsible for ensuring product compliance with the new food safety criteria including those specified for the food-borne pathogen *L. monocytogenes*. The ability of *L. monocytogenes* to proliferate during the manufacture and storage of permissive ready-to-eat foods is probably the most important factor regarding the risk for listeriosis. Currently, there are published studies pertaining to the behavior of *L. monocytogenes* in seven PDO cheeses (Feta, Galotyri, Graviera, Kasseri, Katiki, Manouri and Pichtogalo Chanion). This chapter aims at reviewing the available scientific literature regarding the behavior of *L. monocytogenes* in these Greek PDO cheeses, as well as the different interventions that have been proposed aiming at preventing the pathogen's proliferation.

Chapter II - Although many different serotypes of *Listeria monocytogenes* have been isolated from foods, only a few such as 1/2a, 1/2b, and 4b account for the vast majority of clinical cases, and in particular most outbreaks of listeriosis have involved a small number of closely related clones in serotypes 1/2a and 4b. An epidemic clone (EC) of *L. monocytogenes* has been defined as groups of isolates that are genetically related and presumably of a common ancestor, but are implicated in different, geographically and temporally unrelated outbreaks. Since the introduction of this concept in 2002, four ECs have been recognized: ECI, ECII, and ECIV in serotype 4b and ECIII in serotype 1/2a. Most recently, in 2011, a novel serotype 1/2a EC that had been causing disease in Canada for the past twenty years was detected and designated as ECV. As *L. monocytogenes* continues to spread throughout the world and cause many different outbreaks, it is reasonable to assume that other novel ECs could be identified in the future. In order to control *L. monocytogenes*, determining the routes by which ECs and outbreak clones (OCs) are transmitted to foods will be extremely helpful. Consequently, the availability of subtyping assays capable of discerning closely related ECs and OCs is extremely important. In the past few years, the number and quality of subtyping assays has increased thanks to the development of DNA-based methods such as pulsed-field gel electrophoresis (PFGE), considered the gold-standard for its high discriminatory power (i.e. the ability to correctly differentiate unrelated strains). PFGE has proven to be a very accurate and reproducible method in subtyping *L. monocytogenes*. However, new sequence-based techniques, such as multilocus-sequence typing (MLST) and single nucleotide polymorphism (SNP) typing, are also currently being used. In particular, multi-virulence-locus sequence typing (MVLST) has been able to accurately identify and differentiate all five ECs of *L. monocytogenes*. This technique also proved very useful in the identification of ECs, when PFGE failed to identify strains belonging to the same ECs due to the presence of different PFGE profiles. Therefore, the use of novel DNA-sequence-based molecular subtyping strategies able to correctly determine the clonal relationship among different isolates is essential to accurately recognize outbreaks and epidemics and identify their routes of transmission. This chapter will review the five currently known ECs of *L. monocytogenes*, including listeriosis outbreaks caused by these ECs during the past few years, and the latest molecular subtyping methods developed to identify them.

Chapter III - Microbial food-borne illnesses have a great impact not only in public health but also represent high economic costs for many countries around the world. *Listeria monocytogenes,* a Gram-positive facultative intracellular pathogen, is estimated to cause nearly 1,600 illnesses each year in the United States. Listeriosis may have different clinical syndromes from a non-invasive form in healthy human usually associated to mild gastroenteritis to severe invasive form, especially during pregnancy and in people with compromised immune system. In this case, it can be a serious and sometimes fatal disease. The transmission can occur by different ways, being the most important one the consumption of contaminated food, especially ready-to-eat products. Many efforts have been made in order to control o minimize the presence of this pathogen in food and food processing areas. Besides the new antilisterial technologies that are being explored such as surface pasteurization or ozone treatments, antimicrobial peptides called bacteriocins produced by GRAS microorganisms such as lactic acid bacteria arise as a potential solution in this field. There are many *Listeria*-active bacteriocins described so far in the literature and products containing purified or semi-purified bacteriocins are already in the market. Moreover, some anti-listerial bacteriocins proved to be active not only in food environments but also in listeria-infected mice models. In this chapter, an updated description of outbreaks, pathogenesis as well as the new technology for controlling *Listeria* is presented.

Chapter IV - The presence of microorganisms in foods during production, packaging, transport and storage is unavoidable. Since January 2005, Regulation 178/2002/EC or General Food Law requires the traceability of the food chain in all its stages (EU, 2002). This directive will enforce the introduction of security mechanisms and controls for foodstuffs.

One of the microorganisms of concern, mainly for ready-to-eat foods, is *Listeria monocytogenes*. Between 2002 and 2006 there was a significant increase in reported cases of human listeriosis in Member States of the European Union (EU) (EFSA, 2007). In 2007 there were 1,639 reported cases, of which 1,635 were subsequently confirmed, in 29 countries. The rate of global reporting was 0.35 cases per 100,000 inhabitants. The proportion of samples exceeding the legal limit for *Listeria monocytogenes* in Member States was higher in ready-to-eat foods based on fish, followed by meat products and cheeses (EFSA and ECDC, 2011). Consequently, knowledge of microbial inactivation and growth behavior is very important for food safety and shelf-life assessment. Important aspects that should be considered as emerging risks are the changes that could take place after sublethal injury, i.e., changes in virulence. This review aims to evaluate *Listeria monocytogenes* inactivation and growth in foodstuffs by simulating the supply chain in order to verify the relation existing between the various treatments that could be used by the industry to increase product lifetime without risk to consumers and sublethal damage.

Chapter V - *Listeria monocytogenes* is a pathogen that affects animals and human beings; it can produce potentially fatal infections in susceptible individuals. This bacterium can cause miscarriages in pregnant women and meningitis in newborns, children and adults who are immunosuppressed. Most cases of Listeriosis are sporadic; although outbreaks have been described due to food consumption. The ability of *L. monocytogenes* to resist stressful environmental conditions makes this pathogen a food industry concern.

Chapter VI - *Listeria monocytogenes* is an ubiquitous organism, widely distributed in the environment. The principal reservoirs are soil, forage and water. Other reservoirs include healthy humans and animals or infected domestic and wild animals. *L.monocytogenes* is also the etiologic agent of listeriosis, which occurs in humans and animals. Since the beginning of the 1980's *L. monocytogenes* has been recognized as an emerging food-borne pathogen after several sporadic and epidemic cases of listeriosis occurred in Europe and the US. Recently the incidence of sporadic cases rose again in Europe. Two main forms of listeriosis have been described in humans: febrile gastroenteritis in healthy individuals and life-threatening invasive infections in susceptible individuals, with the latter posing a serious problem to public health. In fact, invasive human listeriosis is a rare but severe infection, typically causing septicemia, encephalitis and meningitis in defined high-risk groups: young, old, pregnant and immune-compromised, the so called "YOPI". Listeriosis is the fifth most common zoonotic disease in Europe, less common than other diseases (eg. by *Escherichia coli* 0157:H7, *Campylobacter jejuni* or *Salmonella* spp.). It has an incidence of 3.3 cases per 1.000.000 population per year, an estimated case fatality rate of 20 up to 30% and the highest hospitalization rate (90%) of all food -borne pathogens with additional long term sequelae in some patients. In Europe, 55.6% of all human listeriosis cases are reported in patients aged above 60 years, approximately 2.5 times higher than those reported in any other age group. Therefore, although this disease continues to occur in association with pregnancy, it is now predominantly an infection of immune-compromised individuals amongst the older sections of the populations. Data on listeriosis in USA show a similar marked reduction-trend. The majority (99%) of the infections caused by *L.monocytogenes* are thought to be foodborne. The pathogen is able to survive at a broad range of temperature (from 0 to 45°C) and pH (from 4.5 to 9.0), high salt concentrations (10%) and low water activity values (0.92). These properties, together with the severity of human listeriosis infections, make *L. monocytogenes* of particular concern for manufacturers of cold stored "ready to eat" (RTE) foods (Romanova et al., 2002; Van Coillie et al., 2004; Shen et al., 2006). RTE food is a large, heterogeneous category of foodstuffs and can be subdivided in many different ways. According to the Codex definition, RTE include any food that is normally consumed in its raw state or any food handled, processed, mixed, cooked or otherwise prepared into a form in which it is normally consumed without further processing. *L.monocytogenes* has been isolated from a wide variety of RTE products capable of supporting its growth and is responsible for numerous outbreaks associated with the consumption of RTE meat, poultry, dairy, fish and vegetable products. Seafood products have been reported to be contaminated with *L.monocytogenes* and several reports of outbreaks or sporadic cases have been linked to these products in particular with cold or hot-smoked salmon, "gravad" salmon, shrimps, mussels, fermented fish, fish and seafood salads. Concerning RTE meat products, a large outbreak occurred in 2008 in Canada causing 22 deaths and 57 confirmed cases. Although fermented pork meat RTE products as dry and semi-dry sausages have been rarely implicated in food poisoning, more risks should be linked to the consumption of these products because mainly in the manufacturing of traditional products, an empirical application of the hurdles technology often occurs. In the following, through an up-to-date review of (personal and non) published data, the epidemiology of *L.monocytogenes* in two selected RTE food categories will be discussed: fermented meat and smoked fish products. Fermented meat products are often contaminated and are produced without any lethal processing step while smoked fish products (in particular cold smoked ones) are frequently contaminated, have no lethal processing steps and permits growth during an extended storage period.

Chapter VII - The incidence of human listeriosis in Navarra (Spain) was monitored during two different periods of time (1995-2005 and 2006-2011) by active surveillance in collaboration with the main hospitals within this region. A total of 72 cases of invasive listeriosis were detected, with an average incidence rate of 0.75/100,000 inhabitants. The incident rate shows a tendency to increase, as the first period (40 cases within 11 years) showed a rate of 0.65/100,000 while the second period (32 cases within 6 years) showed a rate of 0.86/100,000. Over the whole period studied, 44.4% of the cases were diagnosed among aged population (32 cases out 72), the group most affected by listeriosis, while case fatality (including fetal death) was 57.9% in pregnant women (n=11 out of 19 pregnancy-associated cases). Most of the isolated strains belonged to serotype 4b (n=38 out of 65 strains; 58.5%), but a significant increase of 1/2a serotype has been observed in recent years ($P \leq 0.05$). In addition, serotype 1/2c was isolated from a clinical case, and to the best of our knowledge, it is the first clinical isolation of this serotype in the region. In this chapter, the epidemiology of human listeriosis and how to improve the current Spanish surveillance system will be discussed.

Chapter VIII - Listeria is a motile, Gram-positive, rod-shaped coccobacillus. It is a non-sporeforming, facultatively anaerobic bacterium that can cause a life-threatening disease to both humans and animals known as Listeriosis. Listeria can frequently be isolated from soil, water, food products and vegetation. It is a major food-borne pathogen worldwide, accounting for about 28% of food-related deaths in the USA alone. In 2006, Listeriosis was reported in 23 European Union Member States and it ranked fifth among the most common zoonotic infections in Europe after Campylobacter, Salmonella, Yersinia and Verotoxin-Producing *Escherichia coli* (VTEC) infections. The most pathogenic species of Listeria is *Listeria monocytogenes* that often causes food-borne infections in immuno-compromised hosts, including newborns and the elderly. As a facultative intracellular parasitic bacterium,

L. monocytogenes invades a variety of host cells, such as hepatocytes, fibroblasts and epithelial cells, multiplying in the cytoplasm of these cells. This pathogen is one of the reasons of meningoencephalitis and abortion in ruminants. In neonates, it is the third most common cause of bacterial meningitis after *E. coli* and *Streptococcus agalactiae*. In most Listeria infections cases, the symptoms spontaneously clear in about seven days. However, patients at high risk such as pregnant women require antimicrobial treatment to prevent halt and development of more severe diseases. The duration of antimicrobial treatment depends on the severity of the infection. In Listeriosis treatment, the initial choice of antimicrobials is usually Ampicillin. Some studies also reported a successful treatment using the synergism present in the Trimethoprim-sulfamethoxazole preparations.

Chapter IX - Based on long-term monitoring studies carried out among wild ungulates and aquatic organisms living in woodland and hunting areas and freshwater basins of Russia, we determined a carrier state for both pathogenic and nonpathogenic Listeria species of sika deer, red deer, wild boar, as well as herbivorous and carnivorous fish species. Among the eight currently known listeria species, only two ones, namely Listeria innocua and Listeria monocytogenes have been found in hot- and cold-blooded representatives of the fauna, with Listeria innocua being most often isolated from the samples tested. The prevalence rates among aquatic organisms were 0.8% for L. monocytogenes and 5.2% for L. innocua, while in wild cloven-hoofed species the rates were 2.2 to 12% and 1.5 to 29%, respectively. For wild cloven-hoofed animals, listeria in most cases were found in feces, and only in two cases the agent was found in brain and lymph node of a hunted sika deer, and in the liver of a died wild boar. The carriage state levels among cloven-hoofed species significantly depended on the forms of economic activities and compliance with sanitation requirements. Among fish, the carrier state for listeria was determined in both herbivorous and carnivorous fish species. L. monocytogenes was mainly found in bream, carp, white bream and perch, while L. innocua in bream, pike, white bream, rudd, crucian carp and perch. Listeria of both pathogenic and nonpathogenic species were most frequently found in fish skin and gill tissues. The carried out investigations also indicated that the soil in feeding grounds and rotting plant residues are natural reservoirs for listeria, with the immigration of juvenile fish not checked for listeria carrier state and carcasses of drowned listeria-carrying wildlife being another source of listeria introduction into aquatic fauna of freshwater basins, beside the known ones. In order to identify phylogenetic relationships among the identified isolates, a pulse-electrophoresis of a restricted chromosomal DNA (REA-PFGE) was carried out. The results of the investigations into genetic variability among the isolates collected from wild cloven-hoofed animals using REA-PFGE revealed a variety of pulse electrotypes, suggesting multiple sources of infection. In freshwater fish populations a circulation of three L. monocytogenes clonal variants was found, with the pulse-electrotype isolates as found in different fish species, caught in the waters of the same river, having 100% coincidence. In addition, the pulse electrotype of a perch isolate was identical to a restriction profile of an isolate from sika deer feces found in the same region.

In: Listeria Infections
Editors: A. Romano and C. F. Giordano
ISBN: 978-1-62081-639-4
© 2012 Nova Science Publishers, Inc.

Chapter I

The Behavior of *Listeria monocytogenes* during the Manufacture and Storage of Greek Protected Designation of Origin (PDO) Cheeses

Apostolos S. Angelidis,[1] and Alexandros Govaris[2]*
[1]Laboratory of Milk Hygiene and Technology,
Faculty of Veterinary Medicine, Aristotle University of Thessaloniki,
Thessaloniki, Greece
[2]Laboratory of Hygiene of Foods of Animal Origin,
Faculty of Veterinary Medicine, University of Thessaly, Karditsa, Greece

Abstract

Among the numerous traditional cheese varieties produced throughout Greece today, 21 cheeses have been granted the Protected Designation of Origin (PDO) status, whereas others are awaiting recognition. The Greek PDO cheeses include all types of cheeses (hard, semi-hard and soft cheeses).

Several studies worldwide have reported the occurrence of *Listeria* spp. including *Listeria monocytogenes* in raw milk from sheep and goats. The majority of the Greek PDO cheeses are manufactured by a mixture of sheep and goat milk, which can be used raw, or after pasteurization.

According to the European Commission Regulation (EC) 2073/2005 and its amendment by Regulation (EC) 1441/2007 food business operators are responsible for ensuring product compliance with the new food safety criteria including those specified

* Correspondence: Dr Alexandros Govaris, Laboratory of Hygiene of Foods of Animal Origin, Faculty of Veterinary Medicine, University of Thessaly, 224 Trikalon Street, 43100 Karditsa, Greece. Tel. +30 24410 66086, Fax: +30 24410 66087 Email: agovaris@vet.uth.gr

for the food-borne pathogen *L. monocytogenes*. The ability of *L. monocytogenes* to proliferate during the manufacture and storage of permissive ready-to-eat foods is probably the most important factor regarding the risk for listeriosis.

Currently, there are published studies pertaining to the behavior of *L. monocytogenes* in seven PDO cheeses (Feta, Galotyri, Graviera, Kasseri, Katiki, Manouri and Pichtogalo Chanion). This chapter aims at reviewing the available scientific literature regarding the behavior of *L. monocytogenes* in these Greek PDO cheeses, as well as the different interventions that have been proposed aiming at preventing the pathogen's proliferation.

Introduction

Cheese is a highly nutritious food and a great variety of cheeses are manufactured throughout the world. In Greece there are several traditional cheeses produced at the industrial or artisanal scale both in the mainland, as well as in the Greek islands (Anifantakis, 1991; Litopoulou-Tzanetaki and Tzanetakis, 2011). Twenty one of these traditional Greek cheeses have been granted Protected Designation of Origin (PDO) status (European Commission, 1996, 2002, 2011). As is the case for other Mediterranean countries, PDO cheeses are food commodities bearing strong cultural, social and economic importance. The milk used for PDO cheesemaking should be of good quality, collected from lactating breeds of ruminants raised in austerely specified geographical regions at least 10 days after parturition, and the use of condensed milk, milk powder, caseinates, milk protein concentrates, preservatives or colorants is prohibited (Greek Codex of Foodstuffs and Beverages, 2009).

In general, cheeses can be classified using various classification schemes such as those based on their final moisture content, or their technology of manufacture.

**Table 1. Physicochemical specifications and characteristics
of selected PDO Greek cheeses**

Cheese	Cheese type	Milk type[1]	Ripening (days)[2]	Moisture (%)[3]	FDM (%)[4]
Feta	Soft, white-brined	O (30% C)	60	56	43
Galotyri	Soft, acid-curd	O, C, O/C	60[5]	75	40
Graviera Agrafon	Hard	O (30% C)	90	38	40
Graviera Naxou	Hard	B (20% C/O)	90	38	40
Graviera Kritis	Hard	O (20% C)	90	38	40
Kasseri	Semi-hard	O (20% C)	90	45	40
Katiki Domokou	Soft, acid-curd	C, C/O	n/a	75	40
Manouri	Soft, whey-cheese	O, C, O/C	n/a	60	70
Pichtogalo Chanion	Soft, acid-curd	C, O, C/O	n/a	65	50

[1] B, bovine milk; C, caprine milk; O, ovine milk. Percentages added in parentheses refer to the maximum allowable content of the alternative milk in the milk mixture.
[2] The "ripening" of commercially produced Galotyri is much shorter (*ca.* 1 week or less).
[3] Maximum values imposed by the Greek Codex of Foodstuffs and Beverages.
[4] Minimum values imposed by the Greek Codex of Foodstuffs and Beverages.

Based on their moisture content the 21 Greek PDO cheeses can be classified as hard cheeses (Graviera Agrafon, Graviera Naxou, Graviera Kritis, Kefalograviera, Ladotyri

Mytilinis and San Michali), semi-hard cheeses (Batzos, Formaela Arachovas Parnassou, Kasseri, Metsovone and Sfela) and soft cheeses (Anevato, Feta, Galotyri, Kalathaki Limnou, Katiki Domokou, Kopanisti, Manouri, Pichtogalo Chanion, Xynomyzithra Kritis and Xygalo Siteias). Table 1 presents the specifications outlined in the Greek Codex of Foodstuffs and Beverages (2009) pertaining to the physicochemical characteristics of the Greek PDO cheeses discussed in this chapter, whereas Table 2 presents physicochemical data retrieved from the literature on these PDO cheeses. The microbiological safety of most cheeses is dependent on some crucial factors such as the application (or absence thereof) of thermal treatment (thermization, pasteurization) to the raw milk, growth of lactic acid bacteria, the rate and extent of acidification during cheese manufacture and ripening, heating of curd in certain cheese types, the concentration of the salt in the aqueous phase (SWP) of the cheese and the extent and type of microbial contamination(s) during the various steps of cheesemaking.

Raw milk can contain low levels of *L. monocytogenes* (Greenwood et al., 1991; Rodriguez et al., 1994; Meyer-Broseta et al., 2003). The pasteurization of raw milk, however, which inactivates the low levels of *L. monocytogenes*, is not sufficient to eliminate later risks of *L. monocytogenes* contamination in dairy products. Indeed, the pathogen is often isolated from the food-processing environment, including cheese factories (Kornacki and Gurtler, 2007; Kousta et al., 2010), and several outbreaks of listeriosis have been attributed to the consumption of cheeses (mostly soft cheeses) contaminated with *L. monocytogenes* after manufacturing (Linan et al. 1988; Alterkruse et al., 1998; De Buyser et al., 2001; Lunden et al., 2004; Dewaal et al., 2006). Owing to their technology of manufacture and their resulting physicochemical properties, soft, unripened cheeses present a higher incidence and potential for growth or survival of *L. monocytogenes* than other cheese varieties and are considered foods with an increased risk for listeriosis (Schuchat et al., 1992). Hence, a recent scientific report of the European Food Safety Authority (EFSA) proposed that each Member State of the EU should conduct a survey on *L. monocytogenes* in selected categories of ready-to-eat (RTE) foods (including soft cheeses) at retail (EFSA, 2009). In order to satisfy the EFSA requirements, a study involving samples of soft cheeses available in the Greek retail market was conducted recently. A total of 137 soft cheese samples were tested for *L. monocytogenes* as well as other *Listeria* species both qualitatively and quantitatively. None of the cheeses analyzed were found positive for *L. monocytogenes* (0%; 95% CI = 0.0 - 2.2%). Three samples (2.2%; 95% CI = 0.5 - 6.3%) were positive for other *Listeria* spp. with populations ranging from <5 to 4.5 x 10^2 CFU/g (Angelidis et al., 2012). The reported prevalence estimates of *L. monocytogenes* from studies conducted on soft and fresh cheeses in different countries are quite variable. Estimates range from 0% to values as high as 87%, with the majority of studies reporting prevalence estimates below 10% (Lianou and Sofos, 2007; Ryser, 2007). More recent data from the EU indicate a major improvement in the contamination status of soft and semi-soft cheeses at retail. According to the 2008 Community summary report, only 0.2% of the 2116 soft and semi-soft cheese samples tested (single, retail units collected from 25 EU Member States) were deemed as non-compliant, i.e. contained more than 100 cfu/g of *L. monocytogenes*, while the respective percentage for batch samples was 2.8%. Also, approximately 1.3% of the soft and semi-soft cheeses (single or batch samples from either processing plants or retail) made from pasteurized milk were positive for *L. monocytogenes* (presence in 25 g) (EFSA, 2010).

Table 2. Physicochemical characteristics of selected PDO Greek cheeses

Cheese	S/M%[1,2]	NaCl (%)[1]	pH[1]	a_w
Feta	4.20±1.12 (n=19, Nega and Moatsou, 2012)	2.94 (Anifantakis, 1991) 2.83±0.15 (n=4, Konteles et al., 2009) 2.14±0.1 (Govaris et al., 2011)	4.41 (Anifantakis, 1991) 4.43–4.56 (Belessi et al., 2008) 4.58±0.01 (n=4, Konteles et al., 2009) 4.55±0.03 (Govaris et al., 2011) 4.68±0.35 (n=19, Nega and Moatsou, 2012)	0.957-0.966 (Belessi et al., 2008)
Galotyri		2.76 (Anifantakis, 1991) 1.54±0.12 (n=8, Papageorgiou et al., 1998) 1.8±0.6 (artisan); 1.8±0.1 (industrial) (n=4, Rogga et al., 2005)	3.9 (Anifantakis, 1991) 4.35±0.08 (n=8, Papageorgiou et al., 1998) 4.0±0.1(artisan); 3.8 ± 0.04 (industrial) (n=4, Rogga et al., 2005) 3.8- 4.0 (Samelis and Kakouri, 2007) 3.9-4.4 (Kykkidou et al., 2007)	
"Greek Graviera"		1.49 (Anifantakis, 1991) 1.6±0.3 (n=2, plant-ripened); 1.4±0.3 (n=2, pilot-ripened) (Samelis et al., 2010)	5.94 (Anifantakis, 1991) 5.6±0.1 (Giannou et al., 2009a) 5.6±0.2 (n=2, plant-ripened); 5.6±0.1 (n=2, pilot-ripened) (Samelis et al., 2010)	0.948±0.006 (Giannou et al., 2009a)
Graviera Naxou	3.93±0.59 (n=3, Nega and Moatsou, 2012)		5.45±0.04 (n=3, Nega and Moatsou, 2012)	
Graviera Kritis	5.18-5.48 (Kandarakis et al., 1998) 5.02±1.13 (n=6, Nega and Moatsou, 2012)		5.49-5.51 (Kandarakis et al., 1998) 5.56±0.23 (n=6, Nega and Moatsou, 2012)	
Kasseri	5.39±0.92 (n=3, Anastasiou et al., 2007) 3.92±1.31 (n=9, Nega and Moatsou, 2012)	3.1 (Anifantakis, 1991) ca. 2.2-2.4 (traditional); ca. 2.6-3.1 (acidified) (Kaninarides et al., 1995)	5.7 (Anifantakis, 1991) 4.8, 5.3 (Genigeorgis et al., 1991) 5.69±0.01 (traditional); 5.48± 0.04 (acidified) (n=6, Kaninarides et al., 1995) 5.4-5.6 (Moatsou et al., 2001) 5.67±0.19 (n=3, Anastasiou et al., 2007) 5.67±0.17 (n=9, Nega and Moatsou, 2012)	

Cheese	S/M%[1,2]	NaCl (%)[1]	pH[1]	a_w
Katiki Domokou			4.5-4.6 (Panagou, 2008) 4.5-4.6 (Mataragas et al., 2008) 4.5-4.6 (Kagkli et al., 2010) 4.39±0.04 (n=2, Angelidis et al., 2012)	0.983±0.007 (n=2, Angelidis et al., 2012)
Manouri	2.90±0.02 (spring); 2.65±0.07 (summer) (n=3, Lioliou et al., 2001) 6.30 (n=3, Papageorgiou et al., 1996)	0.83 (Anifantakis, 1991) 2.28±0.08 (n=3, Papageorgiou et al., 1996)	5.45, 5.9 (Anifantakis, 1991) 7.09±0.01 (spring); 7.33±0.07 (summer) (n=3, Lioliou et al., 2001) 5.19±0.92 (n=23, Angelidis et al., 2012)	0.973±0.015 (n=23, Angelidis et al., 2012)
Pichtogalo Chanion		1.02±0.38 (n=62, Papageorgiou et al., 1998) 1.25±0.04 (n=2, Theodoridis et al., 2006)	4.36±0.25 (n=62,Papageorgiou et al., 1998) 4.23±0.19 (n=2, Theodoridis et al., 2006)	0.990±0.003 (n=62, Papageorgiou et al., 1998)

[1] The S/M%, NaCl% and pH values of cheeses can vary depending on differences during manufacture (e.g. choice of starters and ripening conditions) and may also change during retail storage from the values of cheeses immediately upon their manufacture. For experiments in which market cheese samples were used, the reported values refer to those measured at the beginning of each experiment. For experiments where cheesemaking was conducted by the investigators, the values are those measured upon completion of the cheese manufacture (including cheese ripening, where applicable). The reader should consult the respective citations for more details.

[2] S/M, Salt (NaCl) in moisture.

The published data on the prevalence of *L. monocytogenes* in Greek cheeses, however remain quite limited (Theodoridis et al., 1998; Angelidis et al., 2006; Filiousis et al., 2009; Angelidis et al., 2012).

The European legislation specifies microbiological criteria for *L. monocytogenes* in Ready-To-Eat (RTE) foods (European Commission, 2005; 2007). According to these Regulations, manufacturers of RTE foods must be able to demonstrate to the competent authorities the *L. monocytogenes*-food category in which their products belong to (*i.e.*, whether the food products support or not the growth of *L. monocytogenes*). Food products "with pH $\leq$ 4.4 or $a_w \leq 0.92$, products with pH $\leq$ 5.0 and $a_w \leq 0.94$ and products with a shelf-life of less than five days" are considered as RTE foods that are unable to support *L. monocytogenes* growth. For RTE foods that do not meet the fore-mentioned physicochemical and shelf-life limits, one way of providing scientific justification regarding the ability or not to support the growth of the pathogen is through the conduct of challenge tests. In the following sections, the studies in which challenge tests have been employed to decipher the behavior of *L. monocytogenes* in Greek PDO cheeses are discussed. Such studies have been conducted thus far for seven of the Greek PDO cheeses, namely Feta, Kasseri, Pichtogalo Chanion, Graviera, Manouri, Galotyri and Katiki Domokou.

Feta Cheese

Feta is by far the most popular cheese in Greece and probably the most popular white-brined cheese in the world. Most of the small ruminants' milk produced in Greece is used for cheesemaking and particularly for the manufacture of white-brined cheeses such as Feta (Moatsou and Govaris, 2011). In Greek, the name Feta means "slice" and most likely originates from the cheese's properties which allow it to be cut in slices without falling apart. Feta is a soft, rennet-coagulated cheese produced by ovine milk or by a mixture of ovine with caprine milk. When caprine milk is used for Feta cheese manufacture it should not exceed 30% in the final mixture. The fat content of the milk used for Feta cheese manufacture should be at least 6% (Greek Codex of Foodstuffs and Beverages, 2009). Feta is ripened and stored in rectangular tinned or lacquered metal containers covered in brine and undergoes lactic fermentation. An older traditional practice still used at a lower scale is the ripening and preservation of Feta in wooden barrels. In recent years, however, for retail marketing purposes, Feta cheese blocks are frequently also sold under Modified Atmosphere Packaging (MAP) (Alichanidis and Polychroniadou, 2008). Most of the Feta cheese produced in Greece is from pasteurized milk, although in certain cases, e.g. under artisanal production practices or when the farmers themselves produce Feta cheese, thermized or even raw milk can also be used. When pasteurized milk is used for Feta cheese manufacture, lactic acid bacterial strains (starters) are added to the milk, in addition to calcium chloride in a concentration of up to 0.2 g per Kg of milk. Traditionally, the thermophilic yogurt starter cultures, i.e. *Streptococcus salivarius* subsp. *thermophilus* and *Lactobacillus delbrueckii* subsp. *bulgaricus* are used. However, the use of mesophilic lactic starters such as *Lactococcus lactis* subsp. *lactis* or *Lactobacillus plantarum* alone, or in combination with thermophilic starters are also frequently employed in order to achieve more rapid acidification during the first ripening stage (Kandarakis et al., 2001; Karageorgis et al., 2005).

The characteristics of mature Feta cheese should be as follows: maximum moisture content 56%, minimum fat-in-dry matter (FDM) 43%. Feta cheese has a mandatory ripening period of at least 2 months. Fully ripened Feta cheese has an a_w value of *ca.* 0.96 (Bintsis, 2006) and a pH value that should be approximately 4.3 - 4.4. The cheesemaking technology of Feta and other white brined cheeses has been presented in a recent review by Moatsou and Govaris (2011).

Owing to its popularity, the effects of various technological steps on the physicochemical characteristics and organoleptic properties of Feta cheese have been extensively studied by investigators working in the field of food science and technology. Consequently, researchers have studied i) the use of different and/or adjunct starter cultures for the manufacture of Feta such as the use of selected mesophilic starter cultures (Litopoulou-Tzanetaki et al., 1993; Katsiari et al., 2002; Sarantinopoulos et al., 2002; Karageorgis et al., 2005), the application of concentrated lyophilized cultures directly on the cheese milk (Pappa and Anifantakis, 2001a, 2001b) or the use of heat-shocked cultures (Vafopoulou et al., 1989) on the manufacture, microbiological, physicochemical and organoleptic characteristics of Feta, ii) the effects of standardization for casein/fat or the use of different ratios or concentrations of caprine and ovine milk on the properties of Feta (Mallatou et al., 1994; Pappas et al., 1994; Tsigkros et al., 2003), iii) the evolution of the lipolysis and proteolysis (Katsiari et al., 2000; Moatsou et al., 2002; Georgala et al., 2005; Nega and Moatsou, 2012) and of the microbial populations (Tzanetakis and Litopoulou-Tzanetaki, 1992; Xanthopoulos et al., 2000; Manolopoulou et al., 2003; Vassiliadis et al., 2009) during cheese ripening, the microbiology of brines used to mature Feta cheese (Bintsis et al., 2000) and the migration of water-soluble nitrogenous compounds from the cheese blocks into the brine (Michaelidou et al., 2005), iv) the effect of other technological variables such as draining time and aging (Pappas et al., 1996), draining temperature (Kandarakis et al., 2001), rennet type (Kandarakis et al., 1999; Moatsou et al., 2004), microbial coagulants (Alichanidis et al., 1984), salting method and storage time (Pappas et al., 1996) and reduction of sodium content (Katsiari et al., 1997). In addition, studies have focused on the microbiology of Feta cheese from different manufacturers (Rantsiou et al., 2008) and the isolation or determination of selected nutrients (Efthymiou, 1967; Michaelidou et al., 1998; Zlatanos et al., 2002; Kondyli et al., 2002). Lalos et al. (1996) investigated the effects of using cold stored milk and different heat treatments on the quality of the resulting Feta. Mauropoulos and Arvanitoyannis (1999) have described the application of the HACCP system to the Feta cheese production line. Recently, Moschopoulou et al. (2010) reported on the microbiological and physicochemical changes after the application of high-hydrostatic pressure treatments at the 15th day of ripening of Feta cheese.

The Behavior of *L. monocytogenes* during the Manufacture and Ripening of Feta Cheese

The first and, to date, most thorough study regarding the fate of *L. monocytogenes* during the manufacture, ripening and storage of Feta was conducted in 1989 by Papageorgiou and Marth. It should be noted that this study was conducted in the US and bovine milk was used for cheesemaking. Papageorgiou and Marth (1989) investigated the ability of two different *L. monocytogenes* strains (the clinical isolate strain Scott A, and the strain incriminated for the listeriosis soft-cheese outbreak in Los Angeles, strain CA) to grow during the cheese-making process and to survive during ripening and storage of the cheese. Pasteurized milk was inoculated with *ca.* 5 x 10^3 CFU/mL of *L. monocytogenes* and 1% of the traditional thermophilic yogurt starters (*L. bulgaricus, S. thermophilus*) were added at a 1:1 ratio. After the addition of rennet, the coagulum was cut at *ca.* pH 6.4, transferred to rectangular metal hoops and drained for 6 h at room temperature. Subsequently the cheese was ripened initially at 22°C in sterile 12% salt brine for 24 h, then for 4 days in 6% brine until the pH had dropped to 4.3 - 4.4, and finally at 4°C until 90 days of ripening.

According to the results of this study, no measureable growth of *L. monocytogenes* occurred in the contaminated milk during the time preceding the addition of rennet. The pathogen was entrapped in the cheese curd, where, on average, *L. monocytogenes* counts were 0.9 log cfu/g higher than those in the inoculated milk. In contrast, the whey contained only about 3% of the inoculated cells. Pathogen counts in the curd increased during the whey drainage period as well as during the first two days of ripening at 22°C. The combined population average increase (i.e. both due to cell concentration in the curd and due to actual growth during this period) was calculated to be *ca.* 2.3 log cfu/g. The observed *L. monocytogenes* population increase paralleled the drop in the pH from an initial value of 6.65 to 5.0 during the first two days. However, once the pH of the 2-day-old cheese had reached 4.6, growth of the pathogen ceased and *L. monocytogenes* counts in the cheese remained essentially unchanged during the following 3 days of ripening at 22°C (days 2 to 5). No appreciable difference in the behavior of the two strains was observed during the first 5 days of manufacture and ripening.

After 5 days at 22°C, the Feta cheese in 6% brine was transferred at 4°C for completion of ripening. The populations of both strains decreased significantly during storage at 4°C, with *L. monocytogenes* CA being less resistant. Nevertheless, high numbers of both strains could be enumerated even after 90 days of storage, i.e. a time period exceeding the mandatory 2-month ripening period. Hence, compared to the populations enumerated in the respective 2-day-old cheeses, *L. monocytogenes* Scott A displayed a reduction in counts of *ca.* 1.3 log cfu/g, whereas strain CA was reduced by about 3.1 log cfu/g.

The results of this study indicated that when the milk used for Feta cheesemaking had been contaminated with high numbers of *L. monocytogenes*, the pathogen could readily grow during the first stage or ripening when both the acidity and the temperature were favorable for *L. monocytogenes* proliferation and that the subsequent ripening under unfavorable conditions (pH = 4.3 at 4°C) was insufficient to eliminate the pathogen.

The milking period of ewes and goats is seasonal and relatively short, and milk production culminates in the mid- to late-spring. Hence, the year-round production of ovine and caprine milk cheeses is not feasible. Therefore, the freezing of either milk or the freezing and frozen storage of cheese curd after drainage is an option that enables more year-round manufacture of cheese in the Mediterranean countries (Alichanidis et al., 1981). A study conducted by Papageorgiou et al. (1997) tested the ability of two strains of *L. monocytogenes* (Scott A and CA) to survive during frozen storage of Feta cheese curd. The strains were inoculated to pasteurized ewe's milk at *ca.* 1-2 x 10^6 cfu/mL which was made into Feta cheese using the standard procedures described previously (Papageorgiou and Marth, 1989). After 5 h of curd drainage at 21-22°C (pH = 5.4, moisture content = 59.7%, FDM = 57.1%), 200-g cheese pieces (5.5 x 5.5 x 6 cm) were placed in sterile stomacher bags and frozen at -

38°C overnight, and subsequently stored at either -18°C or -38°C for up to 7.5 months. The survival of *L. monocytogenes* during frozen storage was evaluated at 15-day intervals after thawing of samples at 35 ± 1°C within 1 h. Two analyses were conducted per sample. One sub-sample consisted of 10 g of cheese from the outer 1.5-2.0 cm of the curd and the other consisted of 10 g from the center of the cheese curd.

The results of the study showed that *L. monocytogenes* Scott A was much more capable of surviving frozen storage than strain CA. Furthermore, Scott A cells survived better in the outer parts of the frozen cheese curd. For instance, up to 83% of the number of *L. monocytogenes* Scott A cells survived 5.5 months of frozen storage at -38°C. An explanation offered by the authors is the formation of smaller ice crystals in the surface of the curd than in the center. The results of this study emphasize that freezing of unripened Feta cheese curd contaminated with high numbers of *L. monocytogenes* will lead to a progressive decrease in viable pathogen populations but freezing is not sufficient to eliminate *L. monocytogenes* from the curd.

Ramsaran et al. (1998) studied the survival of *L. monocytogenes* during the manufacture and storage of Feta cheese using a mesophilic starter culture. Both pasteurized and raw milk was used in the experimental trials standardized at a protein to fat ratio of 0.96, but the species-origin of milk was not specified. Three experimental conditions were tested: raw or pasteurized milk plus 1% (v/v) *Lactococcus lactis* subsp. *lactis* (culture 188) and raw milk plus a nisin-producing culture formed by combining culture 188 (2% v/v) and *L. lactis* subsp. *lactis* ATCC 11454 (3% v/v). The milk had been inoculated with 10^4 CFU/mL of a bioluminescent *L. monocytogenes* strain prior to the addition of starter. Kid goat lipase was added (300 μg per 4 L of milk) and the cheese was ripened for 1 h before addition of rennet (0.012 % v/v). After 1 h the curd was cut and stirred gently for aprox. 20 min, dipped into forms and allowed to drain for 2 h. The curd was then placed at 18°C, and after 24 h it was dry-salted (3% of the curd weight). One week later the curd was placed in 7% brine and stored at 2 ± 1°C.

The populations of *L. monocytogenes* in the cheese made using raw milk were increased by about 1 log cfu/g at 24 h and remained practically unchanged for up to 75 days. In the trials involving pasteurized milk, an initial decline in the populations of *L. monocytogenes* was observed during curd formation (2 h), but the subsequent average increase was greater compared to the raw-milk trials. As a result, the 24-h *L. monocytogenes* counts of the raw and pasteurized milk trials were practically indistinguishable. The increase in the counts of *L. monocytogenes* between 2 and 24 h maybe at least partially attributed to bacterial concentration, i.e. entrapment of Listeria in the cheese curd. Compared to the raw milk trials, the counts of *L. monocytogenes* in the pasteurized milk trials after 55 days of storage were increased by another 0.5 log cfu/g.

The behavior of the pathogen in the trials using the nisin-producing strain during the first 24 h of cheese manufacture was essentially similar to that of the pasteurized milk trials, and after 24 h, the *L. monocytogenes* counts displayed overall a decreasing trend during ripening, but there was noticeable variation around the average count estimates of each sampling point. The authors used the word "erratic" to describe the behavior of *L. monocytogenes* after the first 24 h and suggested that the effect of nisin might have been influenced by physicochemical changes during ripening and storage. Nonetheless, in the nisin-producing starter trials, the average *L. monocytogenes* counts at each sampling point (10, 20, 30, 40, 55 and 75 days) was lower by 0.5 to 1.5 log cfu/g compared to the lower average count of the two other experimental conditions. For instance, at 75 days, the average counts in the cheese of the nisin-producing starter trials were the same as those of the initial inoculum. The authors suggested that the use of a nisin-producing starter culture constitutes an additional hurdle to the growth of *L.* monocytogenes in Feta cheese. However, even in the nisin-producing starter trials, no appreciable effect on the survival of the pathogen was noted.

Genigeorgis et al. (1991) studied the growth and survival of a five-strain cocktail of *L. monocytogenes* in 24 types of market cheeses available in the U.S., during aerobic storage at 4, 8 or 30°C. The aim of the study was to establish the pathogen's potential to grow in contaminated market cheeses at refrigeration or abuse temperatures, simulating a post-manufacture, cross-contamination scenario, where cheeses may get contaminated after the opening of the package, e.g., via contact with raw foods. Therefore the aim and design of this study was quite different than the two previously discussed studies. Hence, in the Genigeorgis et al. study four different market samples of Feta cheese (two reported as "Domestic Feta" and two reported as "Imported Feta") were used. Portions of the cheeses were aseptically removed and placed in sterile petri dishes or test tubes prior to inoculation with *ca.* 4 log cfu/g. The pH of three of the samples was equal to 4.3, while the fourth sample had a pH of 4.2, in accordance to the expected pH values of fully ripened Feta cheese.

The authors reported that Feta and Kasseri (a pasta-filata Greek PDO cheese, discussed at a later section) were among the cheeses in which *L. monocytogenes* was unable to initiate growth at any of the storage temperatures. Instead, in contaminated Feta cheese samples the populations of *L. monocytogenes* after 4 days of storage at 30°C or 8 days of storage at 4 or 8°C were reduced by more than 2.04 log cfu/g. The results showed that *L. monocytogenes* could not proliferate in Feta cheese with a pH lower than 4.6.

It should be also noted that the species origin of the four Feta cheese samples is not specified in the Genigeorgis et al. study either.

Belessi et al. (2008) studied the survival and acid resistance of a non-pathogenic species of the genus *Listeria, L. innocua*, in Feta cheese, both in the presence and in the absence of fungi. Commercial Feta cheese samples with pH values ranging from 4.43 to 4.56, fat content between 22 and 24% and moisture content between 55 and 57% were used in the study. In a first set of experiments, Feta cheese portions were inoculated with 10^5 cfu/g of *L. innocua* and stored at 3, 5, 10 or 15°C. The results of these trials were in agreement with previously published observations concerning *L. monocytogenes*, as *L. innocua* failed to multiply in the contaminated product at either storage temperature. In fact, gradual decreases in the *L. innocua* counts were observed during storage at all temperatures. In experiments involving artificial contamination of Feta cheese with a cocktail of mold spores, the pH of the cheese increased with time during storage at 5, 10 and 15°C, due to fungal growth and this enhanced the survival of *L. innocua* more than the respective survival during storage at 3°C. In addition, following storage at 3 and 10°C, *L. innocua* cells that had been inoculated in Feta cheese were capable of surviving subsequent exposure for 3 h in broth of pH 2.5, in contrast to cultures that had not been inoculated in Feta cheese. The investigators concluded that the growth of fungi on the surface of Feta cheese may compromise the safety of Feta by increasing the pH of the cheese, enhancing the survival of the bacterium and potentially leading to the development of acid-resistant *Listeria* populations. Acid-adapted *Listeria* cells may be more resistant to gastric acid during the digestive process and thereby a higher proportion of surviving cells may reach the intestine. This is an excellent study that highlights the complexity of microbial interactions in foods and their potential implications for food safety. The conduct of an analogous study in the future using *L. monocytogenes* would be of great significance regarding the behavior of the pathogen when introduced as a post-processing contaminant in Feta cheese.

Recently two studies dealing with possible physical or compositional and packaging interventions in order to enhance the safety of Feta cheese with respect to *L. monocytogenes* were published (Konteles et al., 2009; Govaris et al., 2011). Konteles et al. (2009) evaluated the effects of γ-irradiation on the populations of *L. monocytogenes* NCTC 10357 as well as on the colour, texture and sensory properties of Feta cheese during cold storage. Two sets of experiments were conducted. In the first set, *L. monocytogenes* was inoculated in pasteurised ovine milk (10^3 cfu/mL; "pre-process" contamination) and then 1% v/v of mesophilic starters (*L. lactis* subsp. *lactis* and *L. lactis* subsp. *cremoris*) and rennet were added. The curd was cut and drained at 16 - 18°C for 5 h and then placed in tin-coated vessels where the blocks were turned and dry-salted twice with 3% w/w coarse NaCl over the next 12 h. After 5 days of ripening in the vessels at 16-18°C, the expelled whey was poured-off and replaced with sterile brine (7% w/v NaCl), and the cheese ripened until the pH fell below 4.6. The completion of the 2-month ripening took place at 3 - 4°C. By the end of ripening, the populations of *L. monocytogenes* in "pre-process" contaminated Feta cheese had reached *ca.* 2.0×10^5 cfu/g.

Contaminated Feta samples in brine were vacuum-packaged and subjected to irradiation doses of 1.0, 2.5 or 4.7 KGy and stored at 4°C for 30 days. Several physicochemical (moisture, fat, salt content and pH), color, texture and sensorial parameters were evaluated immediately following the irradiation process (day 0), as well as after storage of the irradiated samples at 4°C for 30 days. No statistical significant differences were recorded among the irradiated and control (non-irradiated) samples for all the above measured physicochemical characteristics. On the day of irradiation, none of the applied doses was sufficient to eliminate *L. monocytogenes* in any of the "pre-process" test samples. The maximum reduction in the *L. monocytogenes* populations (3.8 log cfu/g) was recorded in samples receiving the highest irradiation dose (4.7 KGy). After 30 days of storage of irradiated samples at 4°C, significant reductions in the *L. monocytogenes* populations (compared to day 0) were observed only in the samples that had been exposed to irradiation, i.e. the small reductions in the *L. monocytogenes* populations observed in non-irradiated samples between days 0 and 30 were not statistically significant.

In the "post-process" contamination trials, Feta cheese was manufactured as described above, albeit without using contaminated milk, and ripened for 2 months. The brine used for the final packaging (i.e. prior to irradiation) was contaminated with *ca.* 10^3 *L. monocytogenes* cfu/mL. Following irradiation with either 2.5 or 4.7 KGy, the counts of *L. monocytogenes* decreased at levels below the limit of enumeration (10 cfu/g) in all samples. *L. monocytogenes* populations remained below the limit of enumeration also after 30 days of storage of these irradiated samples at 4°C. On the contrary, in the non-irradiated samples, the populations of *L. monocytogenes* remained practically unchanged during the 30-day storage period. It should be noted that irradiation did not seem to influence the texture of Feta, but the highest dose produced detectable changes in the cheese's color by increasing the cheese's "redness" and decreasing its "yellowness" and "lightness", and also altered Feta's typical aroma, which however, was "restored" after one month of cold storage.

Recently, Govaris et al. (2011) studied the activity of oregano and thyme essential oils against *L. monocytogenes* when the pathogen is introduced as a post-processing contaminant to the cheese. The Feta cheese used for the experiments was obtained from a dairy plant in Greece two months after its production. The average physicochemical values of the cheese used in the experiments were: 49.5 for FDM, 53.4% for moisture content, 2.1% for NaCl, and 4.55 for pH. One hundred-g blocks of Feta were surface-inoculated (10^4 cfu/g) with two strains of *L. monocytogenes* (Scott A and Lmk), which were used either as single strain inocula or as a cocktail at equal concentrations. Thirty min after inoculation with *L. monocytogenes* the inoculated samples were sprayed with essential oil (EO) derived from thyme (0.1 mL/100 g), or from oregano (0.1 or 0.2 mL / 100g). Unsprayed samples served as controls. Immediately after applying the EOs, the cheese blocks were packaged under MAP (50% CO_2 and 50% N_2) and stored at 4°C for 36 days. Uninoculated, yet sprayed test samples were subjected to sensory evaluation and proven acceptable by trained panellists.

The *L. monocytogenes* counts in Feta cheese samples treated with EOs were significantly lower than those of control samples at all sampling points. In Feta cheese sprayed with oregano EO at the lower dose (0.1 mL/100g) viable *L. monocytogenes* populations could be detected up to 18 days of storage at 4°C, whereas in samples sprayed with the higher dose of oregano EO (0.2 mL/100g) viable *L. monocytogenes* populations could be detected only up to 14 days of storage. The antilisterial effect of thyme EO at the concentration tested was similar to that of the oregano EO used at the same level (0.1 mL/100g). Significant strain-dependent differences were not observed in this study. In addition, no significant differences in the behavior of *L. monocytogenes* were observed between the trials involving single strains *vs.* those involving the strain cocktail. This study revealed an antilisterial action of oregano and thyme EOs when applied on the surface of mature Feta cheese stored under MAP at 4°C.

Kasseri Cheese

Kasseri is another Greek PDO cheese and probably the second most popular traditional cheese in Greece. It is a "pasta-filata"-type, semi-soft cheese made from raw or pasteurized ovine milk. Occasionally, a mixture of ovine with caprine milk is used (Anifantakis, 1991). However, when caprine milk is used for Kasseri cheese manufacture it should not exceed 20% in the final mixture. When pasteurized milk is used for Kasseri cheese manufacture, thermophilic or combinations of thermophilic and mesophilic starters (Kaminarides et al., 1999; Anastasiou et al., 2007) are added to the milk, in addition to calcium chloride in a concentration of up to 0.2 g per Kg of milk. The minimum fat content of the milk should be 6% (Greek Codex of Foodstuffs and Beverages, 2009).

For the manufacture of Kasseri cheese, pasteurized milk is cooled to 32°C, inoculated with starter and sufficient rennet is added to allow for coagulation in 35 - 40 min. After milk coagulation, the curd is cut in small pieces (i.e. corn-sized) and allowed to stand for 5 - 10 min. The curd is subsequently heated under continuous stirring at 38 - 40°C for *ca.* 5 min, and then collected from the bottom of the cheese vat, pressed, cut into large blocks and left to drain (ripen) at 15-18°C until the pH reaches 5.2 - 5.3. Then the acidified curd ("baski") is ready for further processing, which includes cutting of the curd into long, thin slices, which are immersed and kneaded into hot (75 - 80°C) water until a homogenous compact structure is formed. The hot curd is transferred onto a table where it is further kneaded and stretched by hand (traditionally), dry-salted and placed into cylindrical moulds. While in the moulds, the cheese is dry-salted 12 - 14 times and turned 5 - 6 times during 2 - 3 days at 18°C. The cheese ripens for at least 3 months at a temperature than should not exceed 18°C, being typically 15°C or less (Anifantakis, 1991; Moatsou et al., 2001; Alichanidis and Polychroniadou, 2008; Greek Codex of Foodstuffs and Beverages, 2009). The moisture content of Kasseri should not exceed 45% and the minimum FDM is set at 40% (Greek Codex of Foodstuffs and Beverages, 2009).

Kaminarides et al. (1995, 1999) compared different methods of Kasseri cheesemaking and studied the effects of using concentrated thermophilic and mesophilic cultures and of the acidification temperature on the quality of Kasseri cheese. The effects of milk pasteurization and other technological parameters on the characteristics of Kasseri cheese made from raw or pasteurized ewes' milk without the addition of starter cultures have been investigated in detail by Moatsou et al. (2001). Anastasiou et al. (2007) have demonstrated that *Streptococcus macedonicus*, a new species isolated from naturally fermented Kasseri (Tsakalidou et al., 1998) can be used as an adjunct starter in Kasseri cheese production. Finally, Arvanitoyannis and Mavropoulos (2000) have described the application of the HACCP system to the Kasseri cheese production line.

The Behavior of *L. monocytogenes* as a Post-Processing Contaminant in Kasseri Cheese during Storage

There is only one study with limited information regarding the fate of *L. monocytogenes* introduced as a post-processing contaminant in Kasseri cheese (Genigeorgis et al., 1991). In this US study, among many different market cheeses, two samples of Kasseri, one "Domestic" (pH = 4.8, SWP = 5.8%) and one "imported" (pH = 5.3, SWP = 5.52%) were inoculated (*ca.* 4.0 log cfu/g) with a five-strain inoculum of *L. monocytogenes* (Scott A, V7, RM-1, VPH-1 and VPH-2). Inoculated samples were stored aerobically at 4, 8 or 30°C. The authors reported *L. monocytogenes* population reductions of more than *ca.* 2 log cfu/g after 4, 8 or 6 days of storage of the "domestic" sample at 30, 8 or 4°C, respectively. Reductions of similar magnitude (i.e. more than *ca.* 2 log cfu/g) were reported for the "imported" sample after 8, 24 or 36 days of storage at 30, 8 or 4°C, respectively. The authors proposed that the higher pH and lower SWP value of the "imported" sample may have led to more prolonged survival of *L. monocytogenes* during storage at low temperatures compared to that observed for the "domestic" sample.

Pichtogalo Chanion Cheese

Pichtogalo Chanion is a soft, acid-curd, spreadable, white cheese made in the island of Crete and specifically in the region of Chania. Caprine, ovine, or a mixture of caprine with ovine milk can be used and the milk can be raw or pasteurized. When pasteurized milk is used for Pichtogalo Chanion cheese manufacture, mesophilic starters (Papageorgiou et al., 1998) are added to the milk, in addition to calcium chloride in a concentration of up to 0.2 g per Kg of milk. The milk coagulation is done at 18-25°C within 2 h and the curd is left to sour for approximately 24 h at room temperature. Thus, the pH of the curd is lowered to 4.2 - 4.6. The curd is then transferred to cheese cloths for *ca.* 8 h for draining. Then, 1% salt is added and the cheese is ready for consumption or retailing under refrigeration (Papageorgiou et al., 1998). The moisture content of Pichtogalo Chanion should not exceed 65% and the minimum FDM is set at 50% (Greek Codex of Foodstuffs and Beverages, 2009). Papageorgiou et al. (1998) demonstrated that high-quality Pichtogalo Chanion cheese can be produced using a mixture of pasteurized ovine and caprine milk and 4% of mesophilic starter culture.

The Behavior of *L. monocytogenes* during the Manufacture and Storage of Pichtogalo Chanion Cheese

Theodoridis et al. (2006) studied the fate of *L. monocytogenes* during the manufacture and storage of Pichtogalo Chanion cheese. For the manufacture of Pichtogalo Chanion cheese equal volumes of pasteurized ovine and caprine milk were used. The milk was inoculated with different levels (2×10^2, 2×10^3, or 2×10^5 cfu/mL) of two *L. monocytogenes* strains (Scott A and CA). After warming the milk to 23°C, 4% (v/v) of the starter culture were added followed by addition of rennet. The starter culture consisted of *L. lactis* subsp. *lactis* (1.3%), *Lactobacillus casei* subsp. *pseudoplantarum* (1.3%), *Lb. casei* subsp. *casei* (1%) and *L. lactis* biovar *diacetylactis* (0.4%). These strains had been isolated and biochemically verified as such from traditionally manufactured Pichtogalo Chanion cheese (Papageorgiou et al., 1998). In one of the high-inoculum trials, raw milk was used and no starter was added. Coagulation took place within 2 h, and after keeping the curd at 23°C for 24 h for souring, the curd was transferred to hoops to drain for 8 h. After draining, 1% NaCl was added and the cheese was refrigerated. Two days later, half of the refrigerated cheese was frozen at -20°C in 150-g portions. For frozen samples, enumeration of *L. monocytogenes* was being conducted after thawing (at 35 ± 1°C within 1 h) of the samples and duplicate 10-g samples were tested (one from the outer 1.5-2.0 cm of the cheese and one from the center).

The average composition of the Pichtogalo Chanion cheese was: 64.5% moisture, 55.3% FDM, 1.3% NaCl. The average pH of the 2-day cheese was 4.23. Although minor differences were observed between trials, the populations of *L. monocytogenes* remained essentially unchanged during the first 12 h of cheesemaking in all trials and up to 24 h in all but two trials, in which reductions of up to 1.3 log cfu/g were recorded. During subsequent storage at 4°C, however, i.e. after souring of the curd for 24 h, significant decreases in the *L. monocytogenes* populations were noted in all trials and the pathogen was inactivated to undetectable levels at 5 to 20 days, depending on the level of the initial inoculum. The average estimated time required for one decimal reduction in the populations of *L. monocytogenes* during the post-souring, sharp inactivation period at 4°C was calculated to be 1.8 days. The results of the freezing experiments showed that *L. monocytogenes* populations declined substantially during the first 15 days of frozen storage, but a small fraction of cells (1% or less) remained viable for up to 90 days.

Overall, the data have shown that the conditions prevailing during Pichtogalo Chanion cheese manufacture are unfavorable for the growth and survival of *L. monocytogenes*. Since, however, Pichtogalo Chanion in an unripened cheese that is ready for consumption 2 days after manufacture, the authors emphasized that every effort must be made to keep this cheese pathogen-free (Theodoridis et al., 2006). Hence, the collection of raw milk must be conducted in a manner that minimizes contamination and the milk should be properly pasteurized.

Graviera Cheese

Graviera is considered as the finest among the traditional Greek hard-cheeses. Many types of Graviera cheese are produced and traded in Greece, distinguished by the name of the production region. Three of these types of Graviera (Graviera Agrafon, Graviera Naxou, Graviera Kritis) have been granted PDO status (European Commission, 1996). Graviera Agrafon is produced using ovine milk or mixtures of ovine with up to 30% caprine milk. Graviera Naxou, on the other hand is manufactured using bovine milk. Mixtures of bovine with ovine and caprine milk are also used, provided that small-ruminant milk does not exceed 20%. Finally, Graviera Kritis is made using ovine milk or mixtures of ovine with up to 20% caprine milk (Greek Codex of Foodstuffs and Beverages, 2009). Thermized or pasteurized milk should be used for the manufacture of Graviera Agrafon and Graviera Kritis, whereas raw or pasteurized milk for Graviera Naxou. Nowadays, most of the Graviera cheese is manufactured using pasteurized milk. In modern cheesemaking facilities, following pasteurization, the milk is cooled to 34 - 36°C. Calcium chloride (up to 0.2 g per Kg of milk), thermophilic and mesophilic lactic acid bacterial cultures (and sometimes also propionibacteria) and rennet are added and coagulation usually takes place in 30 - 40 min. The curd is cut in small pieces (approximately the size of rice grains), left undisturbed for a few minutes and then "cooked" at 48 - 52°C under continuous stirring for approximately 30 min before molding (Anifantakis, 1991). The molds are pressed, drained and then placed into 18 - 20% brine for 2 - 5 days. Ripening of the cheese takes place in wooden shelves in well-ventilated rooms at 12 - 18°C and 85 - 95% relative humidity. Repeated surface dry-saltings and turnings of cheese heads are performed during the ripening period. The minimum ripening time for Graviera is set at 3 months. There are only a limited number of published studies, which however have provided useful data on the microbiological, physicochemical and organoleptic characteristics of Graviera cheese. The physicochemical characteristics and microbiological composition of Graviera Kritis, made from raw ovine milk, at different stages of manufacture and ripening has been described by Litopoulou Tzanetaki and Tzanetakis (2011), whereas Zerfiridis et al. (1984) reported on the characteristics of Graviera cheese made from pasteurized bovine milk. Kandarakis et al. (1998) studied the effects of using different starters on the gross and microbiological composition of Graviera Kritis and Samelis et al. (2010) studied the lactic acid bacterial flora and reported on the detection of bacteriocin genes in ripened Graviera cheeses.

The Behavior of *L. monocytogenes* during the Manufacture and Storage of Graviera Cheese

Giannou et al. (2009a) studied the fate of *L. monocytogenes* on fully ripened Greek Graviera cheese stored at 4, 12, or 25°C in air or vacuum packages. Thermized (63°C for 30 s) milk (ovine: caprine ratio of 90:10), rennet and a commercial starter mixture (*S. thermophilus*, *L. lactis* subsp. *lactis*, *L. lactis* subsp. *diacetylactis* and leuconostocs) were used for cheesemaking. In one of the experimental batches *Enterococcus faecium* KE82, a Graviera cheese isolate producing enterocin (Giannou et al., 2009b) was also added to the starter culture. Approximately 10^3 cfu/cm^2 of a five-strain *L. monocytogenes* cocktail (Scott A, ISS G79, a soft-cheese isolate, ISS G185, a blue-veined cheese isolate, WSLC 1294, a goat cheese isolate and WSLC 1482, a soft cheese isolate) were applied on the surface of fully ripened cheese pieces and the contaminated pieces were either vacuum packed or stored aerobically at 4, 12, or 25°C. *L. monocytogenes* growth was not observed in any of the inoculated experimental cheese batches. However, the death rate of the pathogen was slow, particularly at the lower storage temperatures. Hence, populations of *L. monocytogenes* could be enumerated even after 90 days of storage at 4°C and the highest survival was noted for cheeses stored at 4°C under vacuum (less than 1 log reduction, compared to the initial inoculum). The pathogen survival did not display any significant differences between the batches manufactured with the standard starter culture and the batch manufactured with the additional use of *E. faecium*. The authors proposed that the complete growth inhibition of *L. monocytogenes* should be attributed to the combined antimicrobial effect of several factors, i.e. the relatively low pH and a_w values, the organic acid content and the presence of various bacteriocins (enterocins and plantaricins) produced mainly by indigenous, non-starter LAB. In conclusion, this study satisfactorily addressed the behaviour of the pathogen, should fully ripened Graviera cheeses be accidentally contaminated in retail.

In order to get a more comprehensive outlook into the behaviour of *L. monocytogenes* during the manufacture of Graviera cheese, the above detailed study was subsequently followed by additional challenge studies where the pathogen was introduced as a contaminant in two distinct stages, early during the cheesemaking process (Samelis et al., 2009b). Therefore, the following study addressed the behaviour of *L. monocytogenes* in the core of Graviera cheese during processing and storage by inoculating the pathogen into the thermized (63°C for 30 s) milk (90% ovine, 10% caprine) used for cheesemaking. For the thermized milk challenge experiments a three-strain (Scott A, ISS G79 and ISS G185) cocktail (*ca.* 4 log cfu/mL) was used and a composite commercial starter was added (*S. thermophilus*, *L. lactis* subsp. *lactis*, *L. lactis* subsp. *lactis* var. *diacetylactis* and leuconostocs) in half of the inoculated samples. Inoculated samples were incubated at 37°C for 6 h and then at 18°C for an additional 66 h to simulate the conditions during milk curdling and initial cheese ripening, respectively. In separate experiments, fresh Graviera curd (pH = 6.3 ± 0.2) prepared using the initial steps of a standard in-plant Graviera cheese manufacturing protocol was inoculated (*ca.* 3 log cfu/g) with a cocktail consisting of a "non-pathogenic" *L. monocytogenes* strain and two *L. innocua* strains, namely LMG 11387 and M58, both isolated from raw milk (Samelis et al., 2009a). After stirring of the curd to ensure uniform distribution of the inoculum, the contaminated curd was transferred to small perforated cheese molds (12 cm in diameter) and left to dry. The fresh mini cheeses were kept at 18°C overnight, immersed in 20% brine for 24 h at 12°C, drained at 12°C for an additional 24 h and then transferred to a ripening room (18°C, 90% RH) for 20 days. Subsequently, the cheeses were vacuum-packed and stored at 4°C for up to 60 days after manufacture (Samelis et al., 2009b). In the thermized milk trials, *L. monocytogenes* increased by *ca.* 2 logs in the absence of starter culture and the growth occurred essentially within the first 6 h post-inoculation (i.e. at 37°C). The average *L. monocytogenes* populations increased only marginally in the next 6 h of storage at 18°C, reaching an average maximum of 6.2 log cfu/mL, followed by small reductions thereafter. Similar *L. monocytogenes* growth patterns were observed in the milk trials in the presence of starter culture, although the pathogen's growth at both 6 and 12 h was significantly reduced compared to the respective observed growth in the absence of starter. This growth retarding effect paralleled the faster and more pronounced growth of the starter LAB (as well as drop in the pH) in the "starter culture" trials compared to the growth of the indigenous LAB (and drop in the pH) in the trials without added starter. The behavior of *L. monocytogenes* during cooking of the curd, however, was not evaluated in this study due to restrictions pertaining to artificial in-plant contaminations. In the fresh-curd trials, the "non-pathogenic" cocktail populations decreased (*ca.* 0.8 - 1 log cfu/g) during the early ripening stages with most of this decrease occurring essentially within the first 24 h, coinciding with major increases in the populations of LAB and a significant decrease in the pH (from 6.3 to 5.9). No appreciable changes in the populations of Listeriae were noted during the remaining ripening period at 18°C or 4°C, despite the fact that LAB populations increased to 7.5 - 8.5 log CFU/g. Average day 1 pH values (5.9) decreased to 5.5 by day 11 and remained essentially unchanged thereafter. The results of these trials indicated that the contamination (with three *Listeria* spp. strains) of fresh Graviera cheese curd made using thermized milk and a starter culture consisting of mesophilic and thermophilic LAB did not result in outgrowth of the inoculum during subsequent ripening and storage.

Taking into account the fact that natural potential contaminations of thermized milk or subsequent environmental contaminations during the various steps of cheesemaking should be much lower than the inoculum levels used in this study, when the collective results of all experimental trials conducted in this study are considered, it appears that the use of thermized milk in combination with a commercial, freeze-dried, metabolically active, mixed LAB starter culture having high acidification potential, should, under proper manufacturing conditions, lead to the production of Graviera cheese that would be in accordance with the 100 cfu/g limit of Regulation 2073. The use of pathogenic *L. monocytogenes* strains in the fresh curd trials was a realistic (and understandable) experimental restriction noted by the authors. An analogous study in the future, e.g. in a research pilot plant, enabling the use of a pathogenic *L. monocytogenes* cocktail as a contaminant of thermized milk, in which the *L. monocytogenes* behavior will be monitored consecutively throughout the entire Graviera manufacture and ripening process would certainly add valuable information to the conclusions of this study.

Manouri Cheese

Manouri is the only one of three popular Greek whey-cheeses recognized as PDO (European Commission, 1996). Nowadays, Manouri is being manufactured mainly from whey derived from ovine milk during the manufacture of hard cheeses. If whey derived from the manufacture of soft cheeses is used, then its fat content is enriched by the addition of cream (Anifantakis, 1991). According to Greek standards, Manouri must be manufactured using ovine, caprine or mixtures of ovine with caprine milk whey with a minimum fat content of 2.5% (Greek Codex of Foodstuffs and Beverages, 2009). For Manouri cheese manufacture, milk whey is filtered to remove any existing curd particles. The whey is gradually heated under continuous stirring so that its temperature reaches 88 - 90°C within 40 - 45 min. When the temperature is about 70 - 75 °C, 1% NaCl is added as well as ovine or caprine milk cream at a ratio of up to 25%. At approximately 80°C, the first flakes of denatured whey protein (and co-precipitated caseins from the added milk or cream) are surfaced and the rate of stirring is gradually reduced and eventually paused, and heating continues until the temperature reaches 88-90°C. The denatured whey proteins (coagulum) are "cooked" at this temperature for 15 - 30 min and then the floating "curd" is collected (scooped) and placed in cheese cloths to drain (for *ca.* 4 - 5 h). After draining, the cheese is usually packaged in polyethylene cylindrical bags and refrigerated (4 - 5 °C) until retail distribution (Greek Codex of Foodstuffs and Beverages, 2009). As is the case for other whey cheeses, the final chemical composition of Manouri can vary depending on the composition of the initial whey used for manufacture and further depending on the composition (and quantity) of the full-fat milk or cream added during the heating step. Nonetheless, the Greek Codex of Foodstuffs and Beverages specifies a maximum moisture content of 60% and a minimum FDM of 70%.

Lioliou et al. (2001) have examined the main chemical changes as well as the microbial changes occurring on the surface and the interior of Manouri during storage at 4°C, when the cheese is manufactured by the traditional procedure, i.e. using fat-rich whey derived during the manufacture of Batzos, a semi-hard cheese. Mauropoulos and Arvanitoyannis (1999) have provided an example of implementation of the HACCP system during the manufacture of Manouri cheese.

The Behavior of *L. monocytogenes* During Storage of Manouri Cheese

Manouri is a high-pH, high-moisture, fresh, whey cheese. There is only one published study on the behavior of *L. monocytogenes* in whey cheeses (including Manouri), in which the fate of the pathogen was monitored after inoculating (5×10^2 cfu/g) freshly made Manouri cheese (i.e. cheese immediately upon manufacture) that had been drained for 5 h (Papageorgiou et al., 1996). The experimental Manouri cheese had been manufactured with the addition of 80 Kg of cream (63% fat) to 1000 liters of whey during heating when the whey temperature was 68 - 70°C and with the addition of 15 Kg NaCl when the temperature had reached 73 - 75°C. The cheese had initial pH 6.3, FDM 71.7%, moisture 52.2% (average values). Portions of Manouri were inoculated with two strains of *L. monocytogenes* (Scott A and CA), the inoculum was mixed thoroughly into the cheese mass and the inoculated cheese was stored at 5, 12 or 22°C in plastic containers. At 5°C, following a short lag phase of *ca.* 1 day, *L. monocytogenes* exhibited exponential growth with generation times of 18.5 and 17.8 h for strains CA and Scott A, respectively. As a result, maximum *L. monocytogenes* populations exceeding 8 log cfu/g were recorded after two weeks of refrigerated storage with no appreciable change in the cheese pH. At the 12°C-storage experiments, the *L. monocytogenes* generation times were approximately 3-fold shorter compared to those recorded at 5°C. As a result, maximum *L. monocytogenes* concentrations were recorded much sooner (5 - 7 days post-inoculation) and exceeded 8.5 log cfu/mL. As was the case in the 5°C-experimental trials, the pH of the Manouri remained essentially unchanged (i.e., *ca.* 6.3) during this period. As expected, pronounced *L. monocytogenes* growth was also noted during storage at room temperature with analogously high pathogen concentrations being achieved after only 2-3 days. The results of this study highlight the "vulnerability" of Manouri to potential post-processing listerial contaminations. The extensive heat treatment applied to the whey (and to the milk or cream mixture) during cheese processing is deemed adequate to eliminate expected counts of food borne pathogenic vegetative cells that may be present in the raw milk, cream or whey. However, like other unripened whey-cheeses, in the case of Manouri (high moisture, high pH, low salt) storage at low temperature constitutes the only post-processing antimicrobial hurdle. Owing to its elaborate physiologic adaptive mechanisms, *L. monocytogenes* can readily multiply at low temperatures in the absence of significant additional stresses (Angelidis et al., 2002; Angelidis and Smith, 2003). Strict hygienic practices must therefore be employed during the handling and packaging of Manouri in order to avoid any contaminations after the heat-treatment step (collection, draining and packaging) and post-packaging pasteurization of whey-cheeses has been recommended (Papageorgiou et al., 1996). For Anthotyros, other interventions such as irradiation or addition of nisin have been proposed for the inactivation or the control of *L. monocytogenes* proliferation (Tsiotsias et al., 2002; Samelis et al., 2003). In 1998 the results of two surveys regarding the prevalence of *L. monocytogenes* and *Listeria* spp. in the Greek whey cheeses Anthotyros, Myzithra and Manouri were published (Theodoridis et al., 1998). The surveys were conducted in 1990 and 1996 and 167 commercial samples were tested in each survey. The reported percentages of positive whey cheeses for *Listeria* spp. and *L. monocytogenes* were 15% and 13.8% (1990), and 6% and 1.8% (1996), respectively. Although the number of the Greek whey cheeses examined in a subsequent study (Angelidis et al., 2012) was relatively small ($n = 63$), the results of the latter study may indicate an improvement with respect to the hygienic status of whey cheeses, given that only one sample (of Anthotyros) tested positive for *Listeria* spp. and no samples were found positive for *L. monocytogenes* (Angelidis et al., 2012).

Galotyri Cheese

Galotyri is a soft, acid-curd, spreadable cheese, usually made from ovine milk (Anifantakis, 1991), although the use of caprine milk or a mixture of ovine with caprine milk is also permitted (Greek Codex of Foodstuffs and Beverages, 2009). In the traditional manufacturing process, immediately after milking, the milk is boiled and placed in a clay pot where it is left for 24 h. It is then salted (3 - 4% NaCl), mixed and left for another two days with periodical stirring. Subsequently, the naturally acidified cheese is placed in cheese cloths or leather bags. The same procedure is repeated using milk from subsequent milkings until the bags are filled. Then the bags are closed hermetically and transferred to cold ($< 8^{\circ}$C) and dry storage rooms, where the cheese ripens for at least two months in the case it is manufactured from raw milk. Often, the cheese ripens in wooden barrels instead of bags (Litopoulou-Tzanetaki and Tzanetakis, 2011). In recent years Galotyri is also produced commercially using pasteurized milk and starters in single batches. Consequently, "ripening" is shortened to one week or less at 4°C. In this sense commercially available Galotyri can be considered a "fresh" (non-ripened) acidic (pH of *ca.* 4), low-salt (< 2%) cheese (Rogga et al., 2005). The maximum allowable moisture content and the minimum FDM are 75% and 40%, respectively (Greek Codex of Foodstuffs and Beverages, 2009). A recent study examined the microbiological and safety status of 12 batches of commercial Galotyri produced by two plants (one industrial and one artisan) and marketed in Epirus, a northwestern province of Greece (Samelis and Kakouri, 2007). *L. monocytogenes* was detected (< 10 cfu/g) at the time of purchase in one industrial and two artisanal batches, but all batches were negative via culture enrichment after one week of storage at 4°C (Samelis and Kakouri, 2007). Another study examined the effects of treatment with nisin, on the microbiological and sensory properties of Galotyri during aerobic storage at 4°C (Kykkidou et al., 2007). Nisin, at 50 or 150 IU/g, was added after the manufacture of the cheese from pasteurized milk with the addition of commercial starters at a dairy processing plant. Based on the sensory evaluation (appearance and aroma) and microbiological acceptability (with a limit of 5 log cfu/g of yeasts) results of the study, nisin treatments extended the shelf life of fresh Galotyri during aerobic storage at 4°C by *ca.* 7 (50 IU/g) to 21 (150 IU/g) days.

The Behavior of *L. monocytogenes* during the Manufacture and Storage of Galotyri Cheese

The behavior of *L. monocytogenes*, as a post-processing contaminant in Galotyri cheese has been investigated by Papageorgiou et al. (1998) and Rogga et al. (2005). In the first study (Papageorgiou et al., 1998), Galotyri was obtained from local markets and upon transfer to the laboratory the cheese was inoculated (3.5 - 7.5 $\times$ 10^5 cfu/g) with *L. monocytogenes* (strains Scott A or CA). The inoculum was mixed thoroughly into the cheese mass and the inoculated cheese was stored at 5 or 12°C in plastic containers. The average physicochemical composition of the cheeses was determined just prior to the inoculations (moisture 68%, FDM 50.1%, NaCl 1.54%, pH 4.35) and remained essentially unchanged during storage. The populations of both *L. monocytogenes* strains decreased significantly during storage at 5°C, particularly during the first week of storage, reaching low (< 10 cfu/g) levels after one to two weeks. Viable *L. monocytogenes* could be detected for up to 16 - 24 days post-inoculation. Similarly, significant reductions in the *L. monocytogenes* populations were also observed during the 12°C-storage trials. A noticeable *L. monocytogenes* "tailing" effect was evident in all trials.

The study addressed the behavior of *L. monocytogenes* introduced as a post-processing contaminant in Galotyri cheese. Given the numerous handling steps (described above) involved during the manufacture of Galotyri, a future study simulating *L. monocytogenes* contamination scenarios after the milk-boiling step would provide essential additional data regarding the behavior of the pathogen during the initial steps of cheese manufacture.

In the second study, the survival of *L. monocytogenes* was evaluated as a post-processing contaminant of freshly produced Galotyri cheese (Rogga et al., 2005), and additional factors were investigated compared to the study by Papageorgiou et al. (1998). The experimental setting involved the use of Galotyri produced at a commercial scale (purchased from the retail outlets of two local dairy plants), as well as "pilot" Galotyri, prepared in the laboratory in order to evaluate the effects of certain deviations of modern Galotyri production practices from the traditional manufacturing practices. The manufacture of pilot cheeses also enabled their inoculation while at the beginning of draining, a processing step when the risk for cross-contamination is higher (for instance, during placement of the curd to a potentially contaminated cheese cloth).

Both types of commercial Galotyri were produced from pasteurized ovine milk with the addition of commercial or natural starters and their manufacturing process involved a short draining (10 - 18 h at 15°C) and holding period under refrigeration (4 - 5 days after preparation). A five-strain cocktail *L. monocytogenes* (Scott A, N-7144 and N-7155, two meat isolates, DC-LM1 and DC-LM4, two cheese isolates) was used to inoculate (*ca.* 10^3 or 10^7 cfu/g) commercially manufactured Galotyri (containing less than 2% salt), of the artisan (pH = 4) or of the industrial (pH = 3.8) type. The "pilot" Galotyri was manufactured using freshly milked ovine milk, heated to 90°C over a gas burner with the addition of 3% NaCl.

After milk cooling, 0.7% (w/v) of a commercially produced industrial or artisan cheese was added as starter. After 2 h at room temperature, the milks were transferred at 30°C for 2 days, being periodically agitated. The coagulated milks were placed in disinfected cheese cloths and left to drain (6 - 8 h at 15°C followed by overnight draining at 4°C) by hanging. After cheese draining, cheese portions were placed in plastic containers and inoculated with the same five-strain inoculum (*ca.* 10^3 cfu/g). Contaminated samples were stored aerobically at 4 or 12°C. The highly structured experimental design enabled the investigators to reveal interesting differences in the microbiological and physicochemical composition between the different types of Galotyri and assign or at least correlate the observed differences with differences in manufacturing practices.

Some of the many interesting findings of this study are briefly summarized as follows: overall, the commercial artisan Galotyri had a higher content of yeasts and bacterial contaminants associated with plant hygiene (e.g. enterobacteria) than the respective industrial product, and in the "pilot" cheeses, the batch-to-batch inoculation practice resulted in enhanced presence of the above contaminants. *L. monocytogenes* declined rapidly in both types of commercial cheese, particularly during the first 3 days of storage, when average declines of 1.3 - 1.6 and 3.7 - 4.6 log cfu/g were noted in cheese samples inoculated with the low- and high inocula, respectively.

Interestingly, these declines in the populations of *L. monocytogenes* were independent of the cheese type or the storage temperature. At 4°C, the survival of *L. monocytogenes* during the subsequent storage period was characterized by a strong "tailing" effect, independent of the initial inoculation level. Thus, 1.4 - 1.8 log cfu/g of survivors could be enumerated after 4 weeks of storage of all cheeses at 4°C. At 12°C, low numbers (1.2 - 1.7 log cfu/g) of *L. monocytogenes* also survived for 14 days. The survival of *L. monocytogenes* in "pilot" Galotyri appeared to be affected by both the origin of the batch-to-batch starter inoculum, as well as by storage temperature.

In artisan-type "pilot" cheese made using natural starters (pH *ca.* 4.4; NaCl *ca.* 3%) *L. monocytogenes* was inactivated at 14 and 21 days of storage at 12 and 4°C, respectively. However, when an industrial starter was used during "pilot" Galotyri cheesemaking, viable populations of the pathogen could be enumerated at the end of the observation period (28 days of storage at both temperatures).

Both studies have provided evidence that Galotyri does not support the growth of *L. monocytogenes* when the pathogen is introduced as a post-manufacturing contaminant. Rather, the pathogen counts decreased with a rate that was more pronounced during the first days post-inoculation. However, the strong *L. monocytogenes* "tailing" effect exhibited in both studies, and in particular the fact that the survival of *L. monocytogenes* was independent of the initial inoculum in the Rogga et al. (2005) study suggest that inactivation of even a low post-processing contamination of Galotyri cheese under commercial conditions of distribution and storage many not be assured.

Katiki Domokou Cheese

Katiki is a soft, fresh, acid-curd, spreadable cheese produced by caprine milk or mixtures of it with ovine milk in the area of Domokos (central Greece). Katiki is an unripened cheese consumed within a few days after manufacture. Raw or pasteurized milk can be used, but nowadays the cheese is manufactured mainly using pasteurized milk and a mesophilic starter culture (Panagou, 2008; Litopoulou-Tzanetaki and Tzanetakis, 2011). The milk is heated at 75°C for 30 s, cooled at 27-28°C and placed in a cheese vat with or without the addition of rennet to sour and curdle at 20-22°C. The curd is then transferred to cheese cloths for draining. The drained cheese is then salted, mixed, packaged and stored at a temperature lower than 4°C (Greek Codex of Foodstuffs and Beverages, 2009; Litopoulou-Tzanetaki and Tzanetakis, 2011). The maximum allowable moisture content and the minimum FDM values for Katiki are set to 75% and 40%, respectively (Greek Codex of Foodstuffs and Beverages, 2009).

The Behavior of *L. monocytogenes* During Storage of Katiki Domokou Cheese

Panagou (2008) inoculated (*ca.* 10^6 cfu/g) commercially manufactured Katiki obtained from a local market (pH = 4.5 - 4.6) with a five-strain cocktail (NTCT 10527, and the cheese isolates Scott A, LMBF-123, LMBF-131 and LMBF-133) of *L. monocytogenes*. The contaminated cheeses were stored at 5, 10, 15 or 20°C. The emphasis of this work was on the use of neural networks (elaborate predictive microbiology tools) to determine the survival of *L. monocytogenes* in Katiki during storage at constant temperatures. The results of the study showed clear inactivation trends in the populations of *L. monocytogenes* at all storage temperatures. Interestingly, an initial "shoulder", followed by a log-linear declining phase and an extended "tailing" phase, characterized all inactivation curves (Panagou, 2008). Similar observations regarding the reductions of *L. monocytogenes* during storage at different temperatures were later also observed in artificially contaminated processed cheese (Angelidis et al., 2010). As a result, although the populations of *L. monocytogenes* in contaminated Katiki were rapidly decreased (albeit, with different rates, depending on storage temperature) in all trials during the first 1 - 2 weeks of storage, *L. monocytogenes* surviving populations of up to 2 log cfu/g could be enumerated until the end of the experiments (*ca.* 10 days at 20°C or 40 days at 5°C). The average populations of LAB increased from 6.2 - 6.5 cfu/g to 8.0 - 8.2 cfu/g during storage and a small decrease in the pH was noted during the same time period (from 4.6 - 4.5 to 4.2 - 4.3). The author proposed that the presence of "tailing" could be attributed to possible heterogeneity in the *L. monocytogenes* cells and potentially to the development of defensive/adaptive mechanisms in response to acid stress.

A subsequent study was published in the same year, focusing again on modeling of the survival of *L. monocytogenes* during storage of commercial samples of Katiki cheese (Mataragas et al., 2008). In this study, the *L. monocytogenes* strain cocktail, the inoculum level and the storage temperatures were the same as those described by Panagou (2008). However, acid-adapted *L. monocytogenes* cells were also used in certain experimental trials. The reported results regarding the growth of LAB and the drop in pH in the contaminated cheeses during storage were identical to those reported by Panagou (2008) and did not differ between experiments involving acid-adapted or non-acid adapted *L. monocytogenes* cells. Interestingly, however, and in contrast to the shape of the survival curves in the first study, the shape of the survival curves (of both the acid-adapted and non-acid adapted inoculum trials) in the Mataragas et al. (2008) study was bi-phasic, i.e., the rapid inactivation of the pathogen proceeded without an initial "shoulder" phase. Instead, following a rapid log-linear decrease in the populations of *L. monocytogenes* during the first 5-10 days of storage, the subsequent inactivation was much lower, displaying a "tail". As a result, *L. monocytogenes* surviving populations (1-2 log cfu/g) could be enumerated until the end of storage (11 days at 20°C or 40 days at 5°C).

Acid-adapted *L. monocytogenes* cells were inactivated at the same rate as non-acid-adapted cells within a given storage temperature. However, the survival was temperature-dependent, with faster inactivation rates observed at elevated storage temperatures. This study illustrated the usefulness of challenge tests in combination with mathematical modeling as tools for describing and estimating bacterial growth in foods.

A third study pertaining to the survival of *L. monocytogenes* in artificially contaminated commercial Katiki cheese was published in the following year (Kagkli et al., 2009). Five strains of *L. monocytogenes* were either used individually or as a cocktail for inoculation of Katiki cheese. Contaminated cheeses were inoculated at *ca.* 10^6 cfu/g and stored at the same temperatures as in previous studies (Panagou, 2008; Mataragas et al., 2008). In order to monitor the fate, during storage, of individual strains comprising the cocktail inoculum, several colonies were being picked from the highest dilution from *L. monocytogenes*-selective plates at several time points throughout cheese storage and subjected to Pulse-Field Gel Electrophoresis typing. The results regarding the growth of LAB and the drop in pH in the contaminated cheeses during storage were identical to those previously reported by the other two Katiki cheese studies (Panagou, 2008; Mataragas et al., 2008). Similar to the results of previous studies *L. monocytogenes* counts decreased with storage time, with the *L. monocytogenes* populations remaining viable for a longer storage time at low temperatures. However, the shape of the inactivation curves appeared to be neither tri-phasic (Panagou, 2008), nor bi-phasic (Mataragas et al., 2008).

The results also indicated that different strains displayed a different survival capability at different storage temperatures. For instance, *L. monocytogenes* Scott A was the most persistent strain both individually or when mixed with other *L. monocytogenes* strains, surviving the longest at all tested temperatures. The increased survival capacity of this particular strain over other *L. monocytogenes* strains has been also demonstrated in previously conducted, single-strain inoculum challenge studies involving other Greek PDO cheeses (e.g., Papageorgiou et al., 1996, 1998b). All three published studies have demonstrated the inability of *L. monocytogenes* to proliferate in artificially contaminated, commercial samples of Katiki cheese (with a pH of 4.5 - 4.6 at the time of inoculation) when the pathogen is introduced as a post-processing contaminant at high initial levels. Instead, pathogen populations decreased during storage under both refrigeration (5°C) and temperature abusive conditions (10, 15 or 20°C). It is noteworthy, however, that whereas in all three studies the overall decreasing trends were similar, there were noticeable differences in the shape of the inactivation curves among studies, even though the experimental set-up (inoculum preparation, inoculum level, inoculation procedure and storage of contaminated samples) was very similar.

Table 3. Behavior of *Listeria monocytogenes* during the manufacture and storage of selected PDO Greek cheeses when the pathogen is introduced during cheese manufacture, or as a post-processing contaminant

Cheese	Contamination stage / inoculum type (strains) / inoculum level (cfu per mL, g or cm^2)	Comments	Behavior of *L. monocytogenes*	Reference
Feta	Milk, post pasteurization / single-strain, Scott A or CA / 5 x 10^3.	Thermophilic starters (*L. bulgaricus, S. thermophilus*).	Growth of *ca.* 1.5 log cfu/g during the initial 2 d of ripening at 22°C. Slow but significant reduction during ripening and storage at 4°C, but survival of both strains for more than 90 d. Strain CA was less tolerant than Scott A.	Papageorgiou and Marth, 1989
Feta	Milk, raw or post pasteurization / one bioluminescent strain / 10^4.	Mesophilic starters (*L. lactis* subsp. *lactis* nisin-producing or not).	Growth (*ca.* 1.0 log cfu/g) during the initial 24 h of ripening at 18°C. Reduction (*ca.* 1 log) during ripening (75 d at 2°C), only in trials with a nisin-producing starter. Survival without reduction in non-nisin producing starter trials for up to 75 d at 2°C.	Ramsaran et al., 1998
Feta	Milk, post pasteurization / strain NCTC 10357 / 10^3	Mesophilic starters (*L. lactis* subsp. *lactis*, *L. lactis* subsp. *cremoris*).	Populations in the 60-d ripened cheese (at 4°C) were *ca.* 2 x 10^5.	Konteles et al., 2009
Feta	60-d ripened cheese / single or cocktail, Scott A or Lmk / surface contamination 10^4.	Storage under MAP (50% CO_2, 50% N_2).	Fast decline in counts. Undetectable populations after 30 d of storage at 4°C.	Govaris et al., 2011
Galotyri	Market samples, post-processing / single-strain, Scott A or CA / uniform contamination 3.6-7.5 x 10^5.		Fast reduction during storage at 5 or 12°C. Viable cells present for up to 27 d at 12°C and 24 d at 5°C.	Papageorgiou et al., 1998
Galotyri	Market samples or laboratory samples at draining / cocktail of Scott A, N-7144, N-7155, DCLM1, DC-LM4 / uniform contamination 1 x 10^3 or 1 x 10^7.	Commercially and laboratory manufactured cheeses of the industrial and artisan types were tested.	Fast reduction at 4 or 12°C with pronounced "tailing". In commercial cheese, survival for up to 28 d at 4°C, independent of initial inoculum. Populations declined independent of storage temperature. In laboratory cheese, survival throughout 28 d of storage at both temperatures in industrial-type cheese, but only for 14 and 21 d of storage at 12 and 4°C, respectively in artisan-type cheese.	Rogga et al., 2005

Cheese	Contamination stage / inoculum type (strains) / inoculum level (cfu per mL, g or cm²)	Comments	Behavior of *L. monocytogenes*	Reference
Graviera	Fully-ripened (>90 days) cheese / cocktail of Scott A, ISS G79, ISS G185, WSLC 1294, WSLC 1482 / surface contamination 10^3.	Mesophilic and thermophilic starters (*S. thermophilus*, *L. lactis* subsp. *lactis*, *L. lactis* subsp. *diacetylactis*, leuconostocs) with or without *E. faecium* KE82 Ent⁺. Storage under vacuum or air at 4, 12 or 25°C.	No growth on the cheese surface. Long survival with slow reduction rate during storage. The lower the storage temperature, the higher and longer the pathogen survived. Greater survival under vacuum.	Giannou et al., 2009a
Graviera	A: Milk, post thermization / cocktail of Scott A, ISS G79, ISS G185 / 10^4. B: Fresh cheese curds (pH=6.3±0.2) before molding / cocktail of *L. innocua* LMG11387 and M58 and "non-pathogenic" *L. monocytogenes* / 10^3.	A: No starter or mesophilic and thermophilic starters (*S. thermophilus*, *L. lactis* subsp. *lactis*, *L. lactis* subsp. *diacetylactis*, leuconostocs). B: Molded cheeses were kept at 18°C overnight, immersed in 20% brine at 12°C for 24 h, drained at 12°C for 24 h, ripened at 18°C for 20 d and then stored at 4°C under vacuum.	A: Increase during 6 h at 37 and 6 h at 18°C in the absence (*ca.* 2 log) and presence (*ca.* 1.5 log) of starters. Slight reductions during the following 60 h at 18°C. B: Small (*ca.* 0.8 log) decrease in the first 24 h of ripening. No further reduction until 60 d of ripening.	Samelis et al., 2009
Kasseri	Market samples / cocktail of Scott A, V7, RM-1, VPH1, VPH2 / surface contamination *ca.* 10^4	One sample of pH=4.8 and one sample of pH=5.3 were used.	No growth. "Maximum death" of 2.04 log after 8 d at 30°C, 24 d at 8°C or 36 d at 4°C (pH=5.3) or 4 d at 30°C, 8 d at 8°C or 6 d at 4°C (pH=5.3).	Genigeorgis et al., 1991
Katiki	Market samples / cocktail of Scott A, NCTC 10527, LMBF-123, LMBF-131, LMBF-133 / uniform contamination 10^6 cfu/g.	Application of the neural network modeling approach to describe the kinetic behavior of the pathogen in Katiki.	Fast reduction at 5, 10, 15 or 20°C. Tri-phasic inactivation curves ("shoulder", log-linear and "tailing: phase). Up to 2 log cfu/g survivors by the end of the experiments (10 d at 20°C or 40 d at 5°C).	Panagou, 2008

Table 3. (Continued)

Cheese	Contamination stage / inoculum type (strains) / inoculum level (cfu per mL, g or cm^2)	Comments	Behavior of *L. monocytogenes*	Reference
Katiki	Market samples / cocktail of Scott A, NCTC 10527, LMBF-123, LMBF-131, LMBF-133 / uniform contamination 10^6 cfu/g.	Acid-adapted and non-acid adapted inoculum was used. Various models were fitted to the survival data and the best model identified through thorough statistical evaluation.	Fast initial reduction at 5, 10, 15 or 20°C. Bi-phasic inactivation curves (log-linear and "tailing: phase). No difference in survival between acid-adapted and non-adapted cells. Longer survival at lower storage temperatures. 1-2 log cfu/g survivors until the end of the experiments (11 d at 20°C or 40 d at 5°C).	Mataragas et al., 2008
Katiki	Market samples / individual (single-strain) or cocktail of TS124, TS125, TS128, TS131, TS133 / uniform contamination 10^6 cfu/g.	PFGE was used to monitor the behavior of each strain in the mixture.	Fast reduction during storage at 5, 10, 15 or 20°C. Faster reduction at higher temperatures. Different strains displayed different survival capability at different storage temperatures. Survivors up to 2 log cfu/g by the end of the experiments (10 d at 20°C or 30 d at 5°C).	Kagkli et al. 2009
Manouri	Cheese immediately post-manufacture / single-strain, Scott A or CA / uniform contamination 5 x 10^2.	Cheese made with the addition of 80 Kg cream (63% fat content) and 15 Kg NaCl to 1000 L whey.	Growth to very high cell densities (> 8 log) during storage at 5, 12 and 22°C.	Papageorgiou et al., 1996
Pichtogalo Chanion	Raw milk or milk, post pasteurization / single-strain, Scott A or CA / 2 x 10^2, 2 x 10^3 or 2 x 10^5.	No starter (raw milk trial) or mesophilic starters (pasteurized milk trials) (*L. lactis* subsp. *lactis*, *L. lactis* biovar *diacetylactis*, *Lb. casei* subsp. *casei*, *Lb. casei* subsp. *pseudoplantarum*).	No change during the first 12 h of cheesemaking. Significant decrease during subsequent storage at 4°C. Inactivation to undetectable levels at 5 to 20 d.	Theodoridis et al., 2006

Conclusion

This work summarized the experimental set-up and the main findings of published studies dealing with the behavior of *L. monocytogenes* during the manufacture and storage of seven PDO Greek cheeses. Table 3 briefly summarizes the behavior of *L. monocytogenes* during the manufacture and storage of these seven PDO Greek cheeses when the pathogen is introduced during cheese manufacture, or as a post-processing contaminant, including some of the central points of the studies' experimental set-up. Greek PDO cheeses maintain a good safety record with respect to listeriosis, being associated wth none of the reported cheese-borne outbreaks worldwide. In order, to avoid contamination of Greek PDO cheeses with *L. monocytogenes,* control measures such as Good Manufacturing Practices (GMP) and HACCP should be applied by the dairy industry.

References

Alichanidis, E., Polychroniadou, A., Tzanetakis, N., Vafopoulou, A., 1981. Teleme cheese from deep-frozen curd. *Journal of Dairy Science* 64, 732-739.

Alichanidis, E., Anifantakis, E.M., Polychroniadou, A., Nanou, M., 1984. Suitability of some microbial coagulants for Feta cheese manufacture. *Journal of Dairy Research* 51, 141-147.

Alichanidis, E., Polychroniadou, A., 2008. Characteristics of major traditional regional cheese varieties of East-Mediterranean countries: a review. *Dairy Science and Technology* 88, 495-510.

Alterkruse, S.F., Timbo, B.B., Mowbray, J.C., Bean, N.H., Potter, M.E., 1998. Cheese-associated outbreaks of human illness in the United States, 1973 to 1992: sanitary manufacturing practices protect consumers. *Journal of Food Protection* 61, 1405-1407.

Anastasiou, R., Georgalaki, M., Manolopoulou, E., Kandarakis, I., De Vuyst, L., Tsakalidou, E., 2007. The performance of *Streptococcus macedonicus* ACA-DC 198 as starter culture in Kasseri cheese production. *International Dairy Journal* 17, 208-217.

Angelidis, A.S., Smith, L.T., Smith, G.M., 2002. Elevated carnitine accumulation by *Listeria monocytogenes* impaired in glycine betaine transport is insufficient to restore wild-type cryotolerance in milk whey. *International Journal of Food Microbiology* 75, 1-9.

Angelidis, A.S., Smith, G.M., 2003. Role of the glycine betaine and carnitine transporters in adaptation of *Listeria monocytogenes* to chill stress in defined medium. *Applied and Environmental Microbiology* 69, 7492-7498.

Angelidis, A.S., Chronis, E.N., Papageorgiou, D.K., Kazakis, I.I., Arsenoglou, K.C., Stathopoulos, G.A., 2006. Non-lactic acid, contaminating microbial flora in ready-to-eat foods: A potential food-quality index. *Food Microbiology*, 23, 95-100.

Angelidis, A.S., Boutsiouki, P., Papageorgiou, D.K., 2010. Loss of viability of *Listeria monocytogenes* in contaminated processed cheese during storage at 4, 12 and 22°C. *Food Microbiology* 27, 809-818.

Angelidis, A.S., Georgiadou, S.S., Zafiropoulou, V., Velonakis, E.N., Papageorgiou, D.K., Vatopoulos, A., 2012. A survey of soft cheeses in Greek retail outlets highlights a low prevalence of *Listeria* spp. *Dairy Science and Technology* 92, 189-201.

Anifantakis, E. M., 1991. Greek cheeses: a tradition of centuries. *National Dairy Committee of Greece.* Athens, Greece.

Arvanitoyannis, I.S., Mavropoulos, A.A., 2000. Implementation of the hazard analysis critical control point (HACCP) system to Kasseri/Kefalotyri and Anevato cheese production lines. *Food Control* 11, 31-40.

Belessi, C.-I. A., Papanikolaou, S., Drosinos, E. H., Skandamis, P. N., 2008. Survival and acid resistance of *Listeria innocua* in Feta cheese and yogurt, in the presence or absence of fungi. *Journal of Food Protection* 71, 742-749.

Bintsis, T., Litopoulou-Tzanetaki, E., Davies, R., Robinson, R.K., 2000. Microbiology of brines used to mature feta cheese. *International Journal of Dairy Technology* 53, 106-112.

Bintsis, T., 2006. Quality of the brine. In: *Brined cheeses.* Tamine, A., (Ed.). Blackwell Publishing, Oxford, U.K.

De Buyser, M., Dufour, B., Maire, M., Lafarge, V., 2001. Implication of milk and milk products in food-borne diseases in France and different industrialized countries. *International Journal of Food Microbiology* 67, 1-17.

Dewaal, C.S., Hicks, G., Barlow, K., Alderton, L., Vegosen, L., 2006. Foods associated with foodborne illness outbreaks from 1990 through 2003. *Food Protection Trends* 26, 466–473.

Efthymiou, C., 1967. Major free fatty acids of Feta cheese. *Journal of Dairy Science* 50, 20-24.

European Commission, 1996. Commission Regulation (EC) No. 1107/96 of 12 June 1996 on the registration of geographical indications and designations of origin under the procedure laid down in Article 17 of Council Regulation (EEC) No 2081/921107/96. *Official Journal of the European Union* L148, 1-16.

European Commission, 2002. Commission Regulation (EC) No 1829/2002 of 14 October 2002 amending the Annex to Regulation (EC) No 1107/96 with regard to the name 'Feta'. *Official Journal of the European Union* L277, 10-14.

European Commission, 2005. Commission Regulation (EC) No. 2073/2005 of 15 November 2005 on microbiological criteria for foodstuffs. *Official Journal of the European Union* L338, 1-26.

European Commission, 2007. Commission Regulation (EC) No 1441/2007 of 5 December 2007 amending Regulation (EC) No 2073/2005 on microbiological criteria for foodstuffs. *Official Journal of the European Union* L 332, 12-29.

European Commission, 2011. Commission implementing Regulation (EU) No 766/2011 of 29 July 2011 entering a name in the register of protected designations of origin and protected geographical indications [Ξύγαλο Σητείας (Xygalo Siteias)/Ξίγαλο Σητείας (Xigalo Siteias) (PDO)]. *Official Journal of the European Union* L 200, 12-13.

European Food Safety Authority (EFSA), 2009. Report of the Task Force on Zoonoses Data Collection on proposed technical specifications for a survey on *Listeria monocytogenes* in selected categories of ready-to-eat food at retail in the EU. *EFSA Journal* 300, 1-66.

EFSA, 2010. The Community summary report on trends and sources of zoonoses, zoonotic agents and food-borne outbreaks in the European Union in 2008. *EFSA Journal* 8, 1-368.

Filiousis, G., Johansson, A., Frey, J., Perreten, V., 2009. Prevalence, genetic diversity and antimicrobial susceptibility of *Listeria monocytogenes* isolated from ope-air markets in Greece. *Food Control* 20, 314-317.

Genigeorgis, C., Carniciu, M., Dutulescu, D., Farver, T.B., 1991. Growth and survival of *Listeria monocytogenes* in market cheeses stored at 4 to 30°C. *Journal of Food Protection* 54, 662-668.

Georgala, A., Moschopoulou, E., Aktypis, A., Massouras, T., Zoidou, E., Kandarakis, I., Anifantakis, E., 2005. Evolution of lipolysis during the ripening of traditional Feta cheese. *Food Chemistry* 93, 73-80.

Giannou, E., Kakouri, A., Matijasic, B.B., Rogelj, I., Samelis, J., 2009a. Fate of *Listeria monocytogenes* on fully ripened Greek Graviera cheese stored at 4, 12, or 25°C in air or vacuum packages: in situ PCR detection of a cocktail of bacteriocins potentially contributing to pathogen inhibition. *Journal of Food Protection* 72, 531-538.

Giannou, E., Lianou, A., Kakouri, A., Kallimanis, A., Drainas, C., Samelis, J., 2009b. Identification and biopreservation potential of *Enterococcus* spp. Isolated from fully ripened Graviera, a traditional hard Greek cheese. *Italian Journal of Food Science* 21, 135-147.

Govaris, A., Botsoglou, E., Sergelidis, D., Chatzopoulou, P. S., 2011. Antibacterial activity of oregano and thyme essential oils against *Listeria monocytogenes* and *Escherichia coli* O157:H7 in feta cheese packaged under modified atmosphere. *LWT – Food Science and Technology* 44, 1240-1244.

Greek Codex of Foodstuffs and Beverages, 2009. Article 83: Cheeses products. *National Printing Office*, Athens, Greece.

Greenwood, M.H., Roberts, D., Burden, P., 1991. The occurrence of *Listeria* species in milk and dairy products: a national survey in England and Wales. *International Journal of Food Microbiology* 12, 197-206.

ISO 11290-1:1996/Amd 1-2004, 2004. Microbiology of food and animal feedingstuffs – Horizontal method for the detection and enumeration of *Listeria monocytogenes* – Part 1: Detection method. International Organization for Standardization, Geneva, Switzerland.

Kagkli, D.-M., Iliopoulos, V., Stergiou, V., Lazaridou, A., Nychas, G.-J., 2009. Differential *Listeria monocytogenes* strain survival and growth in Katiki, a traditional Greek soft cheese, at different storage temperatures *Applied and Environmental Microbiology* 75, 3621-3626.

Kaminarides, S.E., Siaravas, V., Potetsianaki, I., 1995. Comparison of 2 methods of making kneaded plastic cheese from ewe's milk. *Lait* 75, 181-189.

Kaminarides, S., Paraschopoulos, N., Beri, I., 1999. Combined effects of concentrated thermophilic and mesophilic cultures and conditions of curd acidifications on the manufacture and quality of kasseri cheese. *International Journal of Dairy Technology* 52, 11-19.

Kandarakis, I.G., Moschopoulou, E.E., Moatsou, G.A., Anifantakis, E., 1998. Effect of starters on gross and microbiological composition and organoleptic characteristics of Graviera Kritis cheese. *Lait* 78, 557-568.

Kandarakis, I., Moschopoulou, E., Anifantakis, E., 1999. Use of fermentation produced chymosin from *E. coli* in the manufacture of Feta cheese. *Milchwissenschaft* 54, 24-26.

Kandarakis, I., Moatsou, G., Georgala, A., Kaminarides, S., Anifantakis, E., 2001. Effect of draining temperature on the biochemical characteristics of Feta cheese. *Food Chemistry*, 72, 369-378.

Karageorgis, S.B., Papageorgiou, D.K., Mantis, A.I., Georgakis, S.A., 2005. Use of mesophilic lactic acid bacteria in the manufacture of Feta cheese. *Journal of the Hellenic Veterinary Medical Society* 56, 197-218.

Katsiari, M.C., Voutsinas, L.P., Alichanidis, E., Roussis, I.G., 1997. Reduction of sodium content in Feta cheese by partial substitution of NaCl by KCl. *International Dairy Journal* 7, 465-472.

Katsiari, M.C., Alichanidis, E., Voutsinas, L.P., Roussis, I.G., 2000. Proteolysis in reduced sodium Feta cheese made by partial substitution of NaCl by KCl. *International Dairy Journal* 10, 635-646.

Katsiari, M.C., Voutsinas, L.P., Kondyli, E., Alichanidis, E., 2002. Flavour enhancement of low-fat Feta-type cheese using a commercial adjunct culture. *Food Chemistry* 79, 193-198.

Kondyli, E., Katsiari, M.C., Masouras, T., Voutsinas, L.P., 2002. Free fatty acids and volatile compounds of low-fat Feta-type cheese made with a commercial adjunct culture. *Food Chemistry* 79, 199-205.

Konteles, S., Sinanoglou, V.J., Batrinou, A., Sflomos, K., 2009. Effects of γ-irradiation on *Listeria monocytogenes* population, colour, texture and sensory properties of Feta cheese during cold storage. *Food Microbiology* 26, 157-165.

Kornacki, J.L., Gurtler, J.B., 2007. In: Ryser, E.T., Marth, E.H., (eds) Listeria, listeriosis and food safety, 3rd edn. CRC Press, Boca Raton, FL.

Kousta, M., Mataragas, M., Skandamis, P., Drosinos, E.H., 2010. Prevalence and sources of cheese contamination with pathogens at farm and processing levels *Food Control* 21, 805-815.

Kykkidou, S., Pournis, N., Kostoula, O.K., Savvaidis, I.N., 2007. Effects of treatment with nisin on the microbial flora and sensory properties of a Greek soft acid-curd cheese stored aerobically at 4°C. *International Dairy Journal* 17, 1254-1258.

Lalos, G., Voutsinas, L.P., Pappas, C.P., Roussis, I.G., 1996. Effect of a sub-pasteurization treatment of cold stored ewe's milk on the quality of Feta cheese. *Milchwissenschaft* 51, 78-82.

Lianou, A., Sofos, J.N., 2007. A review of the incidence and transmission of *Listeria monocytogenes* in ready-to-eat products in retail and food service environments. *Journal of Food Protection* 70, 2172-2198.

Linan, M.J., Mascola, L., Dong Lou, X., Goulet, V., May, S., Salminen, C., Hird, D.W., Yonekura, M.L., Hayes, P., Weaver, R., Audurier, A., Plikaytis, B.D., Fannin, S.L., Kleks, A., Broome, C.V., 1988. Epidemic listeriosis associated with Mexican-style cheese. *New England Journal of Medicine* 319, 823-828.

Lioliou, K., Litopoulou-Tzanetaki, E., Tzanetakis, N., Robinson, R.K., 2001. Changes in the microflora of manouri, a traditional Greek whey cheese, during storage. *International Journal of Dairy Technology* 54, 100-106.

Litopoulou-Tzanetaki, E., Tzanetakis, N., Vafopoulou-Mastrojiannaki, A., 1993. Effect of the type of lactic starter on microbiological chemical and sensory characteristics of Feta cheese. *Food Microbiology* 10, 31-41.

Litopoulou-Tzanetaki, E., Tzanetakis, N., 2011. Microbiological characteristics of Greek traditional cheeses. *Small Ruminant Research* 101, 17-32.

Lunden, J., Tolvanen, R., Korkeala, H., 2004. Human listeriosis outbreaks linked to dairy products in Europe. *Journal of Dairy Science* 87(suppl.), E6-E11.

Mallatou, H., Pappas, C.P., Voutsinas, L.P., 1994. Manufacture of Feta cheese from sheep's milk, goats' milk or mixtures of these milks. *International Dairy Journal* 4, 641-664.

Manolopoulou, E., Sarantinopoulos, P., Zoidou, E., Aktypis, A., Moschopoulou, E., Kandarakis, G., Anifantakis, E., 2003. Evolution of microbial populations during traditional Feta cheese manufacture and ripening. *International Journal of Food Microbiology* 82, 153-161.

Mataragas, M., Stergiou, V., Nychas, G.-J.E., 2008. Modelling survival of *Listeria monocytogenes* in the traditional Greek soft cheese Katiki. *Journal of Food Protection* 71, 1835-1845.

Mauropoulos, A.A., Arvanitoyannis, I.S., 1999. Implementation of hazard analysis critical control point to Feta and Manouri cheese production lines. *Food Control* 10, 213-219.

Michaelidou, A., Alichanidis, E., Urlaub, H., Polychroniadou, A., Zerfiridis, G.K., 1998. Isolation and identification of some major water-soluble peptides in Feta cheese. *Journal of Dairy Science* 81, 3109-3116.

Michaelidou, A.-M., Alichanidis, E., Polychroniadou, A. Zerfiridis, G. 2005. Migration of water-soluble nitrogenous compounds of Feta cheese from the cheese blocks into the brine. *International Dairy Journal* 15, 663-668.

Moatsou, G., Kandarakis, I., Moschopoulou, E., Anifantakis, E., Alichanidis, E., 2001. Effect of technological parameters on the characteristics of kasseri cheese made from raw or pasteurized ewes' milk. *International Journal of Dairy Technology* 54, 69-77.

Moatsou, G., Massouras, T., Kandarakis, I., Anifantakis, E., 2002. Evolution of proteolysis during the ripening of traditional Feta cheese. *Lait* 82, 601-611.

Moatsou, G., Moschopoulou, E., Georgala, A., Zoidou, E., Kandarakis, I., Kaminarides, S., Anifantakis, E., 2004. Effect of artisanal liquid rennet from kids and lambs abomasa on the characteristics of Feta cheese. *Food Chemistry* 88, 517-525.

Moatsou, G., Govaris, A., 2011. White brined cheeses: A diachronic exploitation of small ruminants milk in Greece. *Small Ruminant Research* 101, 113-121.

Moschopoulou, E., Anisa, T., Katsaros, G., Taoukis, P., Moatsou, G., 2010. Application of high-pressure treatment on ovine brined cheese: effect of composition and microflora throughout ripening. *Innovative Food Science and Engineering Technologies* 11, 543-550.

Meyer-Broseta, S., Diot, A., Bastian, S., Rivière, J., Cerf, O., 2003. Estimation of low bacterial concentration: *Listeria monocytogenes* in raw milk. *International Journal of Food Microbiology* 80, 1-15.

Nega, A., Moatsou, G., 2012. Proteolysis and related enzymatic activities in ten Greek cheese varieties. *Dairy Science and Technology* 92, 57-73.

Panagou, E.Z., 2008. A radial basis function neural network approach to determine the survival of *Listeria monocytogenes* in Katiki, a traditional Greek soft cheese. *Journal of Food Protection* 71, 750-759.

Papageorgiou, D.K., Marth, E.H., 1989. Fate of *L. monocytogenes* during the manufacture, ripening and storage of Feta cheese. *Journal of Food Protection* 52, 82-87.

Papageorgiou, D.K., Bori, M., Mantis, A., 1996. Growth of *Listeria monocytogenes* in the whey cheeses Myzithra, Anthotyros, and Manouri during storage at 5, 12, and 22°C. *Journal of Food Protection* 59, 1193-1199.

Papageorgiou, D.K., Bori, M., Mantis, A., 1997. Survival of *L. monocytogenes* in Frozen Ewe's milk and Feta cheese curd. *Journal of Food Protection* 60, 1041-1045.

Papageorgiou, D.K., Abrahim, A., Bori, M., Doundounakis, S., 1998a. Chemical and bacteriological characteristics of Pichtogalo Chanion cheese and mesophilic starter cultures for its production. *Journal of Food Protection* 61, 688-692.

Papageorgiou, D.K., Bori, M., Mantis, A. 1998b. Survival of *Listeria monocytogenes* during storage of soft cheeses Galotyri and Touloumotyri at 5°C and 12°C. *Bulletin of the Hellenic Veterinary Medical Society* 49, 48-53.

Pappa, H.C., Anyfantakis, E.M., 2001a. Effect of concentrated starter cultures on the manufacture of Feta cheese. *Milchwissenschaft* 56, 325-329.

Pappa, H.C., Anyfantakis, E.M., 2001b. Effect of different concentrated starter cultures on the proteolysis and organoleptic characteristics of Feta cheese. *Milchwissenschaft* 56, 384-391.

Pappas, C.P., Kondyli, E., Voutsinas, L.P., Mallatou, H., 1994. Effect of standardization of ewes' milk for casein/fat ratio on the composition, sensory and rheological properties of Feta cheese. *International Dairy Journal* 4, 763-778.

Pappas, C.P., Kondyli, E., Voutsinas, L.P., Mallatou, H., 1994. Effects of starter level, draining time and aging on the physicochemical, organoleptic and rheological properties of feta cheese. *Journal of the Society of Dairy Technology* 49, 73-78.

Pappas, C.P., Kondyli, E., Voutsinas, L.P., Mallatou, H., 1996. Effects of salting method and storage time on composition and quality of feta cheese. *Journal of the Society of Dairy Technology* 49, 113-118.

Ramsaran, H., Chen, J., Brunke, B., Hill, A., Griffiths, M.W., 1998. Survival of bioluminescent *Listeria monocytogenes* and *Escherichia coli* O157:H7 in soft cheeses. *Journal of Dairy Science* 81, 1810-1817.

Rantsiou, K., Urso, R., Dolci, P., Comi, G., Cocolin, L., 2008. Microflora of Fetac cheese from four Greek manufacturers. *International Journal of Food Microbiology* 126, 36-42.

Rodriguez, J.L., Gaya, P., Medina, M., Nunez, M., 1994. Incidence of *Listeria monocytogenes* and other *Listeria* spp. in ewe's raw milk. *Journal of Food Protection* 57, 571-575.

Rogga, K.J., Samelis, J., Kakouri, A., Katsiari, M.C., Savvaidis, I.N., Kontominas, M.G., 2005. Survival of *Listeria monocytogenes* in Galotyri, a traditional Greek soft acid-curd cheese, stored aerobically at 4°C and 12°C. *International Dairy Journal* 15, 59-67.

Ryser, E.T., 2007. In: Ryser, E.T., Marth, E.H., (eds) Listeria, listeriosis and food safety, 3rd edn. CRC Press, Boca Raton, FL.

Samelis, J., Kakouri, A., Rogga, K.J., Savvaidis, I.N., Kontominas, M.G., 2003. Nisin treatments to control *Listeria monocytogenes* post-processing contamination on Anthotyros, a traditional Greek whey cheese, stored at 4°C in vacuum packages. *Food Microbiology* 20, 661-669.

Samelis, J., Kakouri, A., 2007. Microbial and safety qualities of PDO Galotyri cheese manufactured at the industrial or artisan scale in Epirus, Greece. *Italian Journal of Food Science* 19, 81-90.

Samelis, J., Lianou, A., Kakouri, A., Delbes, C., Rogelj, I., Matijasic, B.B., Montel, M.-C., 2009a. Changes in the microbial composition of raw milk induced by thermization treatments applied prior to traditional Greek hard cheese processing. *Journal of Food Protection* 72, 783-790.

Samelis, J., Giannou, E., Lianou, A., 2009b. Assuring growth inhibition of listerial contamination during processing and storage of traditional Greek Graviera cheese: compliance with the new European Union regulatory criteria for *Listeria monocytogenes*. *Journal of Food Protection* 72, 2264-2271.

Samelis, J., Kakouri, A., Pappa, E.C., Matijasic, B.B., Georgalaki, M.D., Tsakalidou, E., Rogelj, I., 2010. Microbial stability and safety of traditional Greek Graviera cheese: characterization of the lactic acid bacterial flora and culture-independent detection of bacteriocin genes in the ripened cheeses and their microbial consortia. *Journal of Food Protection* 73, 1294-1303.

Sarantinopoulos, P., Kalantzopoulos, G., Tsakalidou, E., 2002. Effect of *Enterococcus faecium* on microbiological, physicochemical and sensory characteristics of Greek Feta cheese. *International Journal of Food Microbiology* 76, 93-105.

Schuchat, A., Deaver, K.A., Wenger, J.D., Plikaytis, B.D., Mascola, L., Pinner, R.W., Reingold, A.L., Broome, C.V., 1992. Role of foods in sporadic listeriosis. I. Case-control study of dietary risk factors. The Listeria Study Group. *Journal of the American Medical Association* 267, 2041–2045.

Theodoridis, A., Abrahim, A., Sarimvei, S., Panoulis, C., Karaioannoglou, P., Genigeorgis, C., Mantis, A., 1998. Prevalence and significance of *Listeria monocytogenes* in Greek whey cheeses. A comparison between the years 1990 and 1996. *Milchwissenschaft* 53, 147-149.

Theodoridis, A.K., Papageorgiou, D.K., Abrahim, A., Karaioannoglou, P.G., 2006. Fate of *Listeria monocytogenes* during the manufacture and storage of Metsovo and Pichtogalo Chanion cheeses. *Italian Journal of Food Science* 18, 51-61.

Tsakalidou, E., Zoidou, E., Pot, B., Wassil, L., Ludwig, W., Devriese, L.A., Kalantzopoulos, G., Schleifer, K.H., Kersters, K., 1998. Identification of streptococci from Greek Kasseri cheese and description of *Streptococcus macedonicus* sp. nov. *International Journal of Systematic Bacteriology*, 48, 519–527.

Tsigkos, D., Folland, E., Moate, R., Brennan, C.S., 2003. Feta cheese texture: the effect of caprine and ovine milk concentration. *International Journal of Dairy Technology* 56, 233-236.

Tsiotsias, A., Savvaidis, I., Vassila, A., Kontominas, M., Kotzekidou, P., 2002. Control of *Listeria monocytogenes* by low-dose irradiation in combination with refrigeration in the soft whey cheese 'Anthotyros'. *Food Microbiology* 19, 117-126.

Tzanetakis, N., Litopoulou-Tzanetaki, E., 1992. Changes in numbers and kinds of lactic acid bacteria in Feta and Telemes, two Greek cheeses from ewes' milk. *Journal of Dairy Science* 75, 1389-1393.

Vafopoulou, A. Alichanidis, E., Zerfiridis, G., 1989. Accelerated ripening of Feta cheese, with heat-shocked cultures or microbial proteinases. *Journal of Dairy Research* 56, 285-296.

Vassiliadis, A., Psoni, L., Nikolaou, S., Arvanitis, L., Tzanetakis, N., Litopoulou-Tzanetaki, E., 2009. Changes in microbial populations, kinds of lactic acid bacteria and biochemical characteristics of Greek traditional feta cheese during ripening. *International Journal of Dairy Technology* 62, 39-47.

Xanthopoulos, V., Hatzikamari, M., Adamidis, T., Tsakalidou, E., Tzanetakis, N., Litopoulou-Tzanetaki, E., 2000. Heterogeneity of *Lactobacillus plantarum* isolates from Feta cheese throughout ripening. *Journal of Applied Microbiology* 88, 1056-1064.

Zerfiridis, G.K., Vafopoulou-Mastrogiannaki, A., Litopoulou-Tzanetaki, E., 1984. Changes during ripening of commercial Gruyère cheese. *Journal of Dairy Science* 67, 1397-1405.

Zlatanos, S., Laskaridis, S., Feist, C., Sargedos, A., 2002. CLA content and fatty acid composition of Greek Feta and hard cheeses. *Food Chemistry* 78, 471-477.

In: Listeria Infections
Editors: A. Romano and C. F. Giordano

ISBN: 978-1-62081-639-4
© 2012 Nova Science Publishers, Inc.

Chapter II

Epidemic Clones of *Listeria monocytogenes*: Detection, Transmission and Virulence

Sara Lomonaco[*]

Department of Animal Pathology, Faculty of Veterinary Medicine,
Università degli Studi di Torino, Grugliasco, Torino, Italy

Abstract

Although many different serotypes of *Listeria monocytogenes* have been isolated from foods, only a few such as 1/2a, 1/2b, and 4b account for the vast majority of clinical cases, and in particular most outbreaks of listeriosis have involved a small number of closely related clones in serotypes 1/2a and 4b [1]. An epidemic clone (EC) of *L. monocytogenes* has been defined as groups of isolates that are genetically related and presumably of a common ancestor, but are implicated in different, geographically and temporally unrelated outbreaks [1–3]. Since the introduction of this concept in 2002, four ECs have been recognized: ECI, ECII, and ECIV in serotype 4b and ECIII in serotype 1/2a [1,2]. Most recently, in 2011, a novel serotype 1/2a EC that had been causing]disease in Canada for the past twenty years was detected and designated as ECV [4]. As *L. monocytogenes* continues to spread throughout the world and cause many different outbreaks, it is reasonable to assume that other novel ECs could be identified in the future. In order to control *L. monocytogenes*, determining the routes by which ECs and outbreak clones (OCs) are transmitted to foods will be extremely helpful. Consequently, the availability of subtyping assays capable of discerning closely related ECs and OCs is extremely important. In the past few years, the number and quality of subtyping assays has increased thanks to the development of DNA-based methods such as pulsed-field gel electrophoresis (PFGE), considered the gold-standard for its high discriminatory power (i.e. the ability to correctly differentiate unrelated strains). PFGE has proven to be a very

---

[*]Address for correspondence: Sara Lomonaco, Department of Animal Pathology Faculty of Veterinary Medicine, via Leonardo da Vinci 44, 10095 Grugliasco, Torino, Italy. Tel.: +39 011 670 9213; fax: +39 011 670 9224. E-mail address: sara.lomonaco@unito.it

accurate and reproducible method in subtyping *L. monocytogenes* [5]. However, new sequence-based techniques, such as multilocus-sequence typing (MLST) and single nucleotide polymorphism (SNP) typing, are also currently being used [2,6,7]. In particular, multi-virulence-locus sequence typing (MVLST) has been able to accurately identify and differentiate all five ECs of *L. monocytogenes* [2,4]. This technique also proved very useful in the identification of ECs, when PFGE failed to identify strains belonging to the same ECs due to the presence of different PFGE profiles [4,8]. Therefore, the use of novel DNA-sequence-based molecular subtyping strategies able to correctly determine the clonal relationship among different isolates is essential to accurately recognize outbreaks and epidemics and identify their routes of transmission. This chapter will review the five currently known ECs of *L. monocytogenes*, including listeriosis outbreaks caused by these ECs during the past few years, and the latest molecular subtyping methods developed to identify them.

1. Introduction

Listeria monocytogenes is the etiologic agent of the sometimes deadly foodborne disease listeriosis. Although listeriosis is a low incidence disease, it continues to represent a major public health threat due to its high mortality rate (20-30 %), especially among the most susceptible population groups such as infants, elderly, pregnant women and their fetuses and immune-compromised individuals [9].

In the United States alone, the annual medical cost and productivity/premature death loss due to this disease has been estimated to be more than $2 billion per year [10]. *L. monocytogenes* represents a constant issue for the food industry and a serious public health risk, due to its ability to replicate in a large range of environments and to consequently contaminate and grow in various ready-to-eat (RTE) foods [1,9]. RTE products are a particular high-risk food category because they are often ideal substrates for the growth of *L. monocytogenes* and are not usually given further heat treatments after manufacture. As a result, consumption of RTE products has been described as a major cause of listeriosis by the European Food Safety Authority (EFSA) report on zoonoses [11].

Several different RTE foods such as coleslaw, milk, cheese, deli meats and hot dogs have been involved in large foodborne outbreaks of listeriosis [12–17]. The largest outbreaks of listeriosis in North America have been linked to turkey meat, Mexican-style cheese, RTE meats, and most recently cantaloupe [14, 15, 18, 19].

In September 2011, high numbers of listeriosis cases were reported and linked to the consumption of cantaloupe, making this the first outbreak associated with this food. The U.S. Centers for Disease Control and Prevention (CDC) reported 146 cases, with 30 deaths and 1 miscarriage (19), making this the largest listeriosis outbreak in U.S. history, with the highest number of deaths of any other U.S. foodborne listeriosis outbreak since 1998 [15].

According to data from EFSA, a total of 1,645 confirmed cases of listeriosis in the 26 Member States were reported in Europe in 2009, with an increase of 19.1 % compared to 2008 and the highest number of cases since 2003 [11]. The EU notification rate was of 0.4 per 100,000 inhabitants, with higher rates observed in Denmark, Spain and Sweden. The route of transmission was only determined for a small fraction of confirmed cases (4.3 %), and in most of these cases contaminated food was suspected; particularly cheese and milk were mentioned as the vehicle of infection in 26.6 % of cases [11].

In the past, the identification of the food vehicle in foodborne listeriosis outbreaks has been relatively rare in Europe and only three verified *L. monocytogenes* outbreaks linked to cheese and pig meat were reported in 2009 [11]. These outbreaks were responsible for eleven fatal cases, accounting for almost half of the 23 foodborne-related deaths associated with outbreaks in the EU in 2009 [11]. Compared to all reported cases of listeriosis in the EU in 2009, the above three outbreaks were associated with the highest proportion of hospitalized cases and deaths [11]. In Europe, approximately half of all reported cases appear to be associated with dairy products [20]. In fact, many listeriosis outbreaks were associated with the consumption of unpasteurized soft cheeses (Switzerland, 1983-1987); unpasteurized milk (Austria, 1986); Brie made from pasteurized raw milk (France, 1995); contaminated butter (Finland, 1998-1999) and acid curd cheese made from pasteurized milk (Germany, 2006-2007) [21–25].

Most recently in 2009, a multinational outbreak in Austria, Germany and the Czech Republic was reported and linked to the consumption of 'Quargel', a curd cheese. This outbreak accounted for 34 outbreak cases and 8 deaths [26]. In Italy, according to data from the Epidemiological Bulletin of the Ministry of Health, 277 cases of listeriosis were reported from 1998 to 2004 while 534 cases were documented from 2005 to 2010 [27], which translates to an increase in reported cases of about 93 %.

In 1997, a major outbreak of gastrointestinal listeriosis was responsible for over 1,500 cases, particularly children and staff from two elementary schools of the same city in Northern Italy. This outbreak, linked to the consumption of corn and tuna salad, is particularly interesting as *L. monocytogenes* has rarely been associated with these food vehicles and with gastrointestinal symptoms [28].

In 2003 17 European countries took part in a project to establish a European surveillance network on *Listeria* infections in order to develop common methodologies for surveillance of listeriosis in Europe, based on what previously observed in the U.S. with PulseNet [29-31]. This project resulted in the creation of an electronic database on the genetic profiles of the strains identified in the different countries and in various foods [29, 30]. The creation of a common database, harmonization of epidemiologic and microbiological methods and protocols for collaborative investigation are paramount for detecting and investigating international outbreaks [29–31]. In fact, listeriosis cases associated with a single outbreak could potentially be geographically and temporally dispersed thus making the detection of common source outbreaks very difficult [13, 15].

Another factor that makes tracking the source of listeriosis outbreaks so difficult is the long incubation period (3-70 days) between consumption of foods contaminated with *L. monocytogenes* and the appearance of disease symptoms. Therefore the use of molecular subtyping methods is critical as these methods are useful for characterizing strains of foodborne pathogens isolated from different patients and tracking them back through foods to their sources in processing environments.

In this context, excluding unrelated strains from a specific food-related outbreak is essential, as such strains may confound epidemiologic investigations.

Although different serotypes of *L. monocytogenes* have been isolated from foods, only a few (i.e. 1/2a, 1/2b, and 4b), are responsible for the majority of epidemic and clinical sporadic cases [1]. In addition, most outbreaks of foodborne listeriosis have involved a small number of very closely related clones, thus prompting the identification of epidemic clones (ECs) [1].

2. Epidemic Clones (ECs)

Different genotypic methods demonstrated a close relatedness between strains of *L. monocytogenes* belonging to geographically and temporally distinct outbreaks, and that some strains were more likely than others to be isolated from outbreaks of human listeriosis [1, 32]. In particular, findings from early epidemiologic studies with *multilocus enzyme electrophoresis* (MLEE) and later confirmed by techniques such as ribotyping, analysis of allelic variants of virulence genes and pulsed-field gel electrophoresis (PFGE) revealed how several major listeriosis outbreaks were caused by closely related strains (33–36). Most outbreaks of foodborne listeriosis have involved a small number of very closely related clones, most frequently of serotype 4b or 1/2a, thus highlighting the importance of ECs and outbreak clones (OCs) [1, 32].

An EC has been defined as a group of genetically related isolates implicated in *multiple* unrelated outbreaks that are separated in time and space and are presumably of a common ancestor [1, 32, 37]. Evidence has shown that ECs of *L. monocytogenes* caused multiple outbreaks that were separated by several years or decades [1, 4, 32, 37]. Strains belonging to the same EC have been shown to share identical or very highly related virulence gene sequences [2, 8]. However, multiple isolates from the same outbreak within an EC may differ for some genetic characteristic or by their serotype, suggesting that each represents a distinct clone [36, 38–42]. In contrast to EC, an OC has been defined as a strain or group of strains descended asexually from a single ancestral cell that is associated with only a *single* outbreak [37]. The OC definition assumes the clonal relationship of all isolates associated with an outbreak and takes into account the possible existence of slightly different genetic subtypes within ECs [37]. The two concepts of EC and OC can be useful in differentiating between long-term and short-term epidemiology of *L. monocytogenes*, respectively [37].

Five epidemic-associated clonal groups of *L. monocytogenes* have currently been identified: three in serotype 4b (ECI, ECII, ECIV) and two in serotype1/2a (ECIII and ECV) [1, 2, 4, 32]. Since the EC concept was first introduced in 2002 and later revisited in 2003 and 2007, only four ECs were recognized: ECI-IV [1, 2, 32]. In 2011, a novel EC of serotype 1/2a that had been causing time-linked clusters of cases and outbreaks in Canada for the past 20 years was detected and designated ECV [4]. The repeated involvement of ECs in major outbreaks with high case-fatality rates has suggested that ECs may be both well-adapted to foods and food processing plants and highly virulent to humans [1]. Markers specific for a limited number of ECs have repeatedly been observed worldwide [6, 7, 43–47]. Successful identification of ECs and OCs will greatly contribute to studies on the distribution, risk factors and molecular determinants of infectious diseases. In order to allow for appropriate source tracking and attribution and to design more effective intervention strategies, a better understanding of the evolution and ecology of *L. monocytogenes* will be needed. The ability to differentiate strains within *L. monocytogenes* using novel molecular subtyping methods has been crucial for the detection of ECs and OCs, and the sources and routes of transmission to humans [8, 13, 16]. PFGE, targeting restriction enzyme polymorphisms on a whole-genome level, is currently considered the gold-standard technique for subtyping foodborne pathogens in the PulseNet system [5, 13]. PFGE has high discriminatory power (i.e. the ability to correctly differentiate unrelated strains), good epidemiologic concordance (i.e. the ability to group epidemiologically related isolates) and good repeatability between laboratories.

However, PFGE has some limitations as it is laborious, relatively low through-put, has a long response time, and requires precise standardization [48]. Due to its high discriminatory power, PFGE may sometimes confound the epidemiology of *L. monocytogenes,* as even strains belonging to the same outbreak may show different PFGE patterns [4, 16, 19, 49]. For these reasons, alternative methods for subtyping EC strains have been examined in the last few years. For example, multi-virulence-locus sequence typing (MVLST) was developed based on the comparison of nucleotide base changes in the sequences of multiple virulence genes [2, 50]. MVLST was subsequently shown to correctly identify and differentiate all five ECs and possessed both excellent discriminatory power and excellent epidemiologic concordance and thus can be considered the best technique for detection and typing of ECs and OCs [2, 4, 41]. A more detailed description of the molecular methods to detect and screen for ECs and OCs can be found in sections 4 and 5.

2.1. Epidemic Clone I (ECI)

Among the ECs of *L. monocytogenes*, ECI was the first to be defined and is now one of the better characterized ECs. In particular most major foodborne outbreaks of listeriosis in EU and the U.S. have been caused by closely related *L. monocytogenes* strains of serotype 4b [1,32]. A 1981 listeriosis outbreak in Nova Scotia, Canada was responsible for seven adult cases and 34 perinatal infections and occurred as a result of contamination of vegetables through the use of sheep manure as fertilizer [17]. In 1985, 142 cases of human listeriosis resulting in 48 deaths were reported in California, traced to the consumption of a Mexican-style soft cheese that was contaminated with ECI *L. monocytogenes* [14]. In western Switzerland, 122 cases of invasive human disease and 34 deaths due to ECI were reported from 1983 to 1987 and linked to the consumption of a regional pasteurized soft cheese "Vacherin" [22]. In the past, one of the largest outbreaks of listeriosis due to ECI in EU was reported in France in 1992 and linked to the consumption of tongue pork in jelly [51]. This major outbreak was responsible for 279 cases resulting in 22 abortions and 63 deaths. In addition to the outbreaks mentioned above, ECI has also been linked to some other outbreaks [1,32]. Evidence of this association was provided by many different subtyping assays [1,32]. For example, 4b strains of *L. monocytogenes* associated with different outbreaks (California, 1985; Switzerland, 1983-1987; France, 1992) all shared highly similar MLEE types [33,36]. ECI strains from individual outbreaks have also been observed to share a common ribotype (DUP1038) [52]. In general, it has been well established that all ECI strains have some specific characteristics as they harbor restriction fragment length polymorphisms (RFLPs) that discriminate them from other strains of serotype 4b and several unique and specific genomic regions normally missing in other serotype 4b strains [53–55]. Moreover, their genomic DNA is resistant to digestion with Sau3AI, thus suggesting that cytosine nucleotides at GATC sites are protected by methylation [56,57]. In 2001, a DNA region (fragment 85) was found to be specific to ECI and was located in a gene presumed to be associated with cytosine methylation at GATC sites [53]. Subsequent studies confirmed that ECI strains definitely harbor a gene cassette (85M-85R-85S) with GATC-specific restriction-modification functions [56]. These results were the first to provide specific markers to be used for the identification of epidemic-associated strains (53,56). Since then, ECI strains have been often analyzed and characterized, and the availability of complete genome sequences has been very useful in better characterizing ECI and also greatly assisted in the detection of EC-specific markers [1,3].

2.2. Epidemic Clone II (ECII)

In 1998-99, a multistate outbreak of listeriosis in the U.S. caused by a strain of *L. monocytogenes* of serotype 4b resulted in 108 human cases, including 14 deaths and four miscarriages and was linked to the consumption of contaminated hot dogs [13]. This outbreak was characterized by heavy disease and economic burdens and badly damaged the perceived safety of RTE meat products.

Molecular subtyping results from ribotyping (DUP1044A) and PFGE revealed a genetic profile that had seldom been seen before among clinical isolates [13]. One of the specific characteristics for these isolates was to have a mutated region 18, a genomic region that had previously been shown to be conserved among other serotype 4b *L. monocytogenes* strains; therefore these former strains were designated ECII [40,58]. In 2002, another multistate listeriosis outbreak due to consumption of turkey deli products caused 54 illnesses, resulting in eight deaths and three miscarriages [59].

Isolates from this outbreak showed PFGE profiles that were closely related to those of the 1998-99 outbreak [59]. MVLST subsequently confirmed that the 1998 and 2002 outbreaks were caused by the same epidemic clone (ECII) [8]. The high genetic relatedness between isolates from the above two outbreaks was also confirmed with a macroarray-based typing method and differences were observed only in prophages and sequences of internalin-like genes, also among isolates within the same outbreak [40].

The same issue was also observed for PFGE, as the same *Apa*I-PFGE pattern was shared by some isolates belonging to the two outbreaks and many isolates within the same outbreak had different *Apa*I-PFGE patterns [13]. Therefore, the *Apa*I-PFGE results hindered the identification of an epidemiologic link between the two outbreaks, as even one or two band differences in PFGE profiles are deemed significant in CDC's PulseNet protocol and such profiles may not be considered part of the same epidemic or outbreak [13]. Although no other outbreaks in the U.S. have been linked to ECII since 2002, ECII strains seems to have established in a still unknown reservoir in the U.S., especially considering that the 1998 and 2002 outbreaks were characterized by different food vehicles and processing plants [13, 59]. Furthermore, ECII strains were subsequently detected in isolates from U.S. raw poultry processing plants [60] and from numerous RTE meat and poultry processing plants in U.S., tested as part of surveillance and risk-assessment programs by the U.S. Department of Agriculture [61].

In both cases the presence of ECII strains was confirmed with MVLST (62). Recently, ECII strains were observed in EU as they were associated with a time-linked cluster of listeriosis cases that occurred in Belgium in 2006 and 2007, involving 11 patients infected with identical strains of *L. monocytogenes* of serotype 4b [63,64]. The above mentioned findings show that ECII is quite common in the U.S. and is also found in Europe, associated with time-linked cluster [63] and sporadic cases (see section 6).

As observed for ECI, the availability of complete genome sequences was a key to further characterizing ECII strains and allowing the identification of different ECII-specific genetic markers [1, 3].

2.3. Epidemic Clone III (ECIII)

A fatal sporadic case of human listeriosis in 1988 in U.S. was caused by the consumption of turkey franks contaminated with a serotype 1/2a strain of *L. monocytogenes* [65]. In 2000, deli turkey meat produced in the same processing facility was linked to a multistate listeriosis outbreak [16]. Thirty cases of listeriosis were identified in this outbreak, resulting in four deaths and three miscarriages/stillbirths. Human and food *L. monocytogenes* isolates from both episodes were subtyped and results showed the same serotype, and indistinguishable PFGE profiles and ribotypes (DUP-1053A) (16). PFGE profiles for these isolates had been very rarely observed before, thus further suggesting these specific strains were indeed correlated and represented a novel EC, subsequently designated ECIII. A traceback investigation was carried out and identified a single processing plant as the probable source of the outbreak, the same plant that had been implicated in the human sporadic case twelve years earlier [16]. It was therefore suggested that the most likely explanation for the above mentioned findings is that the outbreak strain had persisted in the same plant for at least twelve years, occasionally contaminating food.

In general, strains belonging to the same EC are highly related and may often not be distinguished, even using several molecular typing methods. The backbone genome of *L. monocytogenes* is highly clonal and within ECs, backbone genomes are even more conserved [3, 6, 36, 66, 67]. ECIII strains belonging to the 1988 episode and the 2000 outbreak were apparently identical when only results from ribotyping, PFGE and MVLST were considered (2,16). Subsequent whole-genome sequencing of two *L. monocytogenes* strains from the 1988 sporadic case and two from the 2000 outbreak, allowed the identification of only 11 single nucleotide polymorphisms (SNPs) in the whole backbone genome between these ECIII strains [67]. In contrast, 1,274 polymorphic sites that differentiated the 1988 isolates from the 2000 isolates were observed in a 42 kbp prophage, inserted in the chromosomal *comK* gene [67]. These findings were attributed to extensive recombination in the *comK* prophage that happened within ECIII in a relatively short period of time (twelve years or less) [67]. Food and human isolates shared the same identical prophage sequences within the 1988 episode and 2000 outbreak [67]. On the other hand, significant differences in the prophage sequences were observed between the 1988 episode and the 2000 outbreak, respectively [67]. Findings from this study also supported the previously reported conclusion that prophages in *L. monocytogenes* indeed represent excellent markers for the differentiation of outbreak clones within ECs [67,68].

2.4. Epidemic Clone IV (ECIV)

In 2003 a subgroup of ECI was defined as ECIa [32], a serotype 4b cluster that included two outbreaks in Boston, U.S. (1979 and 1983) [12,69], and the 1989 outbreak in the United Kingdom [70]. The 1979-Boston outbreak was associated with the consumption of pasteurized milk and involved 23 cases from patients with systemic listeriosis from eight local hospitals [69]. In 1983, milk was again associated with another outbreak of listeriosis in humans, which was responsible for 49 cases [12]. Between 1985 and 1989 a marked increase in the incidence of human listeriosis was observed in England, Wales, and Northern Ireland and consumption of contaminated paté was the likely source of infection [70].

Another ECIV outbreak was associated with corn in Italy in 1997 [28]. Interestingly, the corn outbreak was linked to over 1,500 cases with gastrointestinal symptoms, particularly children and staff from two elementary schools of the same city in Northern Italy. The definitive cause of the illness was not identified, but the outbreak was epidemiologically linked to the consumption of corn and tuna salad [28]. This outbreak is particularly interesting, as *L. monocytogenes* has rarely been associated with these symptoms [28]. A common ribotype and similar MLEE profiles were detected among serotype 4b strains implicated in the first three outbreaks mentioned above, and genomics characteristics specific for ECI were absent from ECIa thus suggesting that these outbreaks were sufficiently different from ECI to warrant a different clonal designation - ECIa (53–55,57), subsequently re-classified as ECIV [2].

Controversy still persists as to whether the 1983-outbreak should be considered as ECIV. In fact, MVLST results showed that isolates from the 1983-Boston milk outbreak had a sequence type that differed by a single SNP (*lisR*85) from those of the other two outbreaks and thus the 1983-Boston outbreak was excluded from ECIV and presumed to represent a different clone [2]. However, several later studies observed common MVLST and multiple-locus variable-number tandem-repeat analysis (MLVA) profiles between strains belonging to ECIV and strains belonging to the 1983-Boston outbreak, thus suggesting that this outbreak should be considered part of ECIV [7,42,71]. Moreover, minor genetic differences can be found between isolates within the same listeriosis outbreaks [32] and differences within the same EC have been observed [13, 38, 42, 71]. For examples, three slightly different MLVA profiles were observed for ECIV isolates from the three outbreaks (1979-Boston, 1983-Boston and 1989-UK) [42]. Additionally, since the above outbreaks occurred more than 20-30 years ago, it is possible that differences between epidemiologically linked isolates can be attributed to mutations that occurred during laboratory passages [42]. Overall, the above findings suggest that the 1983-Boston milk outbreak should presently be considered as part of ECIV; however, further analysis is needed to confirm this.

Interestingly, ECIV has not been associated with any additional outbreaks of listeriosis, although markers specific for this clone have been encountered in RTE products in the U.S. [61] and sporadic cases in Portugal and Italy [7,46]. In general, ECIV can be considered one of the ECs that has been so far poorly characterized as phenotypic and genetic features unique to ECIV have yet to be documented [3].

2.5. Epidemic Clone V (ECV)

A nationwide listeriosis outbreak linked to the consumption of RTE meat products contaminated with serotype 1/2a *L. monocytogenes* occurred in Canada in 2008, causing at least 57 cases and 22 deaths [18]. Most isolates associated with this outbreak showed an identical PFGE pattern for *Asc*I while some isolates had an *Asc*I-PFGE pattern that differed by a single fragment shift that was associated with the presence of a 33 kbp prophage [18]. In addition, the presence of a putative mobile genomic island (LGI1) never before seen in other *Listeria* genomes, was also observed [18]. Very similar PFGE patterns were also detected in several serotype 1/2a isolates from surveillance of *L. monocytogenes* and listeriosis in Canada from 1995-2004 [72]. These isolates were responsible for a large amount of sporadic cases and time-linked clusters over a period of several decades in Canada [4,72].

Knabel et al., (2012), subtyped a diverse population of 71 *L. monocytogenes* isolates obtained since 1995 from Canada [4]. Their results demonstrated the presence of a novel EC (ECV) within lineage II of *L. monocytogenes* [4]. In particular, 49 strains were in the same multilocus sequence typing (MLST)-defined clonal complex (CC8) and had the same MVLST-defined sequence type or Virulence Type (VT) (VT59) [4]] The marker for LGI1 was present in only 88 % of ECV isolates, probably due to the location of LGI1 on a putatively mobile genomic island, but was always absent from non-ECV isolates. However, a specific and stable marker for ECV was found in an internal region in the full genome sequences available from isolates of the 2008 outbreak [4, 18]. This marker was present in all ECV isolates tested and only in one non-ECV isolate. This latter isolate proved to be a false-positive ECV as determined by complete sequencing of the marker gene and by MLST and MVLST [4]. Overall, ECV was found to be associated with a wide geographic distribution and was linked to at least 16 time-linked clusters of listeriosis in Canada since 1995, with the most prominent outbreak being the one in 2008 linked to RTE meat products [4].

Recently, some authors [3] have proposed the term ECV to describe serotype 4b isolates associated with the 2000 outbreak of listeriosis in North Carolina, U.S., linked to the consumption of contaminated Mexican-style cheese [73]. This is at odds with the definition of an epidemic clone, which is defined as " [..] groups of genetically related isolates implicated in several outbreaks, geographically and temporally independent, and, presumably of a common ancestor" (1,3,74). In fact, given the definitions of OC and EC, the 2000 outbreak of listeriosis in North Carolina should be referred to as an OC, as only 12 cases over a two-month period were observed in a specific city of North Carolina [73]. In particular, two strains from this outbreak were recently tested with an EC-specific multiplex SNP-typing assay and they all produced an identical profile that differed from other EC strains, but was shared with many other non-EC strains [7].

3. Methods for the Screening and Detection of ECs

The repeated involvement of a few ECs in major outbreaks in recent years [1, 32], suggests that these clones may be particularly adapted to food processing plants or/and may also be particularly pathogenic for humans. In addition, the presence of repeated outbreaks of the same ECs over long periods of time, suggests that these strains may have specific genetic and phenotypic traits that allow them to persist in environmental niches within food processing plants during the interval between different outbreaks [3, 32]. If true, it is reasonable to assume that ECs will be again involved in listeriosis cases in the future. Therefore, the development of rapid molecular subtyping methods would help in understanding the short- and long-term transmission of *L. monocytogenes* and facilitate the characterization, tracking, and control of *L. monocytogenes* strains that are represented by ECs and OCs. Moreover, rapid, simple, inexpensive and accurate screening methods would enhance the detection and control of ECs.

As previously stated, PFGE is currently considered the gold-standard technique for subtyping foodborne pathogen; however, it has some limitations such as it is laborious, requires precise standardization, has a relatively low through-put and long response time, and sometimes is too discriminatory and thus confounds epidemiology [4,8,13,49,75]. Therefore, the availability of several reliable screening and subtyping method for the identification and characterization of ECs and OCs is essential, and some of the alternative fragment-based and sequence-based methods developed and utilized in the past are described below.

4. Fragment-Based Methods

4.1. PCR Methods

In 2001, Herd and Kocks conducted subtractive hybridization studies to identify genetic loci that could be linked to the increased epidemic potential of epidemic-associated *L. monocytogenes* strains [53]. The available genome sequence of EGD-e, an experimentally well-characterized virulent strain, was subtracted from that of a ECI strain from the 1985-California outbreak [53]. Results indicated the presence of 39 fragments in the ECI strain which were either absent or strongly divergent from the genome of EGD-e [53]. Findings from this study have been essential in the identification of EC-specific genetic markers that could be targeted with PCR.

In 2004, Yildirim et al., characterized serotype 4b *L. monocytogenes* strains obtained from foods and food-processing environments and found that a considerable portion of the analyzed strains had genomic DNA resistant to Sau3AI and harbored genetic markers specific to ECI (the 85R-85M-85S cassette) [56]. They also searched for additional ECI-specific genes and two fragments (17B and 133) were found to be conserved among all known ECI strains and absent among other strains of serotype 4b [56]. PCR primers were designed for all fragments deemed specific to ECI such as the 85M-, 85R-, and 85S-cassette and the 17B and 133 DNA regions. These genetic markers can be used to specifically detect ECI and were one of the first markers that could be interrogated with a simple PCR [56].

Concerning ECII, primers were described that provided the first "negative identification" approach for its detection [58]. In particular, all primers derived from six previously identified fragments [53] yielded expected amplicons when non-ECII serotype 4b strains were analyzed. Interestingly, only one primer pair (4bSF7 and 4bSF18) was not able to yield a PCR product when challenged with ECII strains, thus suggesting that sequences corresponding to 4bSF7 and 4bSF18 had a divergent nucleotide sequence or were missing in ECII. The genetic markers identified in this study were the first to specifically identify ECII by means of a "negative-result" PCR assay [58].

In 2007 a multiplex PCR assay was developed to "positively" detect markers specific for ECI, II, and III in addition to confirming the identification of *Listeria* genus, *L. monocytogenes* species and serotypes 1/2a and 4b [76]. Chen and Knabel were able to identify specific genetic markers for each ECs based on findings from whole-genome sequence comparison of three *Listeria* strains belonging to ECI, ECII and ECIII and the availability of 16 newly sequenced *L. monocytogenes* whole-genome sequences (including 3 other ECIII representative strains) [76]. The ECI-specific target corresponded to fragment 17B, already indicated as an ECI marker by other studies [53, 56]. The genomic region 18 linked to the negative genetic markers for ECII [58] was used to identify a positive marker for ECII. The ECIII marker was chosen based on the comparison of three ECIII strains and four other serotype 1/2a strains [76]. ECIV markers were not identified as no whole-genome sequences for ECIV were available at the time. This multiplex PCR correctly identified samples belonging to ECs, with the exception of two false-positive samples erroneously identified as ECII, thus showing a 100 % sensitivity and specificity for all seven pairs, and a 97.5 % specificity for ECII primers [76]. This multiplex PCR assay was recently modified in order to identify ECV, by incorporating primers specific for an internal region within the genome of ECV isolates [4, 18]. Therefore, this assay is now able to provide a fast, dependable, and inexpensive method to rapidly screen presumptive-positive *L. monocytogenes* isolates for *Listeria* spp., *L. monocytogenes*, serotype 1/2a and 4b and EC-specific markers.

4.2. Hybridization Based Methods

DNA Microarray-Based Methods

DNA microarray-based methods are an extension of the hybridization/array technology and are based on the use of thousands of oligonucleotide probes, immobilized on small solid surfaces. The genomic DNA is extracted, labeled and then hybridized to probes of known sequences on the microarray, and sequences in the sample DNA complementary to regions in the arrayed genome can then be detected. Comparative genomic hybridization has been used to characterize many different bacterial species [77–80].

A common approach is represented by spotting most of the coding sequences of a whole-genome from a reference strain on a microarray [81]. Genetic relatedness is determined following hybridization of the DNA of the sample strain onto the array, thus detecting which genes are present (observed hybridization) and which are absent (no hybridization) [81]. Macroarrays were used to confirm that both 1998 and 2002 outbreaks of listeriosis were caused by ECII [40]. Findings from macroarray typing confirmed how isolates from each outbreak were closely related, although some differences among isolates within the same outbreak were observed. Moreover, when 15 randomly chosen serotype 4b clinical isolates were analyzed from a non-outbreak period in 2003, they appeared to be closely related to ECII (40).

In a 2004 study, 52 strains of *L. monocytogenes* were analyzed to compare the resolution of microarray subtyping in regard to that of PFGE, MLST, and ribotyping. The study included 16 EC strains (seven for ECI and three each for ECII, ECIII and ECIV) [82]. The assay produced data that was consistent with PFGE and serotyping, had higher discriminatory power than ribotyping and good reproducibility [82]. Epidemiologically linked strains were grouped together according to epidemic.

Three strains were linked to the 1989-UK outbreak and, interestingly, two clinical isolates grouped together while the third strain, a food isolate, clustered separately [82]. This is consistent with what was later observed by Miya et al., in 2008 [42]. A ECIII strain linked to the multistate deli meat-associated epidemic in 2000 clustered with two strains isolated from the same food-processing plant in 1988 and one isolate from the 1988 human sporadic case associated with turkey frankfurters [82].

Overall, data obtained with microarray typing correlated well with findings from two-enzyme PFGE, and showed better resolution than both ribotyping and MLST using housekeeping genes and ribotyping.

DNA Probes

In 2010, the specificity of DNA probes derived from genomic regions found in the genome of ECII, but absent in the available sequenced genomes of ECI, ECIII, and EGD-e was investigated, in order to identify DNA-based tools that could be used to unambiguously detect ECII strains [83]. Genomic region 18 was identified as a specific marker for the identification of ECII [58], although findings from other studies revealed how this region could also be found in some serotype 4b strains that clearly differed from ECII [40,76]. Therefore new regions were selected and used to design 12 probes [83]. Samples were represented by 12 ECII strains, 19 isolates that shared the same *Asc*I-PFGE profile as ECII strains but were not known to have been involved in outbreaks and 29 strains with PFGE profiles clearly different from those of ECII [83]. Results indicated that five of the tested probes only hybridized with all tested ECII strains and no hybridization was observed with any of the other analyzed serotype 4b strains [83]. Overall, this study allowed the identification of a panel of probes that could unambiguously detect ECII strains [83]. Therefore, developing strain subtyping or detection schemes that combine such probes with previously identified ECI-specific probes [53, 56], could be useful to accurately monitor the major ECs of *L. monocytogenes*.

4.3. Multiple-Locus Variable-Number Tandem Repeat Analysis (MLVA)

MLVA is based on the amplification of tandem repeats (TRs) present in the genome of different pathogenic bacteria [84]. The primers used in this method have the purpose of amplifying all possible TRs in the chromosome. The number of TRs is similar among closely related isolates; size and number of repetitions are subsequently analyzed by a computer and finally the various TR combinations define the MLVA profile [48, 84]. Consequently, MLVA is able to provide accurate information on the genetic correlation between different bacterial strains [48]. MLVA is relatively easy to perform, standardize, automate and interpret because the generated fragments are of known size and sequence. Moreover, this technique has been considered by the CDC as one of the candidates for the second generation of molecular typing methods [85, 86]. However, a potential disadvantage of the method may be linked to the poor availability of reference sequences and also the absence of TRs in some genera, species and strains of foodborne pathogens [48].

In 2008, two MLVA assays were used to analyze sets of *L. monocytogenes* isolates that also comprised ECs [42, 71]. Miya and colleagues developed and validated a MLVA assay to rapidly discriminate serotype 4b *L. monocytogenes* strains and clonal groups. Nine isolates representative of ECs were included in this study: four strains for ECI (1981, 1985, and 1983-87 outbreaks); four for ECIV (1979, 1983 and 1989 outbreaks) and one for ECII (1998 outbreak) [42]. It was possible to observe three slightly different MLVA profiles for ECI and ECIV strains, respectively. ECI, ECII, and ECIV strains grouped in three clusters linked to EC-associated ribotypes DUP-1038B, DUP-1044A, DUP-1042B, respectively [42]. This MLVA scheme has been shown to correctly group together epidemiologically related isolates. One exception was observed as epidemiologically linked ECIV human and food isolates from the 1989 UK outbreak had different MLVA types [42]. However, ECIV contains some of the oldest outbreaks and it is therefore possible to attribute differences between epidemiologically correlated isolates to mutations that occurred during laboratory passage [42].

In another recent study by Sperry and colleagues, a novel MLVA method was developed based on the analysis of eight loci and tested on a set of 193 epidemiologically linked and non-linked *L. monocytogenes* isolates [71]. Samples were comprised of 13 ECI strains (1981, 1985, and 1983-87 outbreaks), eight ECII strains (1998 and 2002 outbreak), two ECIII strains (2000 outbreak and 1988 sporadic listeriosis case) and seven ECIV strains (1983 and 1989 outbreaks) [71]. The ECI isolates grouped together in three main clusters, with only strains from the 1985 California outbreak differing by one locus from other ECI strains [71]. ECII isolates showed three slightly different MLVA profiles and grouped together into three clusters differing by one locus. These findings confirm that slight genetic differences may occur within strains belonging to the same outbreak and same EC. On the other hand, both strains from different outbreaks within ECIII and ECIV had identical MLVA profiles [71]. Overall, MLVA showed strong epidemiologic concordance and can represent a fairly inexpensive high-throughput screening method, useful during epidemiologic investigations of foodborne illness.

4.4. Pulsed-Field Gel Electrophoresis (PFGE)

PFGE, targeting restriction enzyme polymorphisms on a whole-genome level, is currently considered the gold-standard technique for subtyping foodborne pathogens. The PulseNet system (www.cdc.gov/PulseNet) collects from all State Health Laboratories PFGE profiles that were obtained from bacteria causing foodborne disease in the U.S., in order to identify multistate outbreaks related to bacterial foodborne illness [5,13]. In fact, the timely identification of groups of isolates with similar PFGE profiles is useful in epidemiologic investigations, increasing the chances of highlighing a link between contaminated food and clinical cases, even in pre-epidemic phase. In particular, the introduction of PulseNet in 2006 has since allowed the detection of a greater number of outbreaks and their sources [85]. The standardized protocol used by the CDC for PFGE typing of *L. monocytogenes* uses a primary enzyme (*Asc*I) for the screening of correlation between isolates and a secondary one (*Apa*I) to confirm results and obtain further discrimination [5]. Recently, the PulseNet-standardized PFGE protocol for *L. monocytogenes* has been re-evaluated and optimized [87]. Over the years, PFGE has proven to be very useful in epidemiologic investigations of *L. monocytogenes* isolates associated with different epidemics [5, 13, 16, 34, 35, 49, 51] and has been shown to possess high discriminatory power by correctly differentiating unrelated strains, good epidemiologic concordance by properly grouping epidemiologically related isolates and good repeatability between laboratories. However, PFGE has some limitations as it is laborious, relatively low through-put, has a long response time, and requires precise standardization [48]. Although PFGE has some limitations, as previously mentioned, this technique has greatly facilitated the epidemiologic investigations of outbreaks of listeriosis and has been extensively used for subtyping tens of thousands foodborne pathogens worldwide [85].

One of the main issues with PFGE typing is related to its high discriminatory power. In fact PFGE may sometimes provide too much discriminatory power and thus confound epidemiology, as even strains belonging to the same outbreak can show different PFGE profiles [4, 16, 19, 49]. For example, *Apa*I-PFGE hindered the identification of an epidemiologic association between the two ECII outbreaks of 1998 and 2002, as the same *Apa*I-PFGE pattern was shared by some isolates belonging to the two outbreaks and many isolates within the same outbreak had different *Apa*I-PFGE patterns [13]. Also, in the case of ECV, strains with 12 different PFGE profiles were observed with this EC from 1995 - 2010 in Canada, making identification of this EC all but impossible [4]. Most recently, four differing PFGE pattern combinations were observed for the four strains associated with the 2011 cantaloupe outbreak [19]. For the above reasons, alternative methods for detecting and differentiating ECs have been examined in the last few years.

5. Sequence-Based Methods

5.1. Multilocus Sequence Typing (MLST)

MLST is based on the comparison of nucleotide base changes in the sequences of multiple housekeeping genes, generally represented by six or seven genes [88, 89]. In order to determine genetic relatedness, specific nucleotide base changes are considered, rather than the size of DNA fragments. MLST has been applied to the characterization of several foodborne pathogens including *L. monocytogenes*, showing a good correlation with results generated by PFGE [90–92]. However, it has been reported that housekeeping genes, although useful in global phylogenetic studies, may not offer enough variability to distinguish among closely related clones with more recent genetic divergence [2, 50, 93, 94]. In a 2008 study, sequencing of internal fragments of seven housekeeping genes was carried out on a set of 360 highly diverse isolates of *L. monocytogenes* and samples were grouped into clonal complexes (CCs), defined "as groups of profiles differing by no more than one gene from at least one other profile of the group" (6). Reference strains of large outbreaks were included and found to belong to specific CCs. For example, CC1 (defined by its central genotype sequence type 1 - ST1) includes a ECI reference strain; CC6 (ST6) comprises a ECII reference strain; ST11 contains a reference strain for ECIII and finally, CC2 (ST2) includes a ECIV reference strain [6]. Recently CC8 (ST8) has been associated with the newly identified ECV [4].

Another recent MLST study genotyped 300 *L. monocytogenes* isolates and demonstrated that some ECs are associated with highly prevalent CCs detected worldwide [43]. In particular, CC1 and CC2 (containing ECI and ECIV, respectively) were found to have a high prevalence in several isolates from different sources, which may explain their association with major listeriosis outbreaks worldwide [43].

On the contrary, CC6 and ST11 (linked to ECII and ECIII, respectively) were rarely observed, thus possibly indicating that particular conditions allowed the transmission of these ECs [43]. Future research is needed to determine whether ECs represent a distinct subset or if they otherwise completely match MLST-defined CCs.

5.2. Multi-Virulence-Locus Sequence Typing (MVLST)

Virulence genes may be more variable between OCs and ECs, and therefore provide more discriminatory power than housekeeping genes [2, 50, 93, 94]. Therefore, MVLST was developed to include only virulence genes by targeting intragenic regions of three virulence and three virulence-associated genes [2, 50]. MVLST was subsequently shown to correctly identify and differentiate all five currently known ECs and possessed both excellent discriminatory power and epidemiologic concordance [2, 4, 41]. MVLST showed a higher discriminatory power than PFGE, and was able to resolve strains that were indistinguishable by ribotyping or PFGE [50]. MVLST was subsequently used to confirm that the two major listeriosis outbreaks in the U.S. in 1998 and 2002 were part of the same epidemic and belonged to ECII [8]. A total of 21 isolates were analyzed (10 from the 1998 outbreak and 11 from the 2002 outbreak) and compared with 28 epidemiologically unrelated *L. monocytogenes*. Perfect sequence identity was observed for all 21 outbreak strains while significant variation in the six analyzed genes was observed between genetically diverse]isolates [8]. A later study focused on the assessment of discriminatory power and epidemiologic concordance of MVLST through the analysis of 106 well-characterized strains isolated from outbreaks and from other sources (sporadic, environmental, food) [2]. The discriminatory power of MVLST was found to be 0.99 and epidemiologic concordance was E=1 (2), which were further confirmed by the analysis of additional virulence genes and virulence-associated gene regions (41). Overall, MVLST was able to i) correctly identify the first three epidemic clones (ECI, ECII, and ECIII); ii) redefine another epidemic clone (ECIV) and iii) identify a recent novel EC (ECV). MVLST provided results consistent with other subtyping techniques and was able to correctly differentiate unrelated isolates and detect the clonality of epidemic/outbreak isolates. Moreover, MVLST can be applied on its own without necessarily coupling it with other subtyping methods to provide accurate information on ECs, OCs, serotypes and different lineage of *L. monocytogenes* [2].

5.3. Prophage Typing

Chen et al. (2005; 2007) demonstrated that isolates within each EC had identical sequence types and MVLST proved essential for tracking of ECs and useful for understanding the long-term transmission of *L. monocytogenes* [2,8]. However, the identification of the source of specific outbreaks and the differentiation of OCs within the same EC is needed and important for understanding and investigating the short-term epidemiology of *L. monocytogenes*. In 2007, three SNPs that could be used to differentiate three OCs of ECI were identified [38]. Subsequently, Chen and Knabel identified and validated SNPs useful in the differentiation of OCs within ECs II, III, and IV [68]. In particular, 11 SNPs were identified in an arbitrarily chosen prophage locus that were stable within the outbreaks and able to discriminate the 1998 OC from the 2002 OC. Similarly, the sequences of putative prophage regions in ECIII and ECIV isolates provided multiple SNPs that represented accurate epidemiologic markers for distinguishing OCs within these ECs [68]. Overall, prophage regions in *L. monocytogenes* were able to provide epidemiologically relevant SNPs useful in differentiating closely related OCs within ECII, ECIII, and possibly also ECIV [68]. These SNPs could be incorporated into sequence-based or SNP-based subtyping schemes for further investigating the short-term epidemiology of *L. monocytogenes*.

Subsequently, subtyping based on sequences in the *comK* prophage junction fragments (JFs), revealed how different EC strains (including ECII, ECIII, and ECV), were specific to individual meat and poultry processing plants [62]. In particular, *comK* prophage types (PTs) were found to be unique to individual processing plants, or the same between plants that manufactured the same type of product [62]. Based on these findings it was suggested that the concept of defective *comK* prophage be replaced with that of a rapid adaptation island (RAI), containing "adaptons" genes that may allow *L. monocytogenes* to rapidly adapt to different foods and food processing plants [62]. This model may also explain the ability of *L. monocytogenes* to persist, form biofilm and transmit to foods [62]. Overall, prophage typing by sequencing *comK* JFs allows the tracking of persistent strains within individual processing plants, thus presenting an excellent tool for epidemiologic investigations that can lead to the implementation of more efficient strategies to reduce contamination and improve the safety of food products.

5.4. SNP-Based Typing

In contrast to MLST and MVLST, which require sequencing of multiple genes, various methods can be used to detect individual polymorphisms at defined SNP loci (48). In particular, the interrogation of multiple SNPs can help elucidate the relatedness of strains (48). For the discrimination of ECs, informative SNPs were defined as those able to differentiate a specific EC from all other unrelated strains [41].

Multilocus genotyping (MLGT) assays have been recently developed for the high-throughput subtyping of isolates from lineage I, II, III and IV of *L. monocytogenes* based on interrogation of SNPs via multiplexed primer extension reactions [38,95]. A targeted multilocus genotyping (TMLGT) approach was designed to allow for the simultaneous classification of *L. monocytogenes* isolates by lineage, major serotypes, and ECs (ECI, ECII, ECIII, and ECIV) [96]. Six genomic regions containing the selected SNPs were amplified in a multiplex PCR and amplicons acted as a template for the subsequent primer extension reactions utilizing specific probes. Based on DNA sequence alignments, 30 oligonucleotide probes were designed with nucleotides on the 3′ end specific to the selected SNPs. The 5′ end of each probes had a distinctive 24-bp sequence tag that was complimentary to oligonucleotides located on the surface of individual sets of Luminex xMAP fluorescent polystyrene microspheres (Luminex Corporation), used to sort the different extension products. The probes served as allele-specific primers in multiplex extension reactions and after extension and hybridization, the fluorescence intensity was measured for each probe [96]. The TMLGT assay accurately typed 99.6 % of all isolates in relation to lineage, serotype, and EC and showed a 99.9 % typeability and 99.8 % accuracy of isolate assignment [96]. This assay allows the concurrent identification of the four lineages, the four major serotypes, and four of the five currently described ECs of *L. monocytogenes*.

Recently, a multiplex minisequencing assay was developed based on six SNPs that were informative for the four ECs [7]. Minisequencing, based on Snapshot technology™ (Applied Biosystems) requires the preliminary amplification through simplex or multiplex PCR of different fragments of genomic DNA where the SNPs to be interrogated are located. Extension primers are designed to bind in a position immediately adjacent to the selected SNPs and subsequently, a DNA polymerase extends these primers by incorporating a single modified dideoxy nucleotide that coincidently terminates and color-codes DNA strand elongation at each SNP. Specifically, terminator dideoxyNTPs are marked with different colors and emit light at different wavelengths when samples are run through an automated sequencer.

Conveniently, multiple SNPs can be targeted simultaneously by adding tails of different lengths to the 5' end of the extension primers, thus making them different sizes. The generated fragments of different sizes and four different colors are then resolved by capillary electrophoresis with laser-induced fluorescent (LIF) detection, and the different SNP profile of each sample is used to detect and identify the specific EC. Multiple SNPs specific for the different ECs were targeted and detected using this method and when applied to a wide collection of confirmed and non-confirmed EC isolates, this multiplex SNP-typing assay correctly identified all known ECs, and also identified nine strains as ECI, ECII or ECIV, which had been initially misclassified as non-ECs [7]. This assay was intended to provide SNP profiles for the specific identification of the ECs of *L. monocytogenes* (ECI-ECIV) that were known at the time the test was developed. All other non-EC strains share one or more common SNP-typing profiles, which are different from those of ECs [7]. Since the development of this assay, another EC (ECV) has been identified [4].

In-silico determination of the SNP profile for ECV using the available whole-genome sequences for ECV [18] demonstrated that the six selected SNPs should be able to provide a specific profile for this newly identified clone and no new SNPs are needed in the minisequencing assay in order to allow the identification of ECV (Lomonaco and Knabel, unpublished observations).

Preliminary analysis with the above SNP-typing assay were conducted on a single previously characterized ECV strain [18], which showed a specific profile as expected by the in-silico determination of the SNP profile (Figure 1) (Lomonaco and Knabel, unpublished observations).

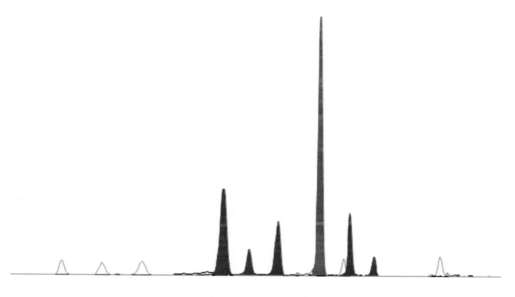

Figure 1. Minisequencing profile obtained with multiplex SNP typing (7) for a single ECV *L. monocytogenes* strain, represented by isolate 08-5923, previously characterized by Gilmour et al., 2010 (18). The observed ECV-specific profile differed from SNP-profiles specific for ECI-ECIV, observed in Lomonaco et al., (2011) (7). Profile was obtained with Peak Scanner software v1.0 from Applied Biosystems. Orange peaks correspond to the internal size standard (GS LIZ120) and blue, green, red and black peaks correspond to G, A, T and C, respectively.

Further analysis of a larger set of ECV strains will be needed to confirm these results. This minisequencing assay can be used to screen for all five currently known ECs in more extensive analysis of food isolates, thus providing valuable insights on the prevalence of these potentially problematic strains in foods and food processing environments. In general, subtyping based on the analysis of SNPs has the potential to provide unequivocal data, which is easy to exchange and compare among different laboratories, has a good potential for automation, and it may be useful for evaluating the epidemiology and dissemination of ECs. Moreover, new SNPs could be incorporated in this SNP-typing assay in order to allow the identification of other ECs that are identified in the future.

5.5. Whole-Genome Sequencing

Several whole-genome sequences of *L. monocytogenes* have been completed in the last few years. In 2004, the whole-genome sequences of three *L. monocytogenes* strains were obtained for representative food isolates of ECI (1985-California outbreak), ECII (1998 U.S. outbreak), and ECIII (1988 sporadic case) [66]. More recently, 16 newly sequenced strains were made available by the *Listeria* sequencing project of the Broad Institute, including three ECIII strains isolated from human cases (two associated with the 2000 outbreak and one from the 1988 sporadic case) [97]. A whole-genome sequence for a ECIV strain associated with the 1997 outbreak in Italy has been recently reported [98] and ECV whole-genome sequences have been completed for two human isolates associated with the 2008 Canada outbreak (18). In a recent publication [99], the availability of draft genomes was announced for another ECII strain of environmental origin (2002 U.S. outbreak) and another ECIV strain from a clinical case (1979-Boston outbreak). Comparative analysis of available whole-genome sequences of *L. monocytogenes* has already greatly contributed to the study and characterization of epidemic-associated strains and will be essential in the future to identify additional EC-specific markers and for understanding short-term evolution. In fact, the ecology and transmission of ECs of *L. monocytogenes* remain largely unknown and additional epidemiologic and ecologic investigations are needed. Moreover, an improved understanding of EC strains may also provide new insights into differences in transmissibility and ability to cause disease among different *L. monocytogenes* subtypes.

6. Prevalence of ECs in Non Epidemic-Associated Sources: Sporadic Cases, Foods and Food Processing Environments

ECs (particularly ECI and ECII) continue to be detected among isolates from food and related environment and apparently sporadic cases of listeriosis [7, 44, 45]. Gray et al. (2004) observed that all four ribotypes previously associated with EC strains were observed from 2.2% to 4.8% in food isolates and were significantly associated with human isolates. In particular, i) ECI-associated ribotype was observed in 12.8 % of human isolates; ii) ECII-associated ribotype in 5.7 %; iii) ECIII-associated ribotype in 8.1 % and finally iv)

ECIV-associated ribotype in 14.4 % of human isolates [39]. In an earlier study, the ECI-associated ribotype, although more commonly linked with human epidemic isolates, had also been observed in 10.5 % of human sporadic cases and 11.8 % of animal cases [36]. Overall, it has been observed that ECI- and ECIV-associated ribotypes were associated with 41 % of human sporadic listeriosis cases [52].

In the U.S., one of the first studies to investigate the presence of EC-specific markers in foods focused on the characterization of several serotype 4b strains of *L. monocytogenes* collected from routine surveys of foods and food-processing environments from 1985 to 2000. Findings from this study revealed that 58.8 % of samples were presumably ECI due to presence of specific genetic markers [56]. Another study has also identified the presence of ECI and ECII strains in a survey of isolates from various food and environmental samples from two turkey processing plants in the U.S. [60]. It must be noted that these isolates showed PFGE profiles that differed from those of established epidemic-associated strains. In addition, slightly different PFGE profiles were observed for isolates showing ECI- or ECII-specific markers, obtained from the same plant but in different sampling times [60]. Results from this study can be attributed to: i) the stable presence of ECs in production facilities or their frequent reintroduction from a source not currently identified and ii) genomic diversification of *L. monocytogenes* isolates with ECI- or ECII-specific markers [60]. Genetic profiles closely related to ECI were also identified in farm isolates, human clinical cases, environmental sources and foods [100]. Findings from this study showed how some PFGE profiles of *L. monocytogenes* are broadly spread and pandemic (100). EC strains were also detected in 8 % of *L. monocytogenes* isolated from RTE foods, when a collection of 502 *L. monocytogenes* isolates from RTE foods and human clinical cases was analyzed [101]. Interestingly, EC strains were found to be significantly overrepresented among isolates obtained from deli and seafood salads, a category of samples contaminated by high levels of *L. monocytogenes* [101].

In Europe, many studies have investigated the presence of EC-specific markers in *L. monocytogenes* isolated from different sources. A 2007 investigation of isolates associated with clinical cases, food and environment in Italy, resulted in the identification of 16 strains with ECI-specific markers and 15 with ECII-specific markers [44]. In particular, ECI and ECII markers were found in 17.6 % and 20.6 % of clinical isolates and in 18 % and 14 % of food isolates, respectively. Both ECI and ECII markers were found in 20 % of environmental isolates. The predominance of ECI and ECII between clinical and environmental isolates (38-40%) compared to those isolated from food (32 %), supports the hypothesis that these clones are particularly well-adapted to specific environments and able to transmit and cause disease in humans [44]. The presence of ECI-, ECII-, and ECIII-specific markers was also observed in 15 samples obtained in another retrospective subtyping study on strains of *L. monocytogenes* isolated from apparently sporadic cases of infection occurring in Northern Italy from 1996 to 2007 [45]. Recently, three strains obtained from human sporadic cases occurred in Northern Italy in 2004, 2005 and 2006, were characterized and showed profiles specific for ECIV, ECI and ECII, respectively [7]. EC specific markers were also found in environmental isolates of *L. monocytogenes*. Strains from different types of sewage sludge were collected between 1999 and 2002 from different sewage treatment plants in France and analyzed [102]. Authors compared PFGE profiles of *L. monocytogenes* obtained from sludge with available data on isolates obtained from food and clinical cases. Interestingly, their results showed how 64.5 % of serotype 4b strains showed PFGE profiles that were closely related to profiles observed in human sporadic or epidemic human strains [102]. PFGE profiles ascribable to ECI and ECIV were also observed in Portugal, for two strains isolated from sporadic cases [46]. In particular, an isolate from a Portuguese human sporadic case collected in 2000 had the same PFGE profile as 17 other isolates, including ECI strains involved in the 1985-California and 1983-87 Switzerland outbreaks [46]. Moreover, two other isolates from human sporadic cases in 1997 and 1998 shared the sample PFGE profile as ECIV isolates linked to the 1989-UK outbreak [46]. Another recent study from Portugal analyzed 1,723 *L. monocytogenes* isolates obtained from fermented meat sausages, processing plant environments, and other raw products [103]. ECI and ECII markers were found in 13.58 % and 33.89 % of samples, respectively. Interestingly, in two facilities the presence of both ECI and ECII isolates was detected and ECI isolates with an indistinguishable PFGE pattern were also obtained [103].

Finally, concerning countries outside the U.S. and EU, there seems to be only one report from Japan about the detection of ECI-specific genetic markers. In particular, two strains of *L. monocytogenes* isolated from chicken meat and two obtained from patients were characteristically resistant to digestion with Sau3AI and showed amplification of three previously identified ECI-specific markers [47].

7. Virulence of Epidemic Clones

L. monocytogenes subtypes appear to differ in their pathogenicity for humans and/or in their ability to transmit to humans [3, 104]. In general, it has been observed that *L. monocytogenes* lineage I strains have been predominantly associated worldwide with human listeriosis (sporadic cases and outbreaks) and they are also more likely to cause human disease when compared to lineage II strains [1, 3]. Numerous investigations have examined whether the epidemic-associated strains were more virulent than other strains of the species [32, 39, 105, 106]. However, while data on molecular subtyping and genetic characterization of ECs is readily available, less is known about the in-vitro and in-vivo virulence phenotypes of these strains in spite of the fact that EC strains have been included in many studies under the assumption of their enhanced virulence [66,107,108]. However, some studies revealed a diversity in virulence-associated phenotypes even among EC strains [1, 32, 106] and controversy still persists on whether EC strains are indeed characterized by a greater pathogenic potential [3,32].

In general, a significant diversity in virulence of *L. monocytogenes* strains belonging to different serotypes and molecular subtypes has been well documented [1,39,104,109,110]. Gray et al., (2004) analyzed food isolates obtained from RTE food products and human isolates from invasive listeriosis cases that occurred in the U.S., mainly from 1997 to 2001. EC-associated ribotypes were observed in different percentages, ranging from a minimum of 2.2 % in foods and 5.7 % in human isolates and a maximum of 4.85 % and 14 % in foods and human isolates, respectively [39]. The same authors also performed a plaque assay on a subset of 133 isolates to evaluate cytopathogenicity; their results expressed the ability to spread between mammalian cells (indicated by plaque area) and infectivity. Three ribotypes were found to differ significantly from the rest in terms of cytopathogenicity. Particularly, ECI-associated DUP-1038B and ECIV-associated DUP-1042B showed larger plaque areas compared to other ribotypes [39]. In contrast, ECIII-associated DUP-1053A showed a lower infectivity compared to other ribotypes. These findings are consistent with other studies on food and human isolates, revealing some subtypes to be more virulent than others [111,112]. However, ECIII comprises serotype 1/2a strains and it is therefore difficult to determine whether the observed differences in infectivity for DUP-1053A are indeed due to differences between epidemic and sporadic strains or can be ascribed to differences between serotypes (1/2a for ECIII and 4b for other EC-associated ribotypes) [39]. Notwithstanding, isolates showing low in-vitro cytopathogenicity may still be able to cause human disease considering that ribotype DUP-1053A was considerably more frequent in human isolates than food isolates (39). It must be noted however, that in-vitro cytopathogenicity cannot be solely defined on the basis of either plaque area or infectivity alone, since correlations between the two can be positive, negative, or absent [39].

L. *monocytogenes* was used as a model organism for the identification of phylogenetic clades significantly associated with isolation from different sources (e.g. humans, animals, and food) [113]. A set of 120 geographically and temporally matched *L. monocytogenes* isolates from different sources was selected from a larger set of previously characterized *L. monocytogenes* isolates [113]. They confirmed what previously observed (39), as isolates of EC-associated ribotypes (DUP-1038B and DUP-1042B) were classified in two clades which formed significantly larger plaques than isolates belonging to other ribotypes (P < 0.05) [113]. Interestingly, *L. monocytogenes* isolates in the above-mentioned clades showed some of the largest mean plaque sizes observed among all of the source-associated clades identified in the study [113]. As also previously observed [39], ECIII-associated ribotype DUP-1053A produced relatively smaller plaques compared to other ribotypes. However, a potential biological explanation for the association of strains with this ribotype with human hosts may be in their enhanced invasiveness for human intestinal epithelial Caco-2 cells, compared to a standard lineage II control strain [113]. Although in-vitro assays do not seem to provide a full measure of virulence potential of *L. monocytogenes* isolates, different findings have provided useful information on the virulence characteristics of *L. monocytogenes* isolates and highlighted the need for future studies [39,113].

Great diversity in virulence potential for *L. monocytogenes* strains has been documented also for EC-associated strains. For example, a ECI food isolate from the 1985-California outbreak associated with Mexican-style cheese was described as showing atypical virulence-associated phenotypic and genotypic characteristics [114]. When compared to standard laboratory control and other lineage I serotype 4b strains, the analyzed ECI strain revealed: i) a significantly reduced invasion efficiency in Caco-2 cells; ii) a significantly greater variation in invasiveness when grown under different conditions; iii) a significantly reduced exponential growth rate, and finally iv) to carry several authentic atypical point mutations resulting in premature stop codons (PMSCs), including a nonsense mutation in *inlB* [114]. Previous studies detected multiple distinct mutations leading to PMSCs in *inlA*, a key virulence gene for *L. monocytogenes* [6,101,114–116]. During the initial stages of an infection, *inlA* plays a critical role in crossing the intestinal barrier (117). Isolates with PMSCs have been shown to represent a substantial fraction of *L. monocytogenes* strains isolated from RTE foods in the U.S. (101). *L. monocytogenes* carrying a PMSC in *inlA* produce a truncated form of *inlA* and such forms have been linked to reduced invasion efficiency and attenuated virulence [114,116]. A recent study screened for all currently known PMSC mutations in *inlA* among a collection of over 1,000 *L. monocytogenes* isolates from RTE foods and human clinical cases in order to determine the prevalence of *inlA* PMSC carrying strains and of EC strains [101]. Interestingly, this study represented the first report of *inlA* PMSC mutations in isolates associated with ECs, particularly ECI, ECIV and ECIII. However, *inlA* PMSC mutations did not appear to be uniformly distributed among ribotypes, including those associated with ECs [101]. Moreover, although *inlA* PMSC mutations were indeed present in a small number of EC strains, these mutations were markedly underrepresented among ECs [101], consistent with the frequent involvement of these EC strains in listeriosis cases worldwide, particularly epidemics [1, 39]. In addition, considering the EC strains that carried a PMSC in *inlA*, the majority were observed in RTE foods and only one in a human case (101). On a subsequent study by the same group, a juvenile male guinea pigs was intragastrically challenged with an ECII strain or a serotype 1/2a strain carrying a PMSC mutation in *inlA* in order to generate a strain-specific dose-response curve [118]. Based on modeling of individual or combined organ data, a significant shift (an approximate $1.3\text{-}\log_{10}$ increase) in the median infectious dose was observed for the strain carrying a PMSC in *inlA* in relation to the ECII strain [118]. Results from this work provide important data for the implementation and development of current and future risk assessments.

Other authors have confirmed that even EC strains (particularly ECI and ECIV) of *L. monocytogenes* can show attenuated virulence in-vitro [106]. In particular, 15 strains of *L. monocytogenes* were obtained from human clinical cases associated with listeriosis outbreaks worldwide. On the whole, three ECI strains and one ECIV strain showed particularly low ability to invade both human intestinal epithelial cells and human hepatic cells and were thus classified as having reduced invasion efficiency [106]. Moreover, a ECIV strain, earlier classified as virulence-impaired in intragastric guinea pig infection experiments [116], showed reduced swarming ability in addition to reduced invasion efficiency. Interestingly, no PMSCs mutations in *inlA* were observed in the four invasion-attenuated strains and these strains were deemed very similar and genetically related to fully invasive strains [106]. However, even though EC strains have shown attenuated virulence in-vitro, a parallel significant reduction in mortality rates was not observed and thus it is possible to hypothesize that most outbreaks of human listeriosis are linked to EC strains not because they are more virulent of other *L. monocytogenes* strains, but rather due to their greater ability to persist in the environment and to survive and replicate in foods [106]. Above all, the results of this study seem to indicate that strains of EC *L. monocytogenes* cannot be considered a priori as highly virulent and that differences in virulence also extend to highly clonal groups commonly associated with listeriosis outbreaks, including ECs [106]. Future studies will be warranted to more accurately determine the association between different genotypic characteristics and virulence.

Conclusion

ECs of *L. monocytogenes* have been associated with major nationwide and international foodborne outbreaks around the world [1]. In particular, the widespread incidence of ECI in both human sporadic and epidemic cases of listeriosis suggests its ubiquity in food processing environments, leading to contamination of food. Overall, findings from the abovementioned studies and the presence of EC strains in different sporadic cases and foods worldwide may suggest that these strains have specific environmental reservoirs in which they can persist and transmit during the intervals between outbreaks. Currently, there are still limited data on prevalence of ECs in isolates from human sporadic cases, animals, food and food processing plants and natural environments. However, considering the repeated involvement of the same EC in geographically and temporally distinct outbreaks, it is possible to hypothesize that these strains have specific environmental niches during the interval between different outbreaks and also possess the ability to transmit widely around the world.

In general, screening for the presence of EC strains in a wider selections of *L. monocytogenes* isolates from different sources will provide valuable data to estimate the prevalence of ECs-associated samples more precisely and to determine the distribution and long-term spread of ECs.

Therefore, the continued development of rapid and reliable subtyping and virulence assays, coupled with the investigation of larger sets of strains, is paramount for improving our understanding of the detection, transmission and virulence of ECs of *L. monocytogenes*.

Acknowledgments

The editorial assistance and support of Dr. Steve Knabel and Dr. Daniele Nucera is gratefully acknowledged. The author would like to apologize for any unintentional omission of relevant works by other colleagues.

References

[1]   Kathariou S. Listeria monocytogenes virulence and pathogenicity, a food safety perspective. *J. Food Prot.* 2002;65(11):1811–29.

[2]   Chen Y, Zhang W, Knabel SJ. Multi-virulence-locus sequence typing identifies single nucleotide polymorphisms which differentiate epidemic clones and outbreak strains of Listeria monocytogenes. *J. Clin. Microbiol.* 2007;45(3):835–46.

[3]   Cheng Y, Siletzky R, Kathariou S. Genomic Divisions/Lineages, Epidemic Clones, and Population Structure. In: Liu D, ed. *Handbook of Listeria monocytogenes.* CRC Press; 2008. p. 337-58.

[4]   Knabel S, Reimer A, Verghese B, Lok M, Ziegler J, Farber J, et al. Sequence typing confirms that a predominant Listeria monocytogenes clone caused human listeriosis cases and outbreaks in Canada from 1988-2010. *J. Clin. Microbiol.* 2012 Feb 15 [Epub ahead of print].

[5]   Graves LM, Swaminathan B. PulseNet standardized protocol for subtyping Listeria monocytogenes by macrorestriction and pulsed-field gel electrophoresis. *Int. J. Food Microbiol.* 2001;65(1-2):55–62.

[6]   Ragon M, Wirth T, Hollandt F, Lavenir R, Lecuit M, Le Monnier A, et al. A new perspective on Listeria monocytogenes evolution. *PLoS Pathog.* 2008;4(9):e1000146.

[7]   Lomonaco S, Knabel SJ, Dalmasso A, Civera T, Bottero MT. Novel multiplex single nucleotide polymorphism-based method for identifying epidemic clones of Listeria monocytogenes. *Appl. Environ. Microbiol.* 2011;77(17):6290–4.

[8]   Chen Y, Zhang W, Knabel SJ. Multi-virulence-locus sequence typing clarifies epidemiology of recent listeriosis outbreaks in the United States. *J. Clin. Microbiol.* 2005;43(10):5291–4.

[9]   Swaminathan B, Gerner-Smidt P. *The epidemiology of human listeriosis.* Microbes Infect. 2007;9(10):1236–43.

[10] Ivanek R, Gröhn YT, Tauer LW, Wiedmann M. The cost and benefit of Listeria monocytogenes food safety measures. *Crit Rev Food Sci Nutr.* 2004;44(7-8):513–23.

[11] EFSA. The European Union summary report on trends and sources of zoonoses, zoonotic agents and food-borne outbreaks in 2009. 2011 p. 378. Report No.: 9(3):2090. Available from: doi:10.2903/j.efsa.2011.2090

[12] Fleming DW, Cochi SL, MacDonald KL, Brondum J, Hayes PS, Plikaytis BD, et al. Pasteurized milk as a vehicle of infection in an outbreak of listeriosis. *N. Engl. J. Med.* 1985;312(7):404–7.

[13] Graves LM, Hunter SB, Ong AR, Schoonmaker-Bopp D, Hise K, Kornstein L, et al. Microbiological aspects of the investigation that traced the 1998 outbreak of listeriosis in the United States to contaminated hot dogs and establishment of molecular subtyping-based surveillance for Listeria monocytogenes in the PulseNet network. *J. Clin. Microbiol.* 2005;43(5):2350–5.

[14] Linnan MJ, Mascola L, Lou XD, Goulet V, May S, Salminen C, et al. Epidemic listeriosis associated with Mexican-style cheese. *N. Engl. J. Med.* 1988;319(13):823–8.

[15] Mead PS, Dunne EF, Graves L, Wiedmann M, Patrick M, Hunter S, et al. Nationwide outbreak of listeriosis due to contaminated meat. *Epidemiol. Infect.* 2006;134(4): 744–51.

[16] Olsen SJ, Patrick M, Hunter SB, Reddy V, Kornstein L, MacKenzie WR, et al. Multistate outbreak of Listeria monocytogenes infection linked to delicatessen turkey meat. *Clin. Infect. Dis.* 2005;40(7):962–7.

[17] Schlech WF 3rd, Lavigne PM, Bortolussi RA, Allen AC, Haldane EV, Wort AJ, et al. Epidemic listeriosis--evidence for transmission by food. *N. Engl. J. Med.* 1983;308(4):203–6.

[18] Gilmour MW, Graham M, Van Domselaar G, Tyler S, Kent H, Trout-Yakel KM, et al. High-throughput genome sequencing of two Listeria monocytogenes clinical isolates during a large foodborne outbreak. *BMC Genomics.* 2010;11:120.

[19] MMWR. Multistate outbreak of listeriosis associated with Jensen Farms cantaloupe --- United States, August--September 2011. 2011 [Accessed 2012 Jan 30]; Available from: http://www.cdc.gov/mmwr/preview/mmwrhtml/mm6039a5.htm?s_cid=mm6039a5_w

[20] Lundén J, Tolvanen R, Korkeala H. Human listeriosis outbreaks linked to dairy products in Europe. *J. Dairy Sci.* 2004;87(E. Suppl.):E6–E11.

[21] Allerberger F, Guggenbichler JP. Listeriosis in Austria--report of an outbreak in 1986. *Acta Microbiol. Hung.* 1989;36(2-3):149–52.

[22] Bille J. Epidemiology of human listeriosis in Europe with special reference to the Swiss outbreak. *Foodborne Listeriosis.* Elsevier. Amsterdam: Miller, A.J., Smith, J.L. and Somkuti,G.A.; 1990. p. 71–4.

[23] Goulet V, Jacquet C, Vaillant V, Rebière I, Mouret E, Lorente C, et al. Listeriosis from consumption of raw-milk cheese. *Lancet.* 1995;345(8964):1581–2.

[24] Koch J, Dworak R, Prager R, Becker B, Brockmann S, Wicke A, et al. Large listeriosis outbreak linked to cheese made from pasteurized milk, Germany, 2006-2007. *Foodborne Pathog.* Dis. 2010;7(12):1581–4.

[25] Maijala R, Lyytikäinen O, Autio T, Aalto T, Haavisto L, Honkanen-Buzalski T. Exposure of Listeria monocytogenes within an epidemic caused by butter in Finland. *Int. J. Food Microbiol.* 2001;70(1-2):97–109.

[26] Fretz R, Pichler J, Sagel U, Much P, Ruppitsch W, Pietzka AT, et al. Update: Multinational listeriosis outbreak due to «Quargel», a sour milk curd cheese, caused by two different L. monocytogenes serotype 1/2a strains, 2009-2010. *Euro Surveill.* 2010;15(16).

[27] Ministero della Salute. Bollettino Epidemiologico [Internet]. [Accessed 2012 Feb 10] Available from: http://www.salute.gov.it/malattieInfettive/datidefcons.jsp

[28] Aureli P, Fiorucci GC, Caroli D, Marchiaro G, Novara O, Leone L, et al. An outbreak of febrile gastroenteritis associated with corn contaminated by Listeria monocytogenes. *N. Engl. J. Med.* 2000;342(17):1236–41.

[29] de Valk H, Jacquet C, Goulet V, Vaillant V, Perra A, Simon F, et al. Surveillance of Listeria infections in Europe. *Euro Surveill.* 2005;10(10):251–5.

[30] Martin P, Jacquet C, Goulet V, Vaillant V, De Valk H. Pulsed-field gel electrophoresis of Listeria monocytogenes strains: the PulseNet Europe Feasibility Study. *Foodborne Pathog. Dis.* 2006;3(3):303–8.

[31] Swaminathan B, Gerner-Smidt P, Ng L-K, Lukinmaa S, Kam K-M, Rolando S, et al. Building PulseNet International: an interconnected system of laboratory networks to facilitate timely public health recognition and response to foodborne disease outbreaks and emerging foodborne diseases. *Foodborne Pathog. Dis.* 2006;3(1):36–50.

[32] Kathariou S. Foodborne outbreaks of listeriosis and epidemic-associated lineages of Listeria monocytogenes. In: Torrence ME, Isaacson RE, eds. *Microbial Food Safety in Animal Agriculture.* Oxford, UK: Blackwell Publishing; 2003. p. 243–56.

[33] Bibb WF, Gellin BG, Weaver R, Schwartz B, Plikaytis BD, Reeves MW, et al. Analysis of clinical and food-borne isolates of Listeria monocytogenes in the United States by multilocus enzyme electrophoresis and application of the method to epidemiologic investigations. *Appl. Environ. Microbiol.* 1990;56(7):2133–41.

[34] Brosch R, Brett M, Catimel B, Luchansky JB, Ojeniyi B, Rocourt J. Genomic fingerprinting of 80 strains from the WHO multicenter international typing study of Listeria monocytogenes via pulsed-field gel electrophoresis (PFGE). *Int. J. Food Microbiol.* 1996;32(3):343–55.

[35] Buchrieser C, Brosch R, Catimel B, Rocourt J. Pulsed-field gel electrophoresis applied for comparing Listeria monocytogenes strains involved in outbreaks. *Can. J. Microbiol.* 1993;39(4):395–401.

[36] Piffaretti JC, Kressebuch H, Aeschbacher M, Bille J, Bannerman E, Musser JM, et al. Genetic characterization of clones of the bacterium Listeria monocytogenes causing epidemic disease. *Proc. Natl. Acad. Sci. US* 1989;86(10):3818–22.

[37] Chen Y, Knabel SJ. Strain Typing. In: Liu D, ed. *Handbook of Listeria monocytogenes.* CRC Press; 2008. p. 203–40.

[38] Ducey TF, Page B, Usgaard T, Borucki MK, Pupedis K, Ward TJ. A single-nucleotide-polymorphism-based multilocus genotyping assay for subtyping lineage I isolates of Listeria monocytogenes. *Appl. Environ. Microbiol.* 2007;73(1):133–47.

[39] Gray MJ, Zadoks RN, Fortes ED, Dogan B, Cai S, Chen Y, et al. Listeria monocytogenes isolates from foods and humans form distinct but overlapping populations. *Appl. Environ. Microbiol.* 2004;70(10):5833–41.

[40] Kathariou S, Graves L, Buchrieser C, Glaser P, Siletzky RM, Swaminathan B. Involvement of closely related strains of a new clonal group of Listeria monocytogenes in the 1998-99 and 2002 multistate outbreaks of foodborne listeriosis in the United States. *Foodborne Pathog. Dis.* 2006;3(3):292–302.

[41] Lomonaco S, Chen Y, Knabel SJ. Analysis of additional virulence genes and virulence gene regions in Listeria monocytogenes confirms the epidemiologic relevance of multi-virulence-locus sequence typing. *J. Food Prot.* 2008;71(12):2559–66.

[42] Miya S, Kimura B, Sato M, Takahashi H, Ishikawa T, Suda T, et al. Development of a multilocus variable-number of tandem repeat typing method for Listeria monocytogenes serotype 4b strains. *Int. J. Food Microbiol.* 2008;124(3):239–49.

[43] Chenal-Francisque V, Lopez J, Cantinelli T, Caro V, Tran C, Leclercq A, et al. Worldwide distribution of major clones of Listeria monocytogenes. *Emerging Infect. Dis.* 2011;17(6):1110–2.

[44] Franciosa G, Scalfaro C, Maugliani A, Floridi F, Gattuso A, Hodzic S, et al. Distribution of epidemic clonal genetic markers among Listeria monocytogenes 4b isolates. *J. Food Prot.* 2007;70(3):574–81.

[45] Mammina C, Aleo A, Romani C, Pellissier N, Nicoletti P, Pecile P, et al. Characterization of Listeria monocytogenes isolates from human listeriosis cases in Italy. *J. Clin. Microbiol.* 2009;47(9):2925–30.

[46] Neves E, Lourenço A, Silva AC, Coutinho R, Brito L. Pulsed-field gel electrophoresis (PFGE) analysis of Listeria monocytogenes isolates from different sources and geographical origins and representative of the twelve serovars. *Syst. Appl. Microbiol.* 2008;31(5):387–92.

[47] Ochiai Y, Batmunkh O, Ogasawara K, Mochizuki M, Hondo R, Ueda F. Genetic variation of Listeria monocytogenes isolates from domestic and imported foods in Japan. *Int. J. Food Microbiol.* 2008;127(1-2):12–7.

[48] Foley SL, Lynne AM, Nayak R. Molecular typing methodologies for microbial source tracking and epidemiological investigations of Gram-negative bacterial foodborne pathogens. *Infect. Genet. Evol.* 2009;9(4):430–40.

[49] Sauders BD, Fortes ED, Morse DL, Dumas N, Kiehlbauch JA, Schukken Y, et al. Molecular subtyping to detect human listeriosis clusters. *Emerging Infect. Dis.* 2003;9(6):672–80.

[50] Zhang W, Jayarao BM, Knabel SJ. Multi-virulence-locus sequence typing of Listeria monocytogenes. *Appl. Environ. Microbiol.* 2004;70(2):913–20.

[51] Jacquet C, Catimel B, Brosch R, Buchrieser C, Dehaumont P, Goulet V, et al. Investigations related to the epidemic strain involved in the French listeriosis outbreak in 1992. *Appl. Environ. Microbiol.* 1995;61(6):2242–6.

[52] Jeffers GT, Bruce JL, McDonough PL, Scarlett J, Boor KJ, Wiedmann M. Comparative genetic characterization of Listeria monocytogenes isolates from human and animal listeriosis cases. *Microbiology (Reading, Engl.).* 2001;147(Pt 5):1095–104.

[53] Herd M, Kocks C. Gene fragments distinguishing an epidemic-associated strain from a virulent prototype strain of Listeria monocytogenes belong to a distinct functional subset of genes and partially cross-hybridize with other Listeria species. *Infect. Immun.* 2001;69(6):3972–9.

[54] Tran HL, Kathariou S. Restriction fragment length polymorphisms detected with novel DNA probes differentiate among diverse lineages of serogroup 4 Listeria monocytogenes and identify four distinct lineages in serotype 4b. *Appl. Environ. Microbiol.* 2002;68(1):59–64.

[55] Zheng W, Kathariou S. Differentiation of epidemic-associated strains of Listeria monocytogenes by restriction fragment length polymorphism in a gene region essential for growth at low temperatures (4 degrees C). *Appl. Environ. Microbiol.* 1995;61(12):4310–4.

[56] Yildirim S, Lin W, Hitchins AD, Jaykus L-A, Altermann E, Klaenhammer TR, et al. Epidemic clone I-specific genetic markers in strains of Listeria monocytogenes serotype 4b from foods. *Appl. Environ. Microbiol.* 2004;70(7):4158–64.

[57] Zheng W, Kathariou S. Host-mediated modification of Sau3AI restriction in Listeria monocytogenes: prevalence in epidemic-associated strains. *Appl. Environ. Microbiol.* 1997;63(8):3085–9.

[58] Evans MR, Swaminathan B, Graves LM, Altermann E, Klaenhammer TR, Fink RC, et al. Genetic markers unique to Listeria monocytogenes serotype 4b differentiate epidemic clone II (hot dog outbreak strains) from other lineages. *Appl. Environ. Microbiol.* 2004;70(4):2383–90.

[59] Gottlieb SL, Newbern EC, Griffin PM, Graves LM, Hoekstra RM, Baker NL, et al. Multistate outbreak of listeriosis linked to turkey deli meat and subsequent changes in US regulatory policy. *Clin. Infect. Dis.* 2006;42(1):29–36.

[60] Eifert JD, Curtis PA, Bazaco MC, Meinersmann RJ, Berrang ME, Kernodle S, et al. Molecular characterization of Listeria monocytogenes of the serotype 4b complex (4b, 4d, 4e) from two turkey processing plants. *Foodborne Pathog. Dis.* 2005;2(3):192–200.

[61] Ward TJ, Evans P, Wiedmann M, Usgaard T, Roof SE, Stroika SG, et al. Molecular and phenotypic characterization of Listeria monocytogenes from U.S. Department of Agriculture Food Safety and Inspection Service surveillance of ready-to-eat foods and processing facilities. *J. Food Prot.* 2010;73(5):861–9.

[62] Verghese B, Lok M, Wen J, Alessandria V, Chen Y, Kathariou S, et al. comK prophage junction fragments as markers for Listeria monocytogenes genotypes unique to individual meat and poultry processing plants and a model for rapid niche-specific adaptation, biofilm formation, and persistence. *Appl. Environ. Microbiol.* 2011;77(10):3279–92.

[63] Yde M, Botteldoorn N, Bertrand S, Collard J, Dierick K. Microbiological and molecular investigation of an increase of human listeriosis in Belgium, 2006-2007. *Euro Surveill.* 2010;15(6).

[64] Kim J-W, Dutta V, Elhanafi D, Lee S, Osborne JA, Kathariou S. A novel restriction-modification system is responsible for temperature-dependent phage resistance in Listeria monocytogenes ECII. *Appl. Environ. Microbiol.* 2012;78(6):1995–2004.

[65] MMWR. Listeriosis associated with consumption of turkey franks. *MMWR Morb. Mortal. Wkly. Rep.* 1989;38(15):267–8.

[66] Nelson KE. Whole genome comparisons of serotype 4b and 1/2a strains of the food-borne pathogen Listeria monocytogenes reveal new insights into the core genome components of this species. *Nucleic Acids Research*. 2004;32:2386–95.

[67] Orsi RH, Borowsky ML, Lauer P, Young SK, Nusbaum C, Galagan JE, et al. Short-term genome evolution of Listeria monocytogenes in a non-controlled environment. *BMC Genomics*. 2008;9:539.

[68] Chen Y, Knabel SJ. Prophages in Listeria monocytogenes contain single-nucleotide polymorphisms that differentiate outbreak clones within epidemic clones. *J. Clin. Microbiol*. 2008;46(4):1478–84.

[69] Ho JL, Shands KN, Friedland G, Eckind P, Fraser DW. An outbreak of type 4b Listeria monocytogenes infection involving patients from eight Boston hospitals. *Arch. Intern. Med*. 1986;146(3):520–4.

[70] McLauchlin J, Hall SM, Velani SK, Gilbert RJ. Human listeriosis and paté: a possible association. *BMJ*. 1991;303(6805):773–5.

[71] Sperry KEV, Kathariou S, Edwards JS, Wolf LA. Multiple-locus variable-number tandem-repeat analysis as a tool for subtyping Listeria monocytogenes strains. *J. Clin. Microbiol*. 2008;46(4):1435–50.

[72] Clark CG, Farber J, Pagotto F, Ciampa N, Doré K, Nadon C, et al. Surveillance for Listeria monocytogenes and listeriosis, 1995-2004. *Epidemiol. Infect*. 2010;138(4): 559–72.

[73] MacDonald PDM, Whitwam RE, Boggs JD, MacCormack JN, Anderson KL, Reardon JW, et al. Outbreak of listeriosis among Mexican immigrants as a result of consumption of illicitly produced Mexican-style cheese. *Clin. Infect. Dis*. 2005;40(5):677–82.

[74] Orskov F, Orskov I. From the national institutes of health. Summary of a workshop on the clone concept in the epidemiology, taxonomy, and evolution of the enterobacteriaceae and other bacteria. *J. Infect. Dis*. 1983;148(2):346–57.

[75] Riley LW. *Molecular Epidemiology of Infectious Diseases: Principles and Practices*. Washington: ASM Press; 2004.

[76] Chen Y, Knabel SJ. Multiplex PCR for simultaneous detection of bacteria of the genus Listeria, Listeria monocytogenes, and major serotypes and epidemic clones of L. monocytogenes. *Appl. Environ. Microbiol*. 2007;73(19):6299–304.

[77] de Greeff A, Wisselink HJ, de Bree FM, Schultsz C, Baums CG, Thi HN, et al. Genetic diversity of Streptococcus suis isolates as determined by comparative genome hybridization. *BMC Microbiol*. 2011;11:161.

[78] den Bakker HC, Moreno Switt AI, Govoni G, Cummings CA, Ranieri ML, Degoricija L, et al. Genome sequencing reveals diversification of virulence factor content and possible host adaptation in distinct subpopulations of Salmonella enterica. *BMC Genomics*. 2011;12:425.

[79] Marsden GL, Davis IJ, Wright VJ, Sebaihia M, Kuijper EJ, Minton NP. Array comparative hybridisation reveals a high degree of similarity between UK and European clinical isolates of hypervirulent Clostridium difficile. *BMC Genomics*. 2010;11:389.

[80] Vejborg RM, Hancock V, Schembri MA, Klemm P. Comparative genomics of Escherichia coli strains causing urinary tract infections. *Appl. Environ. Microbiol*. 2011;77(10):3268–78.

[81] Murray AE, Lies D, Li G, Nealson K, Zhou J, Tiedje JM. DNA/DNA hybridization to microarrays reveals gene-specific differences between closely related microbial genomes. *Proc. Natl. Acad. Sci. US.* 2001;98(17):9853–8.

[82] Borucki MK, Kim SH, Call DR, Smole SC, Pagotto F. Selective discrimination of Listeria monocytogenes epidemic strains by a mixed-genome DNA microarray compared to discrimination by pulsed-field gel electrophoresis, ribotyping, and multilocus sequence typing. *J. Clin. Microbiol.* 2004;42(11):5270–6.

[83] Cheng Y, Kim J-W, Lee S, Siletzky RM, Kathariou S. DNA probes for unambiguous identification of Listeria monocytogenes epidemic clone II strains. *Appl. Environ. Microbiol.* 2010;76(9):3061–8.

[84] Keim P, Price LB, Klevytska AM, Smith KL, Schupp JM, Okinaka R, et al. Multiple-locus variable-number tandem repeat analysis reveals genetic relationships within Bacillus anthracis. *J. Bacteriol.* 2000;182(10):2928–36.

[85] Gerner-Smidt P, Hise K, Kincaid J, Hunter S, Rolando S, Hyytiä-Trees E, et al. PulseNet USA: a five-year update. *Foodborne Pathog. Dis.* 2006;3(1):9–19.

[86] Hyytiä-Trees E, Smole SC, Fields PA, Swaminathan B, Ribot EM. Second generation subtyping: a proposed PulseNet protocol for multiple-locus variable-number tandem repeat analysis of Shiga toxin-producing Escherichia coli O157 (STEC O157). *Foodborne Pathog. Dis.* 2006;3(1):118–31.

[87] Halpin JL, Garrett NM, Ribot EM, Graves LM, Cooper KL. Re-evaluation, optimization, and multilaboratory validation of the PulseNet-standardized pulsed-field gel electrophoresis protocol for Listeria monocytogenes. *Foodborne Pathog. Dis.* 2010;7(3):293–8.

[88] Maiden MC, Bygraves JA, Feil E, Morelli G, Russell JE, Urwin R, et al. Multilocus sequence typing: a portable approach to the identification of clones within populations of pathogenic microorganisms. *Proc. Natl. Acad. Sci. US* 1998;95(6):3140–5.

[89] Maiden MC. Multilocus sequence typing of bacteria. *Annu. Rev. Microbiol.* 2006;60:561–88.

[90] Meinersmann RJ, Phillips RW, Wiedmann M, Berrang ME. Multilocus sequence typing of Listeria monocytogenes by use of hypervariable genes reveals clonal and recombination histories of three lineages. *Appl. Environ. Microbiol.* 2004;70(4): 2193–203.

[91] Revazishvili T, Kotetishvili M, Stine OC, Kreger AS, Morris JG Jr, Sulakvelidze A. Comparative analysis of multilocus sequence typing and pulsed-field gel electrophoresis for characterizing Listeria monocytogenes strains isolated from environmental and clinical sources. *J. Clin. Microbiol.* 2004;42(1):276–85.

[92] Salcedo C, Arreaza L, Alcalá B, de la Fuente L, Vázquez JA. Development of a multilocus sequence typing method for analysis of Listeria monocytogenes clones. *J. Clin. Microbiol.* 2003;41(2):757–62.

[93] Gomes AR, Vinga S, Zavolan M, de Lencastre H. Analysis of the genetic variability of virulence-related loci in epidemic clones of methicillin-resistant Staphylococcus aureus. *Antimicrob. Agents Chemother.* 2005;49(1):366–79.

[94] Packard ER, Parton R, Coote JG, Fry NK. Sequence variation and conservation in virulence-related genes of Bordetella pertussis isolates from the UK. *J. Med. Microbiol.* 2004;53(Pt 5):355–65.

[95] Ward TJ, Ducey TF, Usgaard T, Dunn KA, Bielawski JP. Multilocus genotyping assays for single nucleotide polymorphism-based subtyping of Listeria monocytogenes isolates. *Appl. Environ. Microbiol.* 2008;74(24):7629–42.

[96] Ward TJ, Usgaard T, Evans P. A targeted multilocus genotyping assay for lineage, serogroup, and epidemic clone typing of Listeria monocytogenes. *Appl. Environ. Microbiol.* 2010;76(19):6680–4.

[97] Broad Institute of Harvard and MIT. Listeria monocytogenes Sequencing Project [Internet]. http://www.broadinstitute.org/. [Accessed 2012 Feb 3]. Available from: http://www.broadinstitute.org/annotation/genome/listeria_group/GenomesIndex.html

[98] den Bakker HC, Fortes ED, Wiedmann M. Multilocus sequence typing of outbreak-associated Listeria monocytogenes isolates to identify epidemic clones. *Foodborne Pathog. Dis.* 2010;7(3):257–65.

[99] Chen Y, Strain EA, Allard M, Brown EW. Genome sequences of Listeria monocytogenes strains J1816 and J1-220, associated with human outbreaks. *J. Bacteriol.* 2011;193(13):3424–5.

[100] Fugett EB, Schoonmaker-Bopp D, Dumas NB, Corby J, Wiedmann M. Pulsed-field gel electrophoresis (PFGE) analysis of temporally matched Listeria monocytogenes isolates from human clinical cases, foods, ruminant farms, and urban and natural environments reveals source-associated as well as widely distributed PFGE Types. *J. Clin. Microbiol.* 2007;45:865–73.

[101] Van Stelten A, Simpson JM, Ward TJ, Nightingale KK. Revelation by single-nucleotide polymorphism genotyping that mutations leading to a premature stop codon in inlA are common among Listeria monocytogenes isolates from ready-to-eat foods but not human listeriosis cases. *Appl. Environ. Microbiol.* 2010;76(9):2783–90.

[102] Kerouanton A, Roche SM, Marault M, Velge P, Pourcher A-M, Brisabois A, et al. Characterization of isolates of Listeria monocytogenes from sludge using pulsed-field gel electrophoresis and virulence assays. *J. Appl. Microbiol.* 2010;108(4):1380–8.

[103] Ferreira V, Barbosa J, Stasiewicz M, Vongkamjan K, Moreno Switt A, Hogg T, et al. Diverse geno- and phenotypes of persistent Listeria monocytogenes isolates from fermented meat sausage production facilities in Portugal. *Appl. Environ. Microbiol.* 2011;77(8):2701–15.

[104] Wiedmann M, Bruce JL, Keating C, Johnson AE, McDonough PL, Batt CA. Ribotypes and virulence gene polymorphisms suggest three distinct Listeria monocytogenes lineages with differences in pathogenic potential. *Infect. Immun.* 1997;65(7):2707–16.

[105] Kim SH, Bakko MK, Knowles D, Borucki MK. Oral inoculation of A/J mice for detection of invasiveness differences between Listeria monocytogenes epidemic and environmental strains. *Infect. Immun.* 2004;72(7):4318–21.

[106] Roberts AJ, Williams SK, Wiedmann M, Nightingale KK. Some Listeria monocytogenes outbreak strains demonstrate significantly reduced invasion, inlA transcript levels, and swarming motility in vitro. *Appl. Environ. Microbiol.* 2009;75(17):5647–58.

[107] Peterson LD, Faith NG, Czuprynski CJ. Growth of L. monocytogenes strain F2365 on ready-to-eat turkey meat does not enhance gastrointestinal listeriosis in intragastrically inoculated A/J mice. *Int. J. Food Microbiol.* 2008;126(1-2):112–5.

[108] Donaldson JR, Nanduri B, Burgess SC, Lawrence ML. Comparative proteomic analysis of Listeria monocytogenes strains F2365 and EGD. *Appl. Environ. Microbiol.* 2009;75(2):366–73.

[109] Raybourne RB. Virulence testing of Listeria monocytogenes. *J AOAC Int.* 2002;85(2):516–23.

[110] Roche SM, Gracieux P, Milohanic E, Albert I, Virlogeux-Payant I, Témoin S, et al. Investigation of specific substitutions in virulence genes characterizing phenotypic groups of low-virulence field strains of Listeria monocytogenes. *Appl. Environ. Microbiol.* 2005;71(10):6039–48.

[111] Larsen CN, Nørrung B, Sommer HM, Jakobsen M. In vitro and in vivo invasiveness of different pulsed-field gel electrophoresis types of Listeria monocytogenes. *Appl. Environ. Microbiol.* 2002;68(11):5698–703.

[112] Nørrung B, Andersen JK. Variations in virulence between different electrophoretic types of Listeria monocytogenes. *Lett. Appl. Microbiol.* 2000;30(3):228–32.

[113] Nightingale KK, Lyles K, Ayodele M, Jalan P, Nielsen R, Wiedmann M. Novel method to identify source-associated phylogenetic clustering shows that Listeria monocytogenes includes niche-adapted clonal groups with distinct ecological preferences. *J. Clin. Microbiol.* 2006;44(10):3742–51.

[114] Nightingale KK, Milillo SR, Ivy RA, Ho AJ, Oliver HF, Wiedmann M. Listeria monocytogenes F2365 carries several authentic mutations potentially leading to truncated gene products, including inlB, and demonstrates atypical phenotypic characteristics. *J. Food Prot.* 2007;70(2):482–8.

[115] Jacquet C, Doumith M, Gordon JI, Martin PMV, Cossart P, Lecuit M. A molecular marker for evaluating the pathogenic potential of foodborne Listeria monocytogenes. *J. Infect. Dis.* 2004;189(11):2094–100.

[116] Nightingale KK, Ivy RA, Ho AJ, Fortes ED, Njaa BL, Peters RM, et al. inlA premature stop codons are common among Listeria monocytogenes isolates from foods and yield virulence-attenuated strains that confer protection against fully virulent strains. *Appl. Environ. Microbiol.* 2008;74(21):6570–83.

[117] Lecuit M, Ohayon H, Braun L, Mengaud J, Cossart P. Internalin of Listeria monocytogenes with an intact leucine-rich repeat region is sufficient to promote internalization. *Infect. Immun.* 1997;65(12):5309–19.

[118] Van Stelten A, Simpson JM, Chen Y, Scott VN, Whiting RC, Ross WH, et al. Significant shift in median guinea pig infectious dose shown by an outbreak-associated Listeria monocytogenes epidemic clone strain and a strain carrying a premature stop codon mutation in inlA. *Appl. Environ. Microbiol.* 2011;77(7):2479–87.

In: Listeria Infections
Editors: A. Romano and C. F. Giordano

ISBN: 978-1-62081-639-4
© 2012 Nova Science Publishers, Inc.

Chapter III

Listeria: Epidemiology, Pathogenesis and Novel Potential Treatments

Lucila Saavedra[*][1], *Augusto Bellomio*[2], *Elvira M. Hebert*[1],
Carlos Minahk[2], *Nadia Suarez*[1], *and Fernando Sesma*[1]

[1]Centro de Referencia para Lactobacilos (CERELA-CONICET), Tucumán -Argentina
[2]Instituto Superior de Investigaciones Biológicas (INSIBIO-CONICET),
Tucumán-Argentina

Abstract

Microbial food-borne illnesses have a great impact not only in public health but also represent high economic costs for many countries around the world. *Listeria monocytogenes*, a Gram-positive facultative intracellular pathogen, is estimated to cause nearly 1,600 illnesses each year in the United States.

Listeriosis may have different clinical syndromes from a non-invasive form in healthy human usually associated to mild gastroenteritis to severe invasive form, especially during pregnancy and in people with compromised immune system. In this case, it can be a serious and sometimes fatal disease. The transmission can occur by different ways, being the most important one the consumption of contaminated food, especially ready-to-eat products. Many efforts have been made in order to control o minimize the presence of this pathogen in food and food processing areas.

Besides the new antilisterial technologies that are being explored such as surface pasteurization or ozone treatments, antimicrobial peptides called bacteriocins produced by GRAS microorganisms such as lactic acid bacteria arise as a potential solution in this field.

There are many *Listeria*-active bacteriocins described so far in the literature and products containing purified or semi-purified bacteriocins are already in the market.

[*] Corresponding author: Dr. Lucila Saavedra. CERELA-CONICET, Chacabuco 145, San Miguel de Tucumán, T4000ILC, Argentina, Tel.: +54 381 4310465 ext: 153; fax: +54 381 4005600, E-mail address: lucila@ cerela.org.ar.

Moreover, some anti-listerial bacteriocins proved to be active not only in food environments but also in listeria-infected mice models.

In this chapter, an updated description of outbreaks, pathogenesis as well as the new technology for controlling *Listeria* is presented.

Introduction

Listeria belongs to the family *Listeriaceae*, which are non-spore-forming Gram-positive, motile, rod shaped, facultative-anaerobic bacteria [1-2]. *Listeria* spp. and specially *L. monocytogenes* are ubiquitous. In fact, *L. monocytogenes* can be isolated from polluted water, sludge, soil and plants as well as from different animal sources including wild, domestic and farm animals [3-5]. *L. monocytogenes* appears even to be a habitual resident of the human gut and can be isolated from fecal samples in 2-10% of healthy population [6-7]. Furthermore, the presence of *L. monocytogenes* in raw foods from vegetable or animal origin is very common. Although *L. monocytogenes* is killed by cooking, it can grow under food storage conditions, being the presence of *Listeria* spp. in cooked foods an usual finding [8]. In fact, *L. monocytogenes* can survive and even multiply under conditions that are considered unfavorable for other bacteria. This bacterium can grow in a temperature range from -1.5° to 45° C, environmental pH between 4.1 and 9.6 and it is even able to grow at high salt concentrations (10% NaCl), requiring a water activity as low as 0.92 (11.5% NaCl). In addition, *L. monocytogenes* can survive although not grow in freezing conditions and in dry environments [9-10].

L. monocytogenes is the only member of the family recognized as a human pathogen because it can invade and replicate in human cells, causing the disease known as listeriosis [11]. On the other hand, *L. ivanovii* can cause abortions in ruminants and may even affect humans occasionally [12]. The remaining species of the genus (*L. innocua, L. seeligeri, L. welshimeri, L. grayi, L. marthii* and *L. rocourtiae*) are not pathogenic.

Listeriosis is a serious disease that mainly affects immunocompromised persons. Patients under immunosuppressive therapy and HIV infected alongside people suffering from various types of cancer are the most susceptible population to contract severe forms of the disease [13-14]. Other factors that increase the probability of getting sick are diabetes, alcoholism, liver or kidney disease, newborns, elderly and pregnant women. 16-27% of all cases of listeriosis occur in pregnant women [13] and patients with AIDS have about 65-145% more probability that a healthy person to become ill base on an estimation carried out in Emory University School of Medicine, Atlanta, Georgia [15].

Listeriosis is a worldwide disease with a sporadic incidence but often severe and fatal. 1,685 confirmed cases were reported from 26 European Union countries in 2009 [16], while 1,600 cases per year are reported in the United States [17]. Importantly, nearly 90% of those patients need hospitalization and 250 die [18]. Even though listeriosis was first reported in rabbits in 1926 by Murray *et al.* [19] and as a human disease by Nyfeldt in 1929 [20]; it was finally established as a foodborne disease in as late as 1983. Actually, the first outbreak of listeriosis in which epidemiologists could reliably link the source of contamination with *L. monocytogenes* occurred in Nova Scotia, Canada in 1981, where 18 people died upon ingestion of contaminated coleslaw [21]. Indeed, the transmission of the disease occurs mainly by contaminated ready-to-eat food, especially dairy products, meat and fish [22-25].

There is only one outbreak of neonatal listeriosis that was attributed to the use of contaminated mineral oil in Costa Rica in 1989 [26].

The transmission may also occur from mother to fetus during pregnancy and may lead to stillbirth, septicemia at birth or neonatal meningitis [13]. In addition, babies can become infected during birth from their mothers, who carry the pathogen in the gastrointestinal tract or perianal region [25].

Even though *Listeria* is almost constantly present in foods, the disease is very rare. The minimum infective dose seems to be high and that would be the reason for its low frequency. However, listeriosis is a major public health concern worldwide because the severity of the disease and especially because epidemics are generally associated with industrially processed foods. In fact, *Listeria* epidemics are particularly more frequent in developed countries [7].

Among major outbreaks occurred recently, it can be mentioned the Canadian outbreak in Quebec during the summer of 2008. Nearly 40 people got sick because of contaminated cheese. Luckily, only two deaths were reported [27]. Almost 250 people in total were afflicted with listeriosis that year in Canada, but most cases have been isolated ones and not associated with outbreaks. Another important cheese-related outbreak was reported in Germany from October 2006 till February 2007. In this case, as many as 189 patients were affected [28]. Recently, a major multi-state outbreak took place in the United States, which turned out to be the third most deadly foodborne outbreak in the United States. This outbreak was associated with whole cantaloupes from Jensen Farms, Colorado. 146 people contracted listeriosis and 30 patients died i.e. a 20% mortality rate. In addition, a pregnant woman had a miscarriage [29]. Other multi-state outbreaks were reported before in the United States such as the 1998-1999 outbreaks where at least 50 people were affected in 11 states with a mortality rate of 12% (adult population). The vehicles for transmission were identified as hot dogs and deli meats produced under several brand names by one manufacturer. In fact, the outbreak ceased after the manufacturer recalled contaminated production lots of hot dogs and deli meats [30]. Another major multi-state outbreak was reported in 2005, where 108 cases were described in 24 states with 14 deaths and 4 miscarriages or stillbirths. This outbreak was associated with meat frankfurters [31].

Ivanek *et al.* thoroughly reviewed available data on habitats, hosts and routes of transmission and suggested that three recent human practices contribute in increasing the pathogen load in foods: the storage for long time of refrigerated ready-to-eat foods, feeding of domestic ruminants with *L. monocytogenes* contaminated silage and the spreading of wastewater in agricultural fields or water sources [4].

The Codex Alimentarius Commission (CAC) adopted in 2009 new international standards, codes of practice and guidelines to improve global food safety and defend the health of consumers [32]. Among those directives, the Commission adopted parameters for microbiological testing and environmental monitoring for *L. monocytogenes* in ready-to-eat foods. A maximum level was set for certain food products where *L. monocytogenes* usually cannot grow (100 cfu/g, based on the horizontal method for the detection and enumeration of *L. monocytogenes* - ISO 11290-2:1998), while no *L. monocytogenes* should be present in a 25 g analytical unit in ready-to-eat products where growth is potentially possible under the conditions of storage (based on ISO 11290-1:1996). The parameters will certainly help producers to control and prevent contamination of ready-to-eat foods with this bacterium.

Genome Sequences of *Listeria* Species

In 2001, the genome sequences of *L. monocytogenes* EGDe (serotype 1/2a) and *L. innocua* CLIP 11262 (serotype 6a) were first reported by Glaser et al. [33]. Genome analysis of *L. monocytogenes* EGDe shows a high number of putative transport systems, transcriptional regulators and surface and secreted proteins. This is consistent with the ability of this bacterium to colonize a wide range of ecosystems [33]. Particularly, *L. monocytogenes* EGDe genome encodes for 331 transport proteins, including phosphotransferase system proteins which curiously doubled the number present in *E. coli*). In addition, the capacity of coding many transcriptional regulators allows this bacterium to coordinate gene expression in different environmental conditions inside and outside the host. Moreover, the genome of *L. monocytogenes* EGDe encodes for 133 surface proteins and 86 secreted proteins. Interestingly, the comparative analysis between L. monocytogenes and L. innocua genomes showed that 30 of 133 surface proteins and 23 putative secreted proteins are absent in L. innocua [34].

In recent years, the number of sequenced genomes (complete or incomplete) of different L. monocytogenes serotypes from various sources has grown enormously; many of them are available online. Examples of genomes recently sequenced are: *L. monocytogenes* F2365 (serotype 4b), F6854 (serotype 1/2a) and H7858 (serotype4b) [35]; nonpathogenic *L. monocytogenes* serovar 4a strain M7 [36]; *L. monocytogenes* strains J1816 and J1-220, associated with human outbreaks [37]; *L. monocytogenes* strain HCC23 [38]. The website of the NCBI microbial genomes has bioprojects for 94 genomes of L. monocytogenes, many of them still in draft form (http://www.genomesonline.org; http://www.ncbi.nlm.nih.gov /bioproject).

To date, all sequenced genomes of *L. monocytogenes* are presented as circular chromosomes with sizes ranging from 2.7 to 3.2 Mb with an average G + C content of 38%. These genomes encode approximately to 2,900 genes and more than 60% of these genes have known functions. The expression analysis of complete genome of *L. monocytogenes* EGDe both *in vivo* and *in vitro* trials showed that this bacterium expresses more than 98% of these ORFs in any experimental condition [33, 39].

Recently, the genome of *L.monocytogenes* ScottA (serotype 4b) strain has been released [40]. Since its isolation during the Massachusetts listeriosis outbreak in 1983, the serovar 4b strain Scott A has been widely used as a reference strain for efficacy testing of food processing and preservation techniques, establishment of detection methods in foods, growth and heat resistance studies, and virulence studies [40].

An interesting feature of L. monocytogenes genomes is the fact that there is an important conservation of gene organization, and lack of inversion or "shifts" of long genomic fragments [41-42]. This fact might be attributed to the low occurrence of transposons and insertion sequences (IS) present among genomes of this specie.

Genome evolution in *Listeria* involved limited loss and acquisition of genes. Limited gene loss in *Listeria* did include loss of virulence-associated genes, likely associated with multiple transitions to a saprophytic lifestyle. *Listeria* thus provides an example of a group of bacteria that appears to evolve through a loss of virulence rather than acquisition of virulence characteristics. While *Listeria* includes a number of species-like clades, many of these putative species include clades or strains with atypical virulence associated characteristics.

This information will allow the development of genetic and genomic criteria for pathogenic strains, including development of assays that specifically detect pathogenic *Listeria* strains [43]

The large number of genomic sequences of *L. monocytogenes* strains and other species, either virulent or not, facilitates the application of comparative genomics to identify novel virulence factors. Furthermore, the functional genomic analyses are important to define the role of potential virulence genes and determine their functions during infection. Among the genes associated with pathogenicity, *inlA, inlJ and vip* encode for LPXTG proteins anchored to the peptidoglycan and *aut* encodes a surface protein with autolytic activity called Auto [34]. Another gene associated with pathogenicity is srtA which encodes the sortasa responsible for anchoring LPXTG proteins and several other proteins to the peptidoglycan [44-47].

Life Cycle of *Listeria monocytogenes* Inside the Host

Even though *L. monocytogenes* can behaves as a saprophyte when it is present in the environment, it can become an intracellular parasite by living in the cytosol of a wide range of host cell types [48]. As saprophyte, it is found mainly in soil and water and thus can contaminate vegetables. Moreover, *Listeria* can be present in food processing environments forming biofilms [49-50].

Humans can be infected by *L. monocytogenes* by the ingestion of contaminated foods. After the intake of the pathogen, *Listeria* cells have to deal with harsh environments in the gastrointestinal tract characterized by high osmolarity, low oxygen pressure, low pH, and presence of bile [51]. Nonetheless, *Listeria* is able to survive due to the expression of key proteins such as glutamate decarboxilase that confers acid resistance as described by Colin Hill's group [52], the osmolyte transporter encoded by *opuC* [53], the bile salt hydrolase and the bile exclusion system (BilE) that are crucial for bile stress [54-55]. The key regulator of these responses is the Sigma-B factor (σ^B) [56]. Sigma factors are proteins that may act as RNA polymerase subunits, regulating polymerase affinity for different promoters. *L. monocytogenes* has four alternative sigma factors (σ^B, σ^C, σ^H, σ^L), but only the stress-related σ^B is associated to virulence [56]. It was also suggested that σ^B might modulate the expression dependent on PrfA, the master regulator of *Listeria* pathogenesis [57]. However, it is generally accepted that σ^B role appears to be restricted to the gastrointestinal phase before cell infection [39].

Once in the gut, *Listeria* may enter into the host through the intestinal mucosa by two different mechanisms: on one hand, the bacterium can translocate across the M cells (microfold cells) of Peyer's patches [58]. On the other, *L. monocytogenes* enters by a more efficient pathway, infecting enterocytes i.e. non-phagocytic cells [59], by means of internalin A (InlA) a protein that is covalently anchored to the bacterial cell wall [60]. InlA was first described in 1991 by a seminal work from the Cossart's lab [61]. A few years later, the same group reported for the first time that InlA binds to the transmembrane glycoprotein E-cadherin, which acts as a mammalian cell receptor for internalin A [62].Internalin A-E-cadherin interaction is Ca^{2+}-dependent and occur at the lipid rafts of enterocyte plasma membranes [63]. Upon interaction, a complex signaling process is triggered, which in a simplified view, involves clustering of caveolin-1 and phosphorilation of E-cadherin. This event in turn leads to the ubiquitination of E-cadherin and the association of clathrin, α- and β-catenins [64-65]. These proteins, the natural link between E-cadhein and actin, induce the remodeling of actin, a crucial step for bacterial invasion [66]. Finally, *Listeria* cells end up being taken by the so-called "zipper" mechanism, a clathrin-mediated process that is similar but not identical to the classical endocytic mechanism in clathrin-coated pits [64, 67]. Interestingly, the zipper mechanism was first characterized when the uptake of *L. monocytogenes* by the other main internalin (InlB) was being studied [68]. InlB is a lipoteichoic acid non-covalently bound protein; hence it may be easily released from the cell wall. InlB targets the ubiquitous Met receptor tyrosine kinase [69] enabling *L. monocytogenes* to enter many cell types, *in vitro* at least [70]. The entry of *Listeria* by this second mechanism shares some similarities with the InlA-mediated uptake since it also involves receptor ubiquitination, clathrin recruitment and actin rearrangements, but it has its own features: besides the interaction between InlB N-terminal domain with Met [69], InlB C-terminal domain may bind to glycosaminoglycans [71] as well as C1q, a complement-related protein [72], the three interactions combined guarantees a successful uptake. Upon interaction with InlB, Met dimerizes, undergoes auto-phosphorylation and triggers the recruitment and activation of adaptor proteins crucial for the downstream events [73] i.e. phosphatidylinositol 3-kinase type I recruitment to the uptake site and the concomitant activation of Rac-1 and the complex signaling cascade leading the actin polymerization [74]. Interestingly, Rac-1 activation is associated to lipid rafts, therefore, even though *L. monocytogenes* cell do not interact with cholesterol-rich microdomains in this mechanism, lipid rafts are still involved in the signaling cascade that leads to the cytoskeleton rearrangement [75]. It was very recently shown that septins, GTPases that form filaments and are associated with cellular membrane and cytoskeleton networks during cell division, may take part in the binding of Met receptor to actin [76-77].

Upon endocytosis, *L. monocytogenes* is able to escape from the vacuole where is trapped. It was suggested that *L. monocytogenes* can alter the endocytic vacuole by inhibiting Rab5a-mediated Rac translocation [78], which would activate the NADPH oxidase activity that produces the highly toxic superoxide anion [79]. In this way, *Listeria* is able to delay the cellular antibacterial response. Secondly, *L. monocytogenes* expresses a cholesterol-dependent cytolysin called listeriolysin O (LLO) [80], which needs for optimal activity both a low pH such as the endosomal pH [81] and the activation via reduction of disulfide bonds by the host γ-interferon-inducible lysosomal thiol reductase [82]. LLO would form small pores upon oligomerization in the vacuole membrane [81, 83] allowing Ca^{2+} release from the vacuole and the rise of the endosomal pH hence inhibiting vacuole maturation [84-85]. Since Ca^{2+} induces the fusion of *Listeria*-containing vacuoles with lysosomes, the leakage of this divalent cation would prevent that crucial step [86]. Another important contribution of LLO to *L. monocytogenes* escape from endosomes is that allows the translocation of two phospholipases (PI-PLC and PC-PLC) hence they can hydrolyze the phospholipids present in the endosomal outer leaflet as well as in the inner leaflet of the plasma membrane [87]. These two phospholipases are other important factors for *Listeria* escape. One phospholipase is specific for phosphatidylinositol (PI-PLC) while the other is a broad range phospholipase C (PC-PLC) [88]. They definitely enhance the rupture of vacuole membrane letting *Listeria* free in the cytosol. There are some reports suggesting that PI-PLC but not PC-PLC alongside

LLO would be important for the disruption of endosomal membrane [83, 88] while PC-PLC might be essential for disrupting the double-membrane vacuoles that are formed upon cell to cell spread (see below) [88-89]. However, this is not a completely accepted hypothesis since most of the literature cites that LLO as well as both phopholipases may work together in releasing *Listeria* from both single and double membrane endosomes [65, 90]. Interestingly, even though LLO undoubtedly helps *L. monocytogenes* escaping from the vacuole, its activity is not absolutely required in human cell hosts. On the other hand, PI-PLC and PC-PLC are completely indispensable weapons for that task [91].

One cellular mechanism designed for degradation of cellular components in the cytoplasm is the so-called autophagy [92], essentially involves the sequestration of cellular material in an endoplasmic reticulum-derived double-membrane vacuole: the "phagosome" [93]. This very same mechanism is used by cells to control intracellular parasites as part of an innate defense mechanism [94]. As soon as *L. monocytogenes* escapes from the first endosome it may be trapped by the autophagosome, delaying *Listeria* replication in the cytosol [95]. However, *L. monocytogenes* can also escape from this second "cellular cage" aided mainly by the bacterial factor ActA [96]. This protein helps *Listeria* cells to avoid being recognized by the autophagic machinery because it recruits Arp2/3 complex and Ena/VASP to the bacterial surface in a sort of camouflage [97]. LLO and PC-PLC are also important tools that allow *L. monocytogenes* to avoid being killed by autophagy [96, 98]. Recently, another protein, internalin K (InlK) was identified in helping *Listeria* disguises from autophagic recognition [99]. In this case, InlK recruits the major vault protein, which in turn decorates bacterial surface thus avoiding recognition [99].

After escaping from primary endosomes and autophagosomes, *L. monocytogenes* can grow in the cytosol and then spread from one cell to another without facing the extracellular milieu, thus avoiding complement and antibodies [100]. ActA is the key protein behind *L. monocytogenes* spreading [101]. This surface protein is able to recruit Arp2/3 complex [102], which in turn activates actin polymerization to finally form a long structure (5 μm average) called the "comet tail", because actin polymerizes specifically at one end of *Listeria* cells as it was shown in the classical paper from the Portnoy's group [103]. Bacteria get close to the plasma membrane and then form protrusions till reach and penetrate the neighbor host cell without cellular lysis, being trapped by a double-membrane compartment in the new cell [103]. Then *L. monocytogenes* is able to escape from this vacuole by means of phospholipases and LLO in order to start a new cycle [91].

An important feature of cytosolic *L. monocytogenes* is that it can switch its own metabolism. On one hand, it starts using glycerol as the main carbon energy source [104] but also it is able to use hexose phosphates as carbon source [105], using the hexose phosphate transporter (Hpt) as a permease to steal these metabolites from the host [106]. In fact, *L. monocytogenes* switches from using glycolysis to using the pentose phosphate cycle as the predominant pathway of sugar metabolism [107]. On the other hand, the nitrogen sources for intracellular *Listeria* are arginine and ethanolamine that comes from the hydrolysis of the phospholipid phosphatidylethanolamine by broad range PC-PLC phospholipase [108].

Interestingly, the switch of carbon source is closely related to *Listeria* virulence. In this regard, saprophytic *Listeria* take up sugars as carbon energy source by using the phosphoenol piruvate transport system (PTS), these carbohydrates indirectly inhibit the activity of PrfA, the master regulator of *L. monocytogenes* virulence factors [109]. PrfA is a a symmetrical homodimer belonging to the cAMP receptor protein (Crp)/fumarate nitrate reductase regulator (Fnr) family of bacterial transcription factors, which is tightly regulated in several ways [110]. On one hand, its expression is thermo-regulated i.e. it is almost completely silenced at 30°C while it is efficiently transcribed at 37°C [111]. Moreover, its expression is modulated by three differentially regulated promoters [112]. Worthily, σ^B factor can bind to one of these promoters, prfAp (2). Therefore, the main regulator for *Listeria* stress resistance outside cells (see above) can also partially regulate PrfA expression [113]. On the other hand, it was hypothesized that a cofactor would bind and activate PrfA upon host cell entry; however, such ligand is still uncharacterized [114]. A modern model concerning PrfA activity regulation was proposed recently [115-116]. Briefly, it states that in saprophytic life, sugars would be transported by the PTS and therefore would receive a phosphate group from the EIIB subunit. In this condition, PrfA would be inactive. However, during intracellular life where PTS-independent carbon substrates are being consumed, EIIA would keep phosphorylated thus preventing close interaction with PrfA that can be freed from that complex. Finally, Freitag *et al.* completed this model by proposing that free PrfA would only be fully active upon binding with a cellular cofactor, which would trigger conformational changes in the same way other cAMP receptor proteins are regulated [114]. The conformational change activation theory is supported by the description of a number of PrfA mutants, which are locked in the ON position i.e. they are ever active and have a different conformation as compared to wild type PrfA [117].

Once *L. monocytogenes* translocates the small intestine and replicates in phagocytic cells located close to the site of infection, it can be transported in the blood by macrophages to the spleen and the liver where they are killed by neutrophils and Kuppfer cells in people in good-health [118-119]. However, if the immune system is compromised or does not respond promptly, *Listeria* can further proliferate not only in macrophages but also in hepatocytes [120]. In this regard, it was recently demonstrated by Seveau in an elegant study that LLO alone can drive the internalization of *Listeria monocytogenes* in hepatic cells [121]. This finding does not rule out the role that internalins may play in liver infection; actually, it has been proposed that all three factors i.e. InlA, InlB and LLO may act in a concerted manner in order to guarantee a successful bacterial entry. Interestingly, LLO-mediated uptake in the hepatic cell line studied by Vadia et al does not involve clathrin but depends almost exclusively on pore formation [121]. From the liver and spleen *Listeria* can spread throughout the body, but especially to the central nervous system generating meningo-encephalitis and brain sepsis, life-threatening *Listeria*-associated clinical syndromes because of the tropism that *L. monocytogenes* has for the brain and meninges [122]. Even though there is still no conclusive data about the virulence factors involved in brain infection because only cell culture experiments have been carried out so far [90], some information is available. Since *L. monocytogenes* has to deal with the highly impermeable blood-brain barrier, Greiffenberg *et al.* used human brain microvascular endothelial cells, to get a close approach to *in vivo* conditions, and found that *Listeria* cells are taken up by these cells in an InlB-dependent and wortmannin-insensitive way [123]. In addition to InlB, an important role for the cell wall-anchored autolysin IspC was proposed. In fact it has been proposed that IspC is necessary for crossing the blood-cerebrospinal fluid barrier since ΔIspC mutant exhibited a marked defect in adhesion to and invasion of sheep choroid plexus epithelial cells [124]. An early report stated that the onset of meningo-encephalitis was heavily dependent on the presence of persistent bacteremia [125]. However, this conclusion was challenged since Freitag´s group were able to rule out the involvement of free bacteria in CNS invasion by treating infected mice with systemic gentamicin. They found that *Listeria* was still able to reach CNS even in the absence of free bacteria in the bloodstream [126]. Furthermore, a few years ago, an unexpected reservoir of *L. monocytogenes* was uncovered: it was found that *Listeria* can infect bone marrow myelomonocytic cells during infection, which in turn can release infected cells into the circulation that ultimately invade the central nervous system (CNS), being even more efficient to infect brain as compared to free bacteria [127].

If *L.monocytogenes* infects a pregnant woman, it can reach the uterus, cross the placental barrier and infect the fetus inducing abortion, stillbirth or neonatal meningitis [128]. Even though it can be found during the whole pregnancy, it is most commonly seen during the third trimester [122]. The mechanism underneath fetoplacental infection was studied in detail in animal models, which let the authors reach firm conclusions on the matter. They unquestionably concluded that both InlA and InlB act in a concerted and interdenpendent manner to cross the placental barrier [129]. InlA would bind to the syncytiotrophoblast maternal-fetal interface and InlB, but not InlA, might trigger the downstream signaling cascade that allows *L. monocytogenes* to cross that border [129].

Detection of *Listeria* in Clinical and Food Samples

Listeriosis is commonly diagnosed by the isolation of *L. monocytogenes* from a normally sterile site such as blood, cerebrospinal fluid, placenta, meconium, pleural or pericardial fluid. Currently, there are several methods for the detection and identification of *L. monocytogenes* in food samples and specimens from animal or human. Identification traditionally involved culture methods based on the use of microbiological media to selectively grow and enumerate bacteria followed by the characterization of *Listeria* spp. based on colony morphology, sugar fermentation and haemolytic properties. These methods are the "gold standards"; they are usually sensitive, inexpensive, provide quantitative results and they do not require sophisticated equipment. However, they require several manipulations, many chemicals, media and reagents and they are lengthy. Taking into account these disadvantages, different rapid methods were developed based on molecular techniques or on antibodies; these tests are very sensitive and allow identification of *L. monocytogenes* within 48 h. In addition, there are several tests for the sub-species characterization that are suitable in epidemiological investigations.

1. Methodology for *Listeria* Isolation from Food Samples

Three of the most common methods used to detect *L. monocytogenes* in foods are those developed by the United States Food and Drug Administration (FDA) [130], the Association of Official Analytical Chemists (AOAC) [131] and the International Organization of Standards (ISO Standardization) 11290 [132-134]. These methods vary in the type of selective media that are used. Both the FDA and the ISO methods include a pre-enrichment step allowing injured *L. monocytogenes* cells to recover while AOAC method do not require this step. In the FDA method the pre-enrichment consists of an incubation at 30°C for 4 h in

Listeria Enrichment broth (LEB) without selective agents, then the selective agents (acriflavin, nalidixic acid and cycloheximide) are added and the incubation continue for a total time of 48 h at 30°C. The AOAC method also uses selective enrichment in a broth containing acriflavin and naladixic acid for 48 h at 30°C. The ISO protocol uses a primary enrichment in half Fraser broth at 30°C for 24 h in the presence of selective agents (acriflavin and nalidixic acid) at half concentrations, and then an aliquot is transferred to Fraser broth containing the selective agents at full concentration for an additional enrichment during 48 h at 37°C.

After selective enrichment, cultures are plated on Oxford agar (FDA and AOAC methods), PALCAM agar (FDA and ISO methods) or Agar Listeria Ottavani and Agosti (ALOA for the ISO method) for isolation of possible colonies of *L. monocytogenes.* Oxford agar contains acriflavin, cefofetan, colistin, cycloheximide, phosfomycin, lithium chloride as well as esculin as selective agents; esculin allows detection of β-D-glucosidase activity by *Listeria*, causing a blackening of the colony and surrounding medium. The PALCAM agar contains lithium chloride, polymixin B, acriflavine, ceftazidime, esculin and phenol red; *L. monocytogenes* grows as grey-green colored colony with a black zone. The plating media PALCAM and Oxford have been developed for the selective isolation of listeriae on the basis of the hydrolysis of esculin, which contribute to the differentiation of the listeriae from the other bacteria [135]. However, these media are not able to differentiate *L. monocytogenes* colonies from the other listeriae colonies particularly from those of *L. innocua* [136]. Thus, different chromogenic media such as ALOA chromogenic medium have been developed [137]; ALOA agar contains lithium chloride, nalidixic acid, ceftazidime, cycloheximide (or amphotericin B), polymyxin B solution and L-α-phosphatidylinositol; *Listeria* grows as blue-green regular round colonies while *L. monocytogenes* also shows an opaque halo which helps to easily differentiate them from other species of *Listeria* [134]. Additional variations of ALOA medium are commercialized under different names such as BBL® CHROMagar *Listeria* (Becton Dickinson Diagnostics), BCM® chromogenic agar test (Biosynth International), CompassL.mono® (Biokar Diagnostics).

A different substrate for phosphatidylinositol-specific phospholipase C (PI-PLC) is 5-bromo-4-chloro-3-indolyl-myo-inositol-1-phosphate (X-IP) that stains colonies blue when is cleaved by PI-PLC [138]. Bio-Rad Laboratories have developed RAPID'L.Mono agar, a selective chromogenic medium based on X-IP for the detection of PI-PLC-positive *L. monocytogenes* and *L. ivanovii* which are differentiated by the inability of *L. monocytogenes* to metabolize D-xylose [139]. *L. monocytogenes* produces blue colonies (PI-PLC positive) without yellow halo (xylose negative) while *L. ivanovii* produces green-blue colonies (PI-PLC positive) with yellow halo (xylose positive).

2. Identification of Isolated Cultures

Typical *Listeria* colonies, grown on the above mentioned media, are selected for identification to the species level using additional tests including the Gram-staining reaction, catalase, motility, haemolysis and carbohydrate utilization. *Listeria* strains are Gram-positive rods, aerobic and facultatively anaerobic, non-spore forming, catalase-positive, oxidase-negative, and fermentative in sugars. Most *Listeria* strains are motile at 28°C and non-motile at 37°C [140]. Fermentation of different sugars with the production of acid without gas allows differentiation of the species of *Listeria* (Table 1). Commercial identification kits provide a simple and rapid alternative to traditional biochemical assays, which are time consuming. In addition, some strips test such as API *Listeria* (bio-Mérieux, Marcy-Etoile, France) and Micro-ID® (Remel, USA) have been validated and are now incorporated into standard methodology [130].

The Christie, Atkins, Munch–Petersen (CAMP) test is a very useful tool to differentiate among hemolytic *Listeria* isolates; *L. monocytogenes, L. ivanovii* and *L. seeligeri*. This test is used in the ISO and AOAC protocols and it is optional to be done in the FDA method. The test consists of streaking a β-hemolysin-producing *Staphylococcus aureus* strain (ATCC49444 or 25923, NCTC 7428 or 1803, CIP 5710) and *Rhodococcus equi* (ATCC 6939 or NCTC 1621) parallel to each other on sheep blood agar plate. Suspect *Listeria* cultures are streaked perpendicularly, in between the two indicator microorganisms, without touching them. After 24- and 48-h incubation at 35° C, the zone of influence of the vertical streaks is examined for hemolysis. Hemolysis of *L. monocytogenes* and to a lesser degree *L. seeligeri* is enhanced near the *S. aureus* streak; *L. ivanovii* hemolysis is enhanced near the *R. equi* streak. Other species non-hemolytic do not react in this test. Sometimes, CAMP test cannot correctly differentiate between *L. monocytogenes* and *L. ivanovii* [141]. Hence, commercially available disks impregnated with the β-lysin of *S. aureus* (REMEL, Lenexa, KS) can be used as a simple test to differentiate between haemolytic activities of *Listeria* [130]. As mentioned above, D-xylose and L-rhamnose fermentation can also be used to differentiate *L. monocytogenes* from the other two haemolytic species *L. ivanovii* and *L. seeligeri* (Table 1). Another bacterial enzyme used for the identification of *L. monocytogenes* is D-alanyl aminopeptidase, an enzyme produced by all *Listeria* species except for *L. monocytogenes* [142]. This property is exploited in the Oxoid Biochemical Identification System Mono (OBIS, ThermoScientific) and in the Monocytogenes ID Disc (Biolife, Milan, Italy); a substrate D-alanyl-7-amido-4-methylcoumarin or DL-alanine-β-naphthylamide, respectively, is hydrolyzed releasing a coloured compound.

3. Alternative Rapid Identification Methods

Before choosing a new available commercial test for identifying *L. monocytogenes*, it is important to know whether it has been validated and approved by regulatory authorities such as FDA, ISO or AOAC.

Immunological Methods

There are several immunoassays available as commercial kits that they are validated by regulatory authorities (993.12. 2000). However, only a few kits are specific for *L. monocytogenes* detection, such as VIDAS™LMO 2 (Bio-Mérieux) and Transia ™ Plate *Listeria monocytogenes* (Diffchamb SA, Lyon, France). VIDAS *L. monocytogenes* II (LMO 2) test is a commercially validated available enzyme-linked fluorescent assay (ELFA) that allows rapid screening of samples for the presence of *L. monocytogenes*, since it reduces the detection time to two days [143]. Transia ™ Plate *Listeria monocytogenes* (Diffchamb) is an enzyme-linked immunosorbent assay (ELISA), based on the detection of the *L. monocytogenes* specific P60 protein (invasion-associated protein encoded by the *iap* gene).

Nucleic Acid-Based Methods

Detection of *Listeria* spp. and *L. monocytogenes* by molecular methods is becoming more popular now since these methods are accurate, rapid, sensitive and specific.

DNA Hybridization

DNA hybridization is the simplest molecular method used for the differentiation of *L. monocytogenes* from other *Listeria* species by means of oligonucleotide probes directed against specific virulence factor genes. There are validated commercially kits for testing pure cultures or foods such as GeneTrak DNA hybridization kit (Neogen Corporation, Lansing MI,USA) and AccuProbe® *Listeria monocytogenes* culture identification test (Gen-Probe Inc., San Diego, USA).

Polymerase Chain Reaction (PCR) Based Methods

The polymerase chain reaction (PCR) is a rapid, specific, and sensitive method for the confirmation of *Listeria*. PCR-based strategies for the detection of *L. monocytogenes* have targeted a number of sequences such as the hemolysin *gene hlyA* [144-146], the invasion-associated protein p60 *iap* gene [147], the internalin B *inl*B gene [148] and 16S rRNA [149]. The BAX® System PCR Assay for *L. monocytogenes* (DuPont-Qualicon) is a commercially PCR test for the detection of *L. monocytogenes* in foods and environmental samples. There are also several commercially available kits for the detection of *L. monocytogenes* by real-time PCR, such as the iQ-Check® *Listeria monocytogenes* II kit (Bio-Rad), MicroSeQ® *Listeria monocytogenes* detection Kit (Life Technologies), TaqMan® *Listeria monocytogenes* Detection Kit (Life Technologies), The LightCycler® *Listeria monocytogenes* Detection Kit (Roche/Biotecon).

Table 1. Differentiation of *Listeria* species

Species	Haemolysis	Catalase	Oxidase	Phosphatidylinositol Phospholipase C	Fermentation of		
					L-Rhamnose	D-Mannitol	D-Xylose
L. monocytogenes	+	+	-	+	+	-	-
L. innocua	-	+	-	-	+/-	-	-
L. ivanovii	+	+	-	+	-	-	+
L. grayi	-	+	-	-	+/-	+	-
L. seeligeri	+	+	-	-	-	-	+
L. welshimeri	-	+	-	-	+/-	-	+

From [130].

Sheep blood agar sab, +/- indicates variable biotypes; on ALOA and similar media.

New Technologies in Food Processing to Control *Listeria monocytogenes*

Ready-to-eat (RTE) products are completely processed foods that are consumed without further cooking. Therefore, there is a possibility of the occurrence of food-borne illnesses if contamination by pathogenic bacteria occurs. In this regard, the ability of *L. monocytogenes* to grow at refrigeration temperatures allows it an easy survival and proliferation in RTE products. The economic impact of listeriosis due to big product recalls, severity of the disease, hospitalization and treatment costs has drawn the attention of researchers towards the development of innovative preventive strategies to control the spread of *L. monocytogenes* in foods and food processing environments. Physical, chemical, biological treatments and different combination among them are emerging to control or avoid *L. monocytogenes* growth in food industry, fulfilling the consumer demand for minimally processed, ready-to-eat foods, without any loss in sensory and nutritional attributes [150]

In this section we review new technological developments for the control of spoilage microorganisms, mainly *Listeria* spp. control.

High Pressure Procesing

High Pressure Processing (HPP) is a non-thermal method of food processing where food is subjected to elevated pressures (approximately to 300-700 MPa for vegetative microorganisms inactivation), with or without the addition of heat. HPP retains food quality, maintains natural freshness, and extends microbiological shelf life. The process is also known as high hydrostatic pressure processing (HHP) and ultra high-pressure processing (UHP) [151] [152]. Sensitivity to high pressure varied among *Listeria* strains [153]. Pressure ≥200 MPa causes irreversible protein denaturation, rupture of cytoplasmic membrane and leakage of cell contains [154]. Simpson and Gilmour reported that high pressure inactivation of *Listeria* follows a second-order relationship with processing temperature but in other studies appear to be more sensitive to the effects of pressurization at low temperatures [155-157]. The matrix of the food product has influence on *Listeria* food control by HPP. For example, food with high levels of proteins or glucose favored survival of the pathogen during high pressure treatment but the level of fat in food did not consistently affect survival of *Listeria* [158]. Even though HPP may be ineffective to prevent *L. monocytogenes* growth in certain food products [159], combinations with others antimicrobial compounds yielded good results. For example, food formulation containing bacteriocins [160-161], lactoperoxidase / lactoferrin and lysozyme system [162], or potassium lactate [163] synergistically enhanced the action of high pressure processing against *Listeria*.

Ultrasonic Processing of Food

Ultrasonic treatment can be used to kill bacteria. When applied in a liquid medium, sound waves at a frequency of 20 to 100 kHz may lead to cavitation and changes in pressure that finally have a lethal effect on cells [164], which may be enhanced by mild heat treatment [165]. According to Ugarte et al. ultrasonic treatment of *L. monocytogenes* at 35 and 50°C enhanced inactivation, but at an upper temperature limit for thermosonication (65°C) was evident above which no added killing due to ultrasound was observed [166].

Berrang *et al.* tested the ultrasonication effect to break up biofilm architecture and allow chemical sanitizers to contact cells directly. Those results indicated that the addition of ultrasonication can improve the effectiveness of chlorine or quaternary ammonium sanitizers against *L. monocvtogenes* biofilms [167].

Pulse Electric Fields

Pulse electric fields (PEF) is one of the most appealing non-thermal technologies for preservation of liquid foods due to reduced heating effects compared to traditional pasteurization methods. A typical PEF system is based on a high voltage pulse generator with a treatment chamber [168].

About the effects of PEF on *Listeria* food control, Reina *et al.* observed that the PEF lethal effect on *L. monocytogenes* Scott A was a function of the field strength and treatment time during milk processing [169]. Also, higher field strength or longer treatment time resulted in a greater reduction of viable cells. With treatment at 25°C, 1- to 3-log reductions of *L. monocytogenes* were observed. A 4-log reduction of the bacterium was obtained by increasing the treatment temperature to 50°C.

The combination of PEF with others methods, for example with nisin and ozone resulted in a synergistic effect [170-171].

Ozone Treatment

Ozone is a powerful antimicrobial agent that is suitable for application in food. Molecular ozone or its decomposition products rapidly inactivate microorganisms. When applied to food, ozone is generated on-site and it decomposes quickly, leaving no residues. Ozone is suitable for decontaminating products, equipment, food contact surfaces, and processing environment [172]. There are several reports on the effectiveness of ozone in killing *Listeria spp.* In general, the log CFU reduction depends of time, ozone concentration, temperature, food matrix treatment and the stage of growth of the microorganisms.

Listeria cells from the early log phase of growth are more sensitive than cells from stationary phase and at increasing ozone concentration their elimination are more effective. Regarding the food matrix, the treatments have been more successful in liquids than in solids foods [172-175].

The use of ozone in the processing of foods has recently come to the forefront as a result of the approval by the U.S. Food and Drug Administration of ozone as an anti-microbial agent for food treatment, storage and processing (Federal Register, 2001).

Ionizing Irradiation

Irradiation is a safe, effective, environmentally clean and energy efficient process to improve food safety and quality. Ionizing irradiation may employ gamma rays (cobalt-60 and cesium- 137 as radioactive sources), x-rays (machine generated) or e-beam (high-energy electrons) [152]. This process was shown to be effective in killing *L. monocytogenes* in food [176] [177].

Phage Technology

In recent years, there has been a revival of interest in the use of phages to treat bacterial infections. In fact, phage therapy as a tool to overcome the problem of increasing levels of antibiotic resistance has become widely publicized. Accordingly, the idea that phage could be applied to food products as biocontrol agents has also received more interest among researchers.

In this regard, Carlton et al. studied the bacteriophage P100 for controlling *L. monocytogenes* in foods [178]. They were able to obtain a significant reduction (at least 3.5 logs) or even a complete eradication of *Listeria*. Moreover, no evidence for phage resistance in the *Listeria* isolates recovered from samples was found. These results indicate that P100 can provide an effective and safe measure for the control of *Listeria* contamination in foods and production equipment.

On the other hand, Dykes and Moorhead concluded that the use of nisin combined with listeriophage LH7 has potential to control *L. monocytogenes* in foods [179]. In 2006, *L. monocytogenes* phage was approved by the FDA as a food antimicrobial [180].

Non-Thermal Plasma Technology

Atmospheric plasmas containing high levels of bactericidal molecules (> 100 ppm ozone, nitric oxides, peroxides, etc.) are generated with minimal power under room-temperature conditions in seconds to minutes, with little or no product heating (less than 5 °C). Atmospheric plasma technology (APT) requires a few hundred watts of power and a supply of compressed air or other gas; sometimes, a gas blend is used depending on the reactive gas species being generated [181].

Song *et al.* evaluated the efficacy of atmospheric pressure plasma (APP) in sliced cheese and ham inoculated by 3-strains cocktail of *L. monocytogenes* (ATCC 19114, 19115, and 19111, LMC). In sliced cheese, more than 8 log reductions could be achieved in 120s at 150W. In contrast, reductions after 120s ranged from 0.25 to 1.73 log CFU/g in sliced ham. No viable cells were detected at 125 and 150 W of APP treatment in sliced cheese, irrespective of plasma exposure time, after 1 week at a detection limit of 10^1 CFU/g. Song *et al.* concluded that the inactivation effects of APP on *L. monocytogenes* are strongly dependent on the type of food [182]. In the same trend, Yun *et al.* demonstrate that APP treatment is effective for inactivation of *L. monocytogenes* and applicable for disposable food containers but they concluded that the type of material is crucial and appropriate treatment conditions should be considered for achieving satisfactory inactivation levels [183].

Pulse Ultraviolet Light

Pulsed Ultraviolet (UV)-Light is an emerging processing technology, which has a potential to decontaminate food products. UV-light is pulsed several times per second and each pulse lasts between 100 ns and 2ms. The pulsed UV-light has a modest energy input which can yield high peak power dissipation [184].

Ozer *et al.* investigated the efficacy of pulsed UV-light to inactivate of *Escherichia coli* O157:H7 and *L. monocytogenes* Scott A on salmon fillets. The study demonstrated that about one log reduction (c. 90%) of *E. coli* O157:H7 or *L. monocytogenes* could be achieved at 60s treatment at 8 cm distance without affecting the quality. Similar results were obtained by Keklik *et al.* on unpackaged and vacuum-packaged chicken frankfurters inoculated with *Listeria monocytogenes* Scott A on the top surfaces [185].

Active Packaging System

Modified atmosphere packaging (MAP; 40% CO_2/30% O_2/30% N_2) and vacuum packaging (VP) involve the removal of headspace air, followed by reintroduction of gases that have a different composition than air. In the literature there are controversial findings related to the inhibitory effect of VP/MAP systems on the growth of *L. monocytogenes* in model systems or foods [186-187].

L. monocytogenes is minimally affected by CO_2 levels below 50% [188]. However, there are studies showing that combination of different antimicrobials such as bacteriocins, irradiation, essencial oils, acid organic salts, etc. with MAP may improve the efficacy of the treatment [189-190]. These methodologies are close to a new generation of food packaging technologies called *Active Packaging (AP)*.

Active packing involves the incorporation of certain additives into packaging systems, such as oxygen scavengers, carbon dioxide or chlorine dioxide emitters, ionizing irradiation systems. If antimicrobial agents are used the process is referred as *Antimicrobial Packing (AMP)* [152]. In this regard, the bacteriocins nisin and pediocin were shown to be effective in controlling *L. monocytogenes* using this approach [191-193].

Antimicrobials

Antimicrobials compounds like natural or synthetic chemicals and biological compounds are frequently used to control *L. monocytogenes* in foods. A wide range of products have been assessed to control *L. monocytogenes* in foods. Among them it can be mentioned weak organic acid and ester such as propionate, sorbate, benzoate, [194]; other chemicals such as EDTA [195]; plant extracts such as carvacrol, thymol, eugenol [196], enzymes such as lysozime[197-199].In addition the use of a combination of two or more of them in combination can be particularly fruitful [200-201].

Bacteriocins

Besides the new antilisterial technologies described above, antimicrobial peptides called bacteriocins produced by GRAS microorganisms such as lactic acid bacteria (LAB) arise as a potential solution not only in food preservation but also for therapeutically applications in *Listeria* infections [202-205]. The use of bacteriocin-producing LAB proved to be competitive in the food market. Their application as functional cultures helps to standardize the fermentation process in addition to inhibit the growth of sensitive pathogens such as Listeria. The potential of LAB as biopreservative cultures is based on its prevalent presence during fermentation and storage of food.

Bacteriocins comprise ribosomally synthesized proteinaceous compounds released extracellularly by bacteria that interfere with the growth of other bacteria [202]. Bacteriocins can be classified into four major classes:

I.   Lantibiotic peptides;
II.   Small (< 10 kDa) non- modified peptides. This class is further subdivided into IIa, pediocin-like peptides (anti-listerial peptides having the amino acid motif YGNGV/L in the N-terminal part of the peptide) and IIb, multi-component peptides;
III.   Large (> 10 kDa) proteins, and
IV.   Cyclic peptides.

Paying particular attention to class I and II, there are many *Listeria*-active bacteriocins described so far in the literature [202, 206-214]. They could be used in the industry alone as food preservatives or in combination with other hurdles to increase the antilisteria effect in the so-called hurdle technology, like we described in some cases above.

There are three typical applications of bacteriocins for the bio-preservation of food: 1. the addition, of purified bacteriocins to food products; 2. the inoculation of a food product with bacteriocin-producing LAB that will synthesize the peptide in the product; and 3. the use of an ingredient in food processing that has been previously fermented with abacteriocin-producing bacterium [215].

From a regulatory standpoint, although there are patents for the use of bacteriocin (lacticin 4137, U.S. patent 6,833,150) or fermented products containing bacteriocins from LAB (ALTA ™ 2341, Quest International, Sarasota Fla.), nisin is the only approved in the United States (FDA and FSIS) and in Europe for use in food.

The use of bacteriocin or its bacteriocinogenic strain as biopreservative for food has been extensively reported [208, 216-218]. On the other hand, there is an increase research exploring the potential use of antilisterial bacteriocins as *in vivo* therapeutic agents. Bacteriocins are excellent candidates to substitute antibiotics since they have restricted target specificity which minimizes their impact on commensal microbiota. Furthermore, most bacteriocins are active at low concentrations [203]. We have shown that synthetic enterocin

CRL35, an antilisterial class IIa bacteriocin, in combination with some antibiotics is effective against *L. innocua* 7 and *L. monocytogenes* FBUNT cells [219-220]. Another important feature is that given the nature of bacteriocins, it is unlikely that these substances reach the small intestine, and can affect the intestinal microbiota balance. Most analyzed bacteriocins so far are sensitive to the intestinal proteases, especially alpha-chymotrypsin and trypsin.

One of the first reports about the *in vivo* effectiveness of the bacteriocins in the treatment of *Listeria* infections was conducted by Ingham *et al.* [221]. In this work the group used a mouse model of listeriosis. In this case animals were intravenously administered with a pathogenic strain of *L. monocytogenes*. A fraction of these animals was treated with purified bacteriocin piscicolin 126 before and after challenge with *Listeria*. These authors found that mice that had been given the bacteriocin had a reduced charge of *Listeria* in the organs tested, which also resulted in minor clinical signs of listeriosis.

Gardiner *et al.* have investigated the fate of the two-component lantibiotic lacticin 3147, when administered orally. They found both *ex vivo* and in an animal model (pig), that when the bacteriocin was administered orally or tested in the different liquids simulating the different compartments of the gastrointestinal system, it quickly lost its activity [222].

Corr *et al.* gave the first confirmation that the production of a bacteriocin (salivaricin Abp118) corresponded to the main anti-infective mechanism of a probiotic strain (*Lactobacillus salivarius* UCC118) [223].

An interesting fact was obtained by Bernbom *et al.*, who observed inhibition of *L. monocytogenes* in an *in vitro* intestinal system with continuous flow using a strain producing pediocin AcH [224]. Recently, we found that synthetic enterocin CRL35 is more effective in the inhibition of translocation of *L. monocytogenes* FBUNT than the use of the bacteriocinogenic strain [205].

Conclusion

The progress in studies on the genome, transcriptome and proteome of L.monocytogenes will allow the discovery of new virulence factors involved in pathogenesis allowing the development of methodologies and technologies for rapid detection and treatment. This will ultimately result in further measures in the food industry to reduce the incidence of human listeriosis.

References

[1]   Family III. Listeriaceae fam. nov. In: Vos P, Garrity G, Jones D, Krieg NR, Ludwig W, Rainey FA, et al., editors. *Bergey's Manual of Systematic Bacteriology: Volume 3: The Firmicutes (Bergey's Manual of Systematic Bacteriology*. London: Springer; 2009. p. 244-.

[2]   Validation List, n. List of new names and new combinations previously effectively, but not validly, published. *Int J SysEvolMicrobiol.* [10.1099/ijs.0.022855-0]. 2010;60 (3): 469-72.

[3]   Technical, NOTES. Determination of proteolysis by dye binding. *J Dairy Sci.* 1966;49:504.

[4]   Ivanek, R;Gröhn, YT, Wiedmann, M. *Listeria monocytogenes* in multiple habitats and host populations: review of available data for mathematical modeling. *Foodborne Pathog Dis.* [10.1089/fpd.2006.3.319]. 2006;3(4):319-36.

[5]   Liu, D. Epidemiology. In: Liu D, editor. *Handbook of Listeria monocytogenes*: CRC Press; 2008. p. 27-59.

[6]   Farber, JM, Peterkin, PI. *Listeria monocytogenes*, a food-borne pathogen. *Microbiological Reviews.* 1991;55(3):476-511.

[7]   Who/Fao. Risk assessment of *Listeria monocytogenes* in ready-to-eat foods: World Health Organization, *Food and Agriculture Organization of the United Nations*; 2004.

[8]   Thévenot, D;Dernburg, A, Vernozy-Rozand, C. An updated review of *Listeria monocytogenes* in the pork meat industry and its products. *J ApplMicrobiol.* [10.1111/j.1365-2672.2006.02962.x]. 2006;101(1):7-17.

[9]   Farber, JM;Coates, F, Daley, E. Minimum water activity requirements for the growth of *Listeria monocytogenes. Lett ApplMicrobiol.* [10.1111/j.1472-765X.1992.tb00737.x]. 1992;15(3):103-5.

[10]   Martin, W, Jim, M. Biology. In: Dongyou L, editor. *Handbook of Listeria monocytogenes*: CRC Press; 2008. p. 3-25.

[11]   Vázquez-Boland, JA;Kuhn, M;Berche, P;Chakraborty, T;Domínguez-Bernal, G;Goebel, W, et al. *Listeria pathogenesis* and molecular virulence determinants. *Clin Microbiol Rev.* [10.1128/CMR.14.3.584-640.2001]. 2001;14(3):584-640.

[12]   Guillet, C;Join-Lambert, O;Le Monnier, A;Leclercq, A;Mechaï, F;Mamzer-Bruneel, MF, et al. Human listeriosis caused by *Listeria ivanovii. EmergInfec Dis.* [10.3201/eid1601.091155]. 2010;16(1):136-8.

[13]   Lamont, RF;Sobel, J;Mazaki-Tovi, S;Kusanovic, JP;Vaisbuch, E;Kim, SK, et al. Listeriosis in human pregnancy: a systematic review. *J Perin Med.* [10.1515/JPM.2011.035]. 2011;39(3):227-36.

[14]   Rocourt, J;Jacquet, C, Reilly, A. Epidemiology of human listeriosis and seafoods. *Inter J Food Microbiol.* 2000;62(3):197-209.

[15]   Jurado, RL;Farley, MM;Pereira, E;Harvey, RC;Schuchat, A;Wenger, JD, et al. Increased risk of meningitis and bacteremia due to *Listeria monocytogenes* in patients with human immunodeficiency virus infection. *Clin Infec Dis..* 1993;17(2):224-7.

[16]   ECDC. European Centre for Disease Prevention and Control publishes Annual epidemiological report 2011. *Euro Surveillance: Bulletin Européen Sur Les Maladies Transmissibles = European Communicable Disease Bulletin. 2011*;16(45).

[17]   Exterkate, FA, Veer, GJCMD. Optimal growth of {IStreptococcus cremoris} HP in milk is related to B- and K-casein degradation. *Appl Microbioland Biotechnol.* 1987;25:471-5.

[18]   Scallan, E;Hoekstra, RM;Angulo, FJ;Tauxe, RV;Widdowson, M-A;Roy, SL, et al. Foodborne illness acquired in the United States--major pathogens. *EmergInfec Dis.* [10.3201/eid1701.091101p1]. 2011;17(1):7-15.

[19]   Murray, EGD;Webb, RA, Swann, MBR. A disease of rabbits characterised by a large mononuclear leucocytosis, caused by a hitherto undescribed bacillus Bacterium mono-cytogenes (n.sp.). *J. Pathol. Bacteriol..* [10.1002/path.1700290409]. 1926;29(4):407-39.

[20] Nyfeldt, AA. Etiologie de la mononucleuse infectieuse. *CR Soc Biol.* 1929;101:590-2.

[21] Schlech, WF, 3rd;Lavigne, PM;Bortolussi, RA;Allen, AC;Haldane, EV;Wort, AJ, et al. Epidemic listeriosisevidence for transmission by food. *New Engl. J. Med.* [10.1056/NEJM198301273080407]. 1983;308(4):203-6.

[22] Pinner, RW;Schuchat, A;Swaminathan, B;Hayes, PS;Deaver, KA;Weaver, RE, et al. Role of foods in sporadic listeriosis. II. Microbiologic and epidemiologic investigation. The Listeria Study Group. *JAMA: J Am Med Assoc.* 1992;267(15):2046-50.

[23] Schuchat, A;Deaver, KA;Wenger, JD;Plikaytis, BD;Mascola, L;Pinner, RW, et al. Role of foods in sporadic listeriosis. I. Case-control study of dietary risk factors. The Listeria Study Group. *JAMA: J Am Med Assoc.* 1992;267(15):2041-5.

[24] Mead, PS;Slutsker, L;Dietz, V;McCaig, LF;Bresee, JS;Shapiro, C, et al. Food-related illness and death in the United States. *Emerg Infec Dis.* 1999;5(5):607-25.

[25] Schlech, WF, 3rd. Foodborne listeriosis. *Clinical Infectious Diseases: An Official Publication of the Infectious Diseases Society of America.* [10.1086/314008]. 2000;31(3):770-5.

[26] Schuchat, A;Lizano, C;Broome, CV;Swaminathan, B;Kim, C, Winn, K. Outbreak of neonatal listeriosis associated with mineral oil. *Pediatr Infec Dis J.* 1991;10(3):183-9.

[27] Gaulin, C;Ramsay, D, Bekal, S. Widespread listeriosis outbreak attributable to pasteurized cheese, which led to extensive cross-contamination affecting cheese retailers, Quebec, Canada, 2008. *J Food Prot.* [10.4315/0362-028X.JFP-11-236]. 2012;75(1):71-8.

[28] Koch, J;Dworak, R;Prager, R;Becker, B;Brockmann, S;Wicke, A, et al. Large listeriosis outbreak linked to cheese made from pasteurized milk, Germany, 2006-2007. *Foodborne Pathog Dis.* [10.1089/fpd.2010.0631]. 2010;7(12):1581-4.

[29] CDC. Multistate outbreak of listeriosis associated with Jensen Farms cantaloupe--United States, August-September 2011. *MMWR Morbidity and Mortality Weekly Report. 2011*;60(39):1357-8.

[30] CDC. Update: multistate outbreak of listeriosis--United States, 1998-1999. *MMWR Morbidity and Mortality Weekly Report. 1999*;47(51-52):1117-8.

[31] Mead, PS;Dunne, EF;Graves, L;Wiedmann, M;Patrick, M;Hunter, S, et al. Nationwide outbreak of listeriosis due to contaminated meat. *Epidemiol Infec.* [10.1017/S0950268805005376]. 2006;134(4):744-51.

[32] (CAC), CAC. *Guidelines on the application of general principles of food hygiene to the control of Listeria monocytogenes in ready-to-eat foods.* 2007.

[33] Glaser, P;Frangeul, L;Buchrieser, C;Rusniok, C;Amend, A;Baquero, F, et al. Comparative genomics of *Listeria* species. *Science.* 2001 Oct 26;294(5543):849-52.

[34] Cabanes, D;Sousa, S, Cossart, P. Listeria Genomics In: Wiedmann M, Zhang W, editors. *Genomics of Foodborne Bacterial* Pathogens NY: Springer; 2011. p. 141-70.

[35] Nelson, KE;Fouts, DE;Mongodin, EF;Ravel, J;DeBoy, RT;Kolonay, JF, et al. Whole genome comparisons of serotype 4b and 1/2a strains of the food-borne pathogen *Listeria monocytogenes* reveal new insights into the core genome components of this species. *Nucleic Acids Res.* 2004;32(8):2386-95.

[36] Chen, J;Xia, Y;Cheng, C;Fang, C;Shan, Y;Jin, G, et al. Genome sequence of the nonpathogenic *Listeria monocytogenes* serovar 4a strain M7. *J. Bacteriol.* 2011 Sep;193(18):5019-20.

[37] Chen, Y;Strain, EA;Allard, M, Brown, EW. Genome sequences of *Listeria monocytogenes* strains J1816 and J1-220, associated with human outbreaks. *J. Bacteriol.* 2011 Jul;193(13):3424-5.

[38] Steele, CL;Donaldson, JR;Paul, D;Banes, MM;Arick, T;Bridges, SM, et al. Genome sequence of lineage III *Listeria monocytogenes* strain HCC23. *J. Bacteriol.* 2011 Jul;193(14):3679-80.

[39] Toledo-Arana, A;Dussurget, O;Nikitas, G;Sesto, N;Guet-Revillet, H;Balestrino, D, et al. The Listeria transcriptional landscape from saprophytism to virulence. *Nature.* 2009 Jun 18;459(7249):950-6.

[40] Briers, Y;Klumpp, J;Schuppler, M, Loessner, MJ. Genome sequence of *Listeria monocytogenes* Scott A, a clinical isolate from a food-borne listeriosis outbreak. *J. Bacteriol.* 2011 Aug;193(16):4284-5.

[41] Buchrieser, C;Rusniok, C;Kunst, F;Cossart, P, Glaser, P. Comparison of the genome sequences of *Listeria monocytogenes* and Listeria innocua: clues for evolution and pathogenicity. *FEMS Immunol Med. Microbiol.* 2003 Apr 1;35(3):207-13.

[42] Ragon, M;Wirth, T;Hollandt, F;Lavenir, R;Lecuit, M;Le Monnier, A, et al. A new perspective on *Listeria monocytogenes* evolution. *PLoS Pathog.* 2008;4(9):e1000146.

[43] den Bakker, HC;Cummings, CA;Ferreira, V;Vatta, P;Orsi, RH;Degoricija, L, et al. Comparative genomics of the bacterial genus Listeria: Genome evolution is characterized by limited gene acquisition and limited gene loss. *BMC Genomics.* 2010;11:688.

[44] Bierne, H;Mazmanian, SK;Trost, M;Pucciarelli, MG;Liu, G;Dehoux, P, et al. Inactivation of the srtA gene in *Listeria monocytogenes* inhibits anchoring of surface proteins and affects virulence. *Mol. Microbiol.* 2002 Feb;43(4):869-81.

[45] Cabanes, D;Sousa, S;Cebria, A;Lecuit, M;Garcia-del Portillo, F, Cossart, P. Gp96 is a receptor for a novel *Listeria monocytogenes* virulence factor, Vip, a surface protein. *EMBO J.* 2005 Aug 3;24(15):2827-38.

[46] Sabet, C;Lecuit, M;Cabanes, D;Cossart, P, Bierne, H. LPXTG protein InlJ, a newly identified internalin involved in *Listeria monocytogenes* virulence. *Infect Immun.* 2005 Oct;73(10):6912-22.

[47] Pucciarelli, MG;Calvo, E;Sabet, C;Bierne, H;Cossart, P, Garcia-del Portillo, F. Identification of substrates of the *Listeria monocytogenes* sortases A and B by a non-gel proteomic analysis. *Proteomics.* 2005 Dec;5(18):4808-17.

[48] Lecuit, M. Human listeriosis and animal models. *Microbes Infect.* 2007 Aug;9(10):1216-25.

[49] Lunden, JM;Autio, TJ, Korkeala, HJ. Transfer of persistent *Listeria monocytogenes* contamination between food-processing plants associated with a dicing machine. *J. Food Prot.* 2002 Jul;65(7):1129-33.

[50] Renier, S;Hebraud, M, Desvaux, M. Molecular biology of surface colonization by *Listeria monocytogenes*: an additional facet of an opportunistic Gram-positive foodborne pathogen. *Environ Microbiol.* 2011 Apr;13(4):835-50.

[51] Schuppler, M, Loessner, MJ. The Opportunistic Pathogen *Listeria monocytogenes*: Pathogenicity and Interaction with the Mucosal Immune System. *Int. J. Inflam.* 2010;2010:704321.

[52] Cotter, PD;O'Reilly, K, Hill, C. Role of the glutamate decarboxylase acid resistance system in the survival of *Listeria monocytogenes* LO28 in low pH foods. *J. Food Prot.* 2001 Sep;64(9):1362-8.

[53] Sleator, RD;Wouters, J;Gahan, CG;Abee, T, Hill, C. Analysis of the role of OpuC, an osmolyte transport system, in salt tolerance and virulence potential of *Listeria monocytogenes*. *Appl. Environ. Microbiol.* 2001 Jun;67(6):2692-8.

[54] Begley, M;Sleator, RD;Gahan, CG, Hill, C. Contribution of three bile-associated loci, bsh, pva, and btlB, to gastrointestinal persistence and bile tolerance of *Listeria monocytogenes*. *Infect Immun.* 2005 Feb;73(2):894-904.

[55] Sleator, RD;Wemekamp-Kamphuis, HH;Gahan, CG;Abee, T, Hill, C. A PrfA-regulated bile exclusion system (BilE) is a novel virulence factor in *Listeria monocytogenes*. *Mol Microbiol.* 2005 Feb;55(4):1183-95.

[56] Chaturongakul, S;Raengpradub, S;Wiedmann, M, Boor, KJ. Modulation of stress and virulence in *Listeria monocytogenes*. *Trends Microbiol.* 2008 Aug;16(8):388-96.

[57] Ollinger, J;Bowen, B;Wiedmann, M;Boor, KJ, Bergholz, TM. *Listeria monocytogenes* sigmaB modulates PrfA-mediated virulence factor expression. *Infect Immun.* 2009 May;77(5):2113-24.

[58] Corr, S;Hill, C, Gahan, CG. An in vitro cell-culture model demonstrates internalin- and hemolysin-independent translocation of *Listeria monocytogenes* across M cells. *Microb. Pathog.* 2006 Dec;41(6):241-50.

[59] Lecuit, M. Understanding how *Listeria monocytogenes* targets and crosses host barriers. *Clin Microbiol Infect.* 2005 Jun;11(6):430-6.

[60] Vazquez-Boland, JA;Kuhn, M;Berche, P;Chakraborty, T;Dominguez-Bernal, G;Goebel, W, et al. Listeria pathogenesis and molecular virulence determinants. *Clin. Microbiol. Rev.* 2001 Jul;14(3):584-640.

[61] Gaillard, JL;Berche, P;Frehel, C;Gouin, E, Cossart, P. Entry of L. monocytogenes into cells is mediated by internalin, a repeat protein reminiscent of surface antigens from gram-positive cocci. *Cell.* 1991 Jun 28;65(7):1127-41.

[62] Mengaud, J;Ohayon, H;Gounon, P;Mege, RM, Cossart, P. E-cadherin is the receptor for internalin, a surface protein required for entry of L. monocytogenes into epithelial cells. *Cell.* 1996 Mar 22;84(6):923-32.

[63] Seveau, S;Bierne, H;Giroux, S;Prevost, MC, Cossart, P. Role of lipid rafts in E-cadherin-- and HGF-R/Met--mediated entry of *Listeria monocytogenes* into host cells. *J Cell Biol.* 2004 Aug 30;166(5):743-53.

[64] Bonazzi, M;Veiga, E;Pizarro-Cerda, J, Cossart, P. Successive post-translational modifications of E-cadherin are required for InlA-mediated internalization of *Listeria monocytogenes*. *Cell Microbiol.* 2008 Nov;10(11):2208-22.

[65] Pizarro-Cerda, J, Cossart, P. *Listeria monocytogenes* membrane trafficking and lifestyle: the exception or the rule? *Annu Rev Cell Dev. Biol.* 2009;25:649-70.

[66] Lecuit, M;Hurme, R;Pizarro-Cerda, J;Ohayon, H;Geiger, B, Cossart, P. A role for alpha-and beta-catenins in bacterial uptake. *Proc Natl Acad Sci U S A.* 2000 Aug 29;97(18):10008-13.

[67] Bonazzi, M;Vasudevan, L;Mallet, A;Sachse, M;Sartori, A;Prevost, MC, et al. Clathrin phosphorylation is required for actin recruitment at sites of bacterial adhesion and internalization. *J. Cell Biol.* 2011 Oct 31;195(3):525-36.

[68] Veiga, E, Cossart, P. Listeria hijacks the clathrin-dependent endocytic machinery to invade mammalian cells. *Nat. Cell Biol.* 2005 Sep;7(9):894-900.

[69] Shen, Y;Naujokas, M;Park, M, Ireton, K. InIB-dependent internalization of Listeria is mediated by the Met receptor tyrosine kinase. *Cell.* 2000 Oct 27;103(3):501-10.

[70] Khelef, N;Lecuit, M;Bierne, H, Cossart, P. Species specificity of the *Listeria monocytogenes* InIB protein. *Cell Microbiol.* 2006 Mar;8(3):457-70.

[71] Jonquieres, R;Pizarro-Cerda, J, Cossart, P. Synergy between the N- and C-terminal domains of InIB for efficient invasion of non-phagocytic cells by *Listeria monocytogenes*. *Mol Microbiol.* 2001 Nov;42(4):955-65.

[72] Braun, L;Ghebrehiwet, B, Cossart, P. gC1q-R/p32, a C1q-binding protein, is a receptor for the InIB invasion protein of *Listeria monocytogenes*. *EMBO J.* 2000 Apr 3;19(7):1458-66.

[73] Dokainish, H;Gavicherla, B;Shen, Y, Ireton, K. The carboxyl-terminal SH3 domain of the mammalian adaptor CrkII promotes internalization of *Listeria monocytogenes* through activation of host phosphoinositide 3-kinase. *Cell Microbiol.* 2007 Oct;9(10):2497-516.

[74] Bierne, H;Miki, H;Innocenti, M;Scita, G;Gertler, FB;Takenawa, T, et al. WASP-related proteins, Abi1 and Ena/VASP are required for *Listeria* invasion induced by the Met receptor. *J Cell Sci.* 2005 Apr 1;118(Pt 7):1537-47.

[75] Seveau, S;Tham, TN;Payrastre, B;Hoppe, AD;Swanson, JA, Cossart, P. A FRET analysis to unravel the role of cholesterol in Rac1 and PI 3-kinase activation in the InIB/Met signalling pathway. *Cell Microbiol.* 2007 Mar;9(3):790-803.

[76] Mostowy, S;Janel, S;Forestier, C;Roduit, C;Kasas, S;Pizarro-Cerda, J, et al. A role for septins in the interaction between the *Listeria monocytogenes* INVASION PROTEIN InIB and the Met receptor. *Biophys J.* 2011 Apr 20;100(8):1949-59.

[77] Mostowy, S;Nam Tham, T;Danckaert, A;Guadagnini, S;Boisson-Dupuis, S;Pizarro-Cerda, J, et al. Septins regulate bacterial entry into host cells. *PLoS One.* 2009;4(1):e4196.

[78] Alvarez-Dominguez, C;Madrazo-Toca, F;Fernandez-Prieto, L;Vandekerckhove, J;Pareja, E;Tobes, R, et al. Characterization of a *Listeria monocytogenes* protein interfering with Rab5a. *Traffic.* 2008 Mar;9(3):325-37.

[79] Prada-Delgado, A;Carrasco-Marin, E;Bokoch, GM, Alvarez-Dominguez, C. Interferon-gamma listericidal action is mediated by novel Rab5a functions at the phagosomal environment. *J Biol Chem.* 2001 Jun 1;276(22):19059-65.

[80] Cossart, P;Vicente, MF;Mengaud, J;Baquero, F;Perez-Diaz, JC, Berche, P. Listeriolysin O is essential for virulence of *Listeria monocytogenes*: direct evidence obtained by gene complementation. *Infect Immun.* 1989 Nov;57(11):3629-36.

[81] Beauregard, KE;Lee, KD;Collier, RJ, Swanson, JA. pH-dependent perforation of macrophage phagosomes by listeriolysin O from *Listeria monocytogenes*. *J. Exp. Med.* 1997 Oct 6;186(7):1159-63.

[82] Singh, R;Jamieson, A, Cresswell, P. GILT is a critical host factor for *Listeria monocytogenes* infection. *Nature.* 2008 Oct 30;455(7217):1244-7.

[83] Goldfine, H;Knob, C;Alford, D, Bentz, J. Membrane permeabilization by *Listeria monocytogenes* phosphatidylinositol-specific phospholipase C is independent of phospholipid hydrolysis and cooperative with listeriolysin O. *Proc Natl Acad Sci U S A.* 1995 Mar 28;92(7):2979-83.

[84] Henry, R;Shaughnessy, L;Loessner, MJ;Alberti-Segui, C;Higgins, DE, Swanson, JA. Cytolysin-dependent delay of vacuole maturation in macrophages infected with *Listeria monocytogenes*. *Cell Microbiol.* 2006 Jan;8(1):107-19.

[85] Repp, H;Pamukci, Z;Koschinski, A;Domann, E;Darji, A;Birringer, J, et al. Listeriolysin of *Listeria monocytogenes* forms Ca2+-permeable pores leading to intracellular Ca2+ oscillations. *Cell Microbiol.* 2002 Aug;4(8):483-91.

[86] Shaughnessy, LM;Hoppe, AD;Christensen, KA, Swanson, JA. Membrane perforations inhibit lysosome fusion by altering pH and calcium in *Listeria monocytogenes* vacuoles. *Cell Microbiol.* 2006 May;8(5):781-92.

[87] Schnupf, P, Portnoy, DA. Listeriolysin O: a phagosome-specific lysin. *Microbes Infect.* 2007 Aug;9(10):1176-87.

[88] Smith, GA;Marquis, H;Jones, S;Johnston, NC;Portnoy, DA, Goldfine, H. The two distinct phospholipases C of *Listeria monocytogenes* have overlapping roles in escape from a vacuole and cell-to-cell spread. *Infect Immun.* 1995 Nov;63(11):4231-7.

[89] Marquis, H, Hager, EJ. pH-regulated activation and release of a bacteria-associated phospholipase C during intracellular infection by *Listeria monocytogenes*. *Mol. Microbiol.* 2000 Jan;35(2):289-98.

[90] Cossart, P. Illuminating the landscape of host-pathogen interactions with the bacterium *Listeria monocytogenes*. *Proc Natl Acad Sci U S A.* 2011 Dec 6;108(49):19484-91.

[91] Alberti-Segui, C;Goeden, KR, Higgins, DE. Differential function of *Listeria monocytogenes* listeriolysin O and phospholipases C in vacuolar dissolution following cell-to-cell spread. *Cell Microbiol.* 2007 Jan;9(1):179-95.

[92] Seglen, PO;Gordon, PB, Holen, I. Non-selective autophagy. *Semin Cell Biol.* 1990 Dec;1(6):441-8.

[93] Klionsky, DJ. Autophagy: from phenomenology to molecular understanding in less than a decade. *Nat Rev Mol Cell Biol.* 2007 Nov;8(11):931-7.

[94] Rich, KA;Burkett, C, Webster, P. Cytoplasmic bacteria can be targets for autophagy. *Cell Microbiol.* 2003 Jul;5(7):455-68.

[95] Py, BF;Lipinski, MM, Yuan, J. Autophagy limits *Listeria monocytogenes* intracellular growth in the early phase of primary infection. *Autophagy.* 2007 Mar-Apr;3(2):117-25.

[96] Birmingham, CL;Canadien, V;Gouin, E;Troy, EB;Yoshimori, T;Cossart, P, et al. *Listeria monocytogenes* evades killing by autophagy during colonization of host cells. *Autophagy.* 2007 Sep-Oct;3(5):442-51.

[97] Yoshikawa, Y;Ogawa, M;Hain, T;Yoshida, M;Fukumatsu, M;Kim, M, et al. *Listeria monocytogenes* ActA-mediated escape from autophagic recognition. *Nat Cell Biol.* 2009 Oct;11(10):1233-40.

[98] Ray, K;Marteyn, B;Sansonetti, PJ, Tang, CM. Life on the inside: the intracellular lifestyle of cytosolic bacteria. *Nat Rev Microbiol.* 2009 May;7(5):333-40.

[99] Dortet, L;Mostowy, S;Samba-Louaka, A;Gouin, E;Nahori, MA;Wiemer, EA, et al. Recruitment of the major vault protein by InlK: a *Listeria monocytogenes* strategy to avoid autophagy. *PLoS Pathog.* 2011 Aug;7(8):e1002168.

[100] Mackaness, GB. The influence of immunologically committed lymphoid cells on macrophage activity in vivo. *J Exp Med.* 1969 May 1;129(5):973-92.

[101] Kocks, C;Gouin, E;Tabouret, M;Berche, P;Ohayon, H, Cossart, P. L. monocytogenes-induced actin assembly requires the actA gene product, a surface protein. *Cell.* 1992 Feb 7;68(3):521-31.

[102] Welch, MD;Iwamatsu, A, Mitchison, TJ. Actin polymerization is induced by Arp2/3 protein complex at the surface of *Listeria monocytogenes*. *Nature.* 1997 Jan 16;385(6613):265-9.

[103] Tilney, LG, Portnoy, DA. Actin filaments and the growth, movement, and spread of the intracellular bacterial parasite, *Listeria monocytogenes. J Cell Biol.* 1989 Oct;109(4 Pt 1):1597-608.

[104] Eisenreich, W;Dandekar, T;Heesemann, J, Goebel, W. Carbon metabolism of intracellular bacterial pathogens and possible links to virulence. *Nat Rev Microbiol.* 2010 Jun;8(6):401-12.

[105] Eylert, E;Schar, J;Mertins, S;Stoll, R;Bacher, A;Goebel, W, et al. Carbon metabolism of *Listeria monocytogenes* growing inside macrophages. *Mol Microbiol.* 2008 Aug;69(4):1008-17.

[106] Chico-Calero, I;Suarez, M;Gonzalez-Zorn, B;Scortti, M;Slaghuis, J;Goebel, W, et al. Hpt, a bacterial homolog of the microsomal glucose- 6-phosphate translocase, mediates rapid intracellular proliferation in *Listeria. Proc Natl Acad Sci U S A.* 2002 Jan 8;99(1):431-6.

[107] Joseph, B;Przybilla, K;Stuhler, C;Schauer, K;Slaghuis, J;Fuchs, TM, et al. Identification of *Listeria monocytogenes* genes contributing to intracellular replication by expression profiling and mutant screening. *J. Bacteriol.* 2006 Jan;188(2):556-68.

[108] Goldfine, H;Johnston, NC, Knob, C. Nonspecific phospholipase C of *Listeria monocytogenes*: activity on phospholipids in Triton X-100-mixed micelles and in biological membranes. *J Bacteriol.* 1993 Jul;175(14):4298-306.

[109] Milenbachs, AA;Brown, DP;Moors, M, Youngman, P. Carbon-source regulation of virulence gene expression in *Listeria monocytogenes. Mol Microbiol.* 1997 Mar;23(5):1075-85.

[110] de las Heras, A;Cain, RJ;Bielecka, MK, Vazquez-Boland, JA. Regulation of Listeria virulence: PrfA master and commander. *Curr Opin Microbiol.* 2011 Apr;14(2):118-27.

[111] Johansson, J;Mandin, P;Renzoni, A;Chiaruttini, C;Springer, M, Cossart, P. An RNA thermosensor controls expression of virulence genes in *Listeria monocytogenes. Cell.* 2002 Sep 6;110(5):551-61.

[112] Freitag, NE, Portnoy, DA. Dual promoters of the *Listeria monocytogenes* prfA transcriptional activator appear essential in vitro but are redundant in vivo. *Mol. Microbiol.* 1994 Jun;12(5):845-53.

[113] Nadon, CA;Bowen, BM;Wiedmann, M, Boor, KJ. Sigma B contributes to PrfA-mediated virulence in *Listeria monocytogenes. Infect Immun.* 2002 Jul;70(7):3948-52.

[114] Freitag, NE;Port, GC, Miner, MD. *Listeria monocytogenes* - from saprophyte to intracellular pathogen. *Nat .Rev. Microbiol.* 2009 Sep;7(9):623-8.

[115] Joseph, B;Mertins, S;Stoll, R;Schar, J;Umesha, KR;Luo, Q, et al. Glycerol metabolism and PrfA activity in *Listeria monocytogenes. J Bacteriol.* 2008 Aug;190(15):5412-30.

[116] Stoll, R;Mertins, S;Joseph, B;Muller-Altrock, S, Goebel, W. Modulation of PrfA activity in *Listeria monocytogenes* upon growth in different culture media. *Microbiology.* 2008 Dec;154(Pt 12):3856-76.

[117] Vega, Y;Rauch, M;Banfield, MJ;Ermolaeva, S;Scortti, M;Goebel, W, et al. New *Listeria monocytogenes* prfA* mutants, transcriptional properties of PrfA* proteins and structure-function of the virulence regulator PrfA. *Mol. Microbiol.* 2004 Jun;52(6):1553-65.

[118] Conlan, JW. Early pathogenesis of *Listeria monocytogenes* infection in the mouse spleen. *J. Med. Microbiol.* 1996 Apr;44(4):295-302.

[119] Conlan, JW, North, RJ. Neutrophils are essential for early anti-Listeria defense in the liver, but not in the spleen or peritoneal cavity, as revealed by a granulocyte-depleting monoclonal antibody. *J. Exp. Med.* 1994 Jan 1;179(1):259-68.

[120] Gaillard, JL;Jaubert, F, Berche, P. The inlAB locus mediates the entry of *Listeria monocytogenes* into hepatocytes in vivo. *J. Exp. Med.* 1996 Feb 1;183(2):359-69.

[121] Vadia, S;Arnett, E;Haghighat, AC;Wilson-Kubalek, EM;Tweten, RK, Seveau, S. The pore-forming toxin listeriolysin O mediates a novel entry pathway of L. monocytogenes into human hepatocytes. *PLoS Pathog.* 2011 Nov;7(11):e1002356.

[122] Doganay, M. Listeriosis: clinical presentation. *FEMS Immunol Med Microbiol.* 2003 Apr 1;35(3):173-5.

[123] Greiffenberg, L;Goebel, W;Kim, KS;Weiglein, I;Bubert, A;Engelbrecht, F, et al. Interaction of *Listeria monocytogenes* with human brain microvascular endothelial cells: InlB-dependent invasion, long-term intracellular growth, and spread from macrophages to endothelial cells. *Infect Immun.* 1998 Nov;66(11):5260-7.

[124] Wang, L, Lin, M. A novel cell wall-anchored peptidoglycan hydrolase (autolysin), IspC, essential for *Listeria monocytogenes* virulence: genetic and proteomic analysis. *Microbiology.* 2008 Jul;154(Pt 7):1900-13.

[125] Berche, P. Bacteremia is required for invasion of the murine central nervous system by *Listeria monocytogenes. Microb Pathog.* 1995 May;18(5):323-36.

[126] Drevets, DA;Jelinek, TA, Freitag, NE. *Listeria monocytogenes*-infected phagocytes can initiate central nervous system infection in mice. *Infect Immun.* 2001 Mar;69(3): 1344-50.

[127] Join-Lambert, OF;Ezine, S;Le Monnier, A;Jaubert, F;Okabe, M;Berche, P, et al. *Listeria monocytogenes*-infected bone marrow myeloid cells promote bacterial invasion of the central nervous system. *Cell Microbiol.* 2005 Feb;7(2):167-80.

[128] Abram, M;Schluter, D;Vuckovic, D;Wraber, B;Doric, M, Deckert, M. Murine model of pregnancy-associated *Listeria monocytogenes* infection. *FEMS Immunol Med Microbiol.* 2003 Apr 1;35(3):177-82.

[129] Disson, O;Grayo, S;Huillet, E;Nikitas, G;Langa-Vives, F;Dussurget, O, et al. Conjugated action of two species-specific invasion proteins for fetoplacental listeriosis. *Nature.* 2008 Oct 23;455(7216):1114-8.

[130] Hitchins, AD, Jinneman, K. Chapter 10: Detection and Enumeration of *Listeria monocytogenes. Food and Drug Administration's Bacteriological Analytical Manual* (online)2011.

[131] 993.12., AOM. *Listeria monocytogenes* in Milk and Dairy Products. Selective Enrichment and Isolation Method. Official Methods of Analysis of AOAC INTERNATIONAL. In: O, Volume I, Agricultural Chemicals; Contaminants; Drugs, Horwitz W., ed. *AOAC INTERNATIONAL,* Gaithersburg, MD, USA, 138–141. 2000.

[132] Standardization, IOf. Microbiology of food and animal feeding stuffs –Horizontal method for the detection and enumeration of *Listeria monocytogenes* – Part 1: Detection method. *International Standard ISO* 11290-1, Geneva, Switzerland. 1996.

[133] Standardization, IOf. Microbiology of food and animal feeding stuffs –Horizontal method for the detection and enumeration of *Listeria monocytogenes* – Part 2: Enumeration method. *International Standard ISO* 11290–2, Geneva, Switzerland. 1998.

[134] *Standardization, IOf.* Microbiology of food and animal feeding stuffs – Horizontal method for the detection and enumeration of *Listeria monocytogenes* – Part 1: Detection method. International Standard ISO 11290-1, AMENDMENT 1: Modification of the isolation media and the haemolysis test, and inclusion of precision data, Geneva, Switzerland. 2004.

[135] McLauchlin, J. *Listeria monocytogenes*, recent advances in the taxonomy and epidemiology of listeriosis in humans. *J Appl Bacteriol.* [Review]. 1987 Jul;63(1):1-11.

[136] Poyski, FT;Parenipye, RN;Lashbrook, LC;Peterson, ME;Pelroy, GA, Eklund, MW. Selective and differential medium for isolation of *Listeria monocytogenes* from foods. *J. Food Prot.* 1993;56:326-9.

[137] Vlaemynck, G;Lafarge, V, Scotter, S. Improvement of the detection of *Listeria monocytogenes* by the application of ALOA, a diagnostic, chromogenic isolation medium. *J .Appl .Microbiol.* [Comparative Study]. 2000 Mar;88(3):430-41.

[138] Restaino, L;Frampton, EW;Irbe, RM;Schabert, G, Spitz, H. Isolation and detection of *Listeria monocytogenes* using fluorogenic and chromogenic substrates for phosphatidylinositol-specific phospholipase C. *J. Food Prot.* 1999 Mar;62(3):244-51.

[139] Lauer, WF;Facon, JP, Patel, A. Evaluation of a chromogenic medium for identification and differentiation of *Listeria monocytogenes* in selected foods. *J. AOAC Inter.* 2005 Mar-Apr;88(2):511-7.

[140] Gasanov, U;Hughes, D, Hansbro, PM. Methods for the isolation and identification of *Listeria* spp. and *Listeria monocytogenes*: a review. *FEMS Microbiol Rev.* [Research Support, Non-U.S. Gov't Review]. 2005 Nov;29(5):851-75.

[141] Vazquez-Boland, JA;Dominguez, L;Fernandez, JF;Rodriguez-Ferri, EF;Briones, V;Blanco, M, et al. Revision of the validity of CAMP tests for *Listeria* identification. Proposal of an alternative method for the determination of haemolytic activity by *Listeria* strains. *Acta Microbiol. Hung.* 1990;37(2):201-6.

[142] Clark, AG, McLaughlin, J. Simple color tests based on an alanyl peptidase reaction which differentiate *Listeria monocytogenes* from other *Listeria* species. *J Clin Microbiol.* [Research Support, Non-U.S. Gov't]. 1997 Aug;35(8):2155-6.

[143] Silbernagel, KM;Jechorek, RP;Kaufer, AL;Johnson, RL;Aleo, V;Brown, B, et al. Evaluation of the VIDAS *Listeria* (LIS) immunoassay for the detection of *Listeria* in foods using demi-Fraser and Fraser enrichment broths, as modification of AOAC Official Method 999.06 (AOAC Official Method 2004.06). *J. AOAC Inter.* [Multicenter Study]. 2005 May-Jun;88(3):750-60.

[144] Rodriguez-Lazaro, D;Hernandez, M, Pla, M. Simultaneous quantitative detection of *Listeria* spp. and *Listeria monocytogenes* using a duplex real-time PCR-based assay. *FEMS Microbiol Lett.* [Research Support, Non-U.S. Gov't]. 2004 Apr 15;233(2): 257-67.

[145] Rodriguez-Lazaro, D;Hernandez, M;Scortti, M;Esteve, T;Vazquez-Boland, JA, Pla, M. Quantitative detection of *Listeria monocytogenes* and *Listeria innocua* by real-time PCR: assessment of *hly*, *iap*, and lin02483 targets and AmpliFluor technology. *Appl. Environ. Microbiol.* [Comparative Study Research Support, Non-U.S. Gov't]. 2004 Mar;70(3):1366-77.

[146] Rodriguez-Lazaro, D;Jofre, A;Aymerich, T;Hugas, M, Pla, M. Rapid quantitative detection of *Listeria monocytogenes* in meat products by real-time PCR. *Appl. Environ*

Microbiol. [Comparative Study Research Support, Non-U.S. Gov't]. 2004 Oct;70(10):6299-301.

[147] Cocolin, L;Rantsiou, K;Iacumin, L;Cantoni, C, Comi, G. Direct identification in food samples of *Listeria* spp. and *Listeria monocytogenes* by molecular methods. *Appl. Environ Microbiol.* 2002 Dec;68(12):6273-82.

[148] Jung, YS;Frank, JF;Brackett, RE, Chen, J. Polymerase chain reaction detection of *Listeria monocytogenes* on frankfurters using oligonucleotide primers targeting the genes encoding internalin AB. *J Food Prot.* [Research Support, Non-U.S. Gov't Research Support, U.S. Gov't, Non-P.H.S.]. 2003 Feb;66(2):237-41.

[149] Sontakke, S, Farber, JM. The use of PCR ribotyping for typing strains of *Listeria* spp. *EurJEpidemiol.* 1995 Dec;11(6):665-73.

[150] Gandhi, M, Chikindas, ML. Listeria: A foodborne pathogen that knows how to survive. *Int J Food Microbiol.* 2007 Jan 1;113(1):1-15.

[151] Aymerich, T;Picouet, PA, Monfort, JM. Decontamination technologies for meat products. *Meat Sci.* 2008 Jan;78(1-2):114-29.

[152] Tokarskyy , O, Marshall, DL. Novel Technologies for Microbial Spoilage Prevention. In: Toldrá F, editor. *Handbook of Meat Processing.* Oxford, UK: Wiley-Blackwell; 2010. p. 263-86.

[153] Tay, A;Shellhammer, TH;Yousef, AE, Chism, GW. Pressure death and tailing behavior of *Listeria monocytogenes* strains having different barotolerances. *J Food Prot.* 2003 Nov;66(11):2057-61.

[154] Lado, BH, Yousef, AE. Alternative food-preservation technologies: efficacy and mechanisms. *Microbes Infect.* 2002 Apr;4(4):433-40.

[155] Simpson, RK, Gilmour, A. The effect of high hydrostatic pressure on *Listeria monocytogenes* in phosphate-buffered saline and model food systems. *J Appl Microbiol.* 1997 Aug;83(2):181-8.

[156] Ritz, M;Tholozan, JL;Federighi, M, Pilet, MF. Morphological and physiological characterization of *Listeria monocytogenes* subjected to high hydrostatic pressure. *Appl Environ Microbiol.* 2001 May;67(5):2240-7.

[157] Ritz, M;Tholozan, JL;Federighi, M, Pilet, MF. Physiological damages of *Listeria monocytogenes* treated by high hydrostatic pressure. *Int J Food Microbiol.* 2002 Nov 15;79(1-2):47-53.

[158] Simpson, RK, Gilmour, A. The effect of high hydrostatic pressure on the activity of intracellular enzymes of *Listeria monocytogenes*. *Lett Appl. Microbiol.* 1997 Jul;25(1):48-53.

[159] Lakshmanan, R, Dalgaard, P. Effects of high-pressure processing on *Listeria monocytogenes*, spoilage microflora and multiple compound quality indices in chilled cold-smoked salmon. *J. Appl. Microbiol.* 2004;96(2):398-408.

[160] Chung, YK;Vurma, M;Turek, EJ;Chism, GW, Yousef, AE. Inactivation of barotolerant *Listeria monocytogenes* in sausage by combination of high-pressure processing and food-grade additives. *J. Food Prot.* 2005 Apr;68(4):744-50.

[161] Jofre, A;Garriga, M, Aymerich, T. Inhibition of *Listeria monocytogenes* in cooked ham through active packaging with natural antimicrobials and high-pressure processing. *J. Food Prot.* 2007 Nov;70(11):2498-502.

[162] Vannini, L;Lanciotti, R;Baldi, D, Guerzoni, ME. Interactions between high pressure homogenization and antimicrobial activity of lysozyme and lactoperoxidase. *Int. J. Food Microbiol.* 2004 Jul 15;94(2):123-35.

[163] Aymerich, T;Jofre, A;Garriga, M, Hugas, M. Inhibition of *Listeria monocytogenes* and Salmonella by natural antimicrobials and high hydrostatic pressure in sliced cooked ham. *J. Food Prot.* 2005 Jan;68(1):173-7.

[164] Piyasena, P;Mohareb, E, McKellar, RC. Inactivation of microbes using ultrasound: A review. *Int. J. Food Microbiol.* 2003 Nov 1;87(3):207-16.

[165] Baumann, AR;Martin, SE, Feng, H. Power ultrasound treatment of *Listeria monocytogenes* in apple cider. *J. Food Prot.* 2005 Nov;68(11):2333-40.

[166] Ugarte-Romero, E;Feng, H, Martin, SE. Inactivation of *Shigella boydii* 18 IDPH and *Listeria monocytogenes* Scott A with power ultrasound at different acoustic energy densities and temperatures. *Food Sci.* 2007;4103- 7.

[167] Berrang, ME;Frank, JF, Meinersmann, RJ. Effect of chemical sanitizers with and without ultrasonication on *Listeria monocytogenes* as a biofilm within polyvinyl chloride drain pipes. *J. Food Prot.* 2008 Jan;71(1):66-9.

[168] Wouters, PC;Dutreux, N;Smelt, JPPM, Lelieveld, HLM. Effects of pulsed electric fields on inactivation kinetics of Listeria innocua. *App. Environ. Microbiol.* 1999;12:53-64.

[169] Reina, LD;Jin, ZT;Zhang, QH, Yousef, AE. Inactivation of *Listeria monocytogenes* in milk by pulsed electric field. *J. Food Prot.* 1998 Sep;61(9):1203-6.

[170] Calderón-Miranda, ML;Barbosa-Canovas, GV, Swanson, BG. Transmission electron microscopy of Listeria innocua treated by pulsed electric fields and nisin in skimmed milk. *Int J. Food Microbiol.* 1999;1:31-8.

[171] Unal, R;Kim, JG, Yousef, AE. Inactivation of *Escherichia coli* O1 57:H7, *Listeria monocytogenes*, and *Lactobacillus leichmannii* by combinations of ozone and pulsed electric field. *J. Food Prot.* 2001 Jun;64(6):777-82.

[172] Khadre, Yousef, AE. Sporicidal action of ozone and hydrogen peroxide: a comparative study. *Int. J. Food Microbiol.* 2001 Dec 30;71(2-3):131-8.

[173] Wade, WN;Scouten, AJ;McWatters, KH;Wick, RL;Demirci, A;Fett, WF, et al. Efficacy of ozone in killing *Listeria monocytogenes* on alfalfa seeds and sprouts and effects on sensory quality of sprouts. *J Food Prot.* 2003 Jan;66(1):44-51.

[174] Robbins, JB;Fisher, CW;Moltz, AG, Martin, SE. Elimination of *Listeria monocytogenes* biofilms by ozone, chlorine, and hydrogen peroxide. *J. Food Prot.* 2005 Mar;68(3):494-8.

[175] Fan, L;Song, J;McRae, KB;Walker, BA, Sharpe, D. Gaseous ozone treatment inactivates *Listeria innocua in vitro. J Appl Microbiol.* 2007 Dec;103(6):2657-63.

[176] Sommers, CH, Boyd, G. Elimination of *Listeria monocytogenes* from ready-to-eat turkey and cheese tortilla wraps using ionizing radiation. *J. Food Prot.* 2005 Jan;68(1):164-7.

[177] Bari, ML;Nakauma, M;Todoriki, S;Juneja, VK;Isshiki, K, Kawamoto, S. Effectiveness of irradiation treatments in inactivating *Listeria monocytogenes* on fresh vegetables at refrigeration temperature. *J. Food Prot.* 2005 Feb;68(2):318-23.

[178] Carlton, RM;Noordman, WH;Biswas, B;de Meester, ED, Loessner, MJ. Bacteriophage P100 for control of *Listeria monocytogenes* in foods: genome sequence, bioinformatic

analyses, oral toxicity study, and application. *Regul Toxicol Pharmacol*. 2005 Dec;43(3):301-12.

[179] Dykes, GA, Moorhead, SM. Combined antimicrobial effect of nisin and a listeriophage against *Listeria monocytogenes* in broth but not in buffer or on raw beef. *Int. J. Food Microbiol*. 2002;1:71-81.

[180] Sthal, NZ. Antimicrobials move in new directions: A quick look at products debuts and reformulations. *Meat Processing*. 2007;4:46-8.

[181] Klockow, P, Keener, KM. Safety and quality assessment of packaged spinach treated with a novel ozone generation system. *Lebensmittel-Wissenschaft and Technologie*. 2009;6:1047-53.

[182] Song, HP;Kim, B;Choe, JH;Jung, S;Moon, SY;Choe, W, et al. Evaluation of atmospheric pressure plasma to improve the safety of sliced cheese and ham inoculated by 3-strain cocktail *Listeria monocytogenes*. *Food Microbiol*. 2009 Jun;26(4):432-6.

[183] Yun, H;Kim, B;Jung, S;Kruk, ZA;Kim, DB;Choe, W, et al. Inactivation of *Listeria monocytogenes* inoculated on disposable plastic tray, aluminum foil, and paper cup by atmospheric pressure plasma. *Food Control,*. 2010;8:1182-6.

[184] Demirci, A, Panico, L. Pulsed Ultraviolet Light. . *Food Science and Technology International*. 2008;14:443-6.

[185] Keklik, NM;Demirci, A, Puri, VM. Inactivation of *Listeria monocytogenes* on unpackaged and vacuum-packaged chicken frankfurters using pulsed UV-light. *J. Food Sci.*. 2009;8:431-9.

[186] Wilkinson, BHP;Janz, JAM;Morel, PCH;Purchas, RW, Hendriks, WH. The effect of modified atmosphere packaging with carbon monoxide on the storage quality of master-packaged fresh pork. *Meat Science*. 2006;4:605-10.

[187] Sagoo, SK;Little, CL;Allen, G;Williamson, K, Grant, KA. Microbiological safety of retail vacuum-packed and modified-atmosphere-packed cooked meats at end of shelf life. *J Food Prot*. 2007 Apr;70(4):943-51.

[188] Van Houteghem, N;Devlieghere, F;Rajkovic, A;Gomez, SM;Uyttendaele, M, Debevere, J. Effects of CO$_2$ on the resuscitation of *Listeria monocytogenes* injured by various bactericidal treatments. *Int. J. Food Microbiol*. 2008 Mar 31;123(1-2):67-73.

[189] Jin, T, Zhang, H. Biodegradable polylactic acid polymer with nisin for use in antimicrobial food packaging. *J. Food Sci*. 2008 Apr;73(3):M127-34.

[190] Massani, MB;Morando, PJ;Vignolo, GM, Eisenberg, P. Characterization of a multilayer film activated with *Lactobacillus curvatus* CRL705 bacteriocins. *J. Sci. Food Agric*. Nov 14.

[191] Grower, JL;Cooksey, K, Getty, KJ. Development and characterization of an antimicrobial packaging film coating containing nisin for inhibition of *Listeria monocytogenes*. *J. Food Prot*. 2004 Mar;67(3):475-9.

[192] Nguyen, VT;Gidley, MJ, Dykes, GA. Potential of a nisin-containing bacterial cellulose film to inhibit *Listeria monocytogenes* on processed meats. *Food Microbiol*. 2008 May;25(3):471-8.

[193] de Fatima, FSN;Pires, AC;Camilloto, GP;Santiago-Silva, P;Espitia, PJ, Silva, WA. Recent patents on active packaging for food application. *Recent Pat. Food Nutr. Agric*. 2009 Jun;1(2):171-8.

[194] Glass, KA;McDonnell, LM;Rassel, RC, Zierke, KL. Controlling *Listeria monocytogenes* on sliced ham and turkey products using benzoate, propionate, and sorbate. *J. Food Prot.* 2007 Oct;70(10):2306-12.

[195] Chang, Y;Gu, W, McLandsborough, L. Low concentration of ethylenediaminetetraacetic acid (EDTA) affects biofilm formation of *Listeria monocytogenes* by inhibiting its initial adherence. *Food Microbiol.* 2012 Feb;29(1): 10-7.

[196] Garcia-Garcia, R;Lopez-Malo, A, Palou, E. Bactericidal action of binary and ternary mixtures of carvacrol, thymol, and eugenol against *Listeria innocua. J. Food Sci.* 2011 Mar;76(2):M95-100.

[197] Takahashi, H;Kuramoto, S;Miya, S;Koiso, H;Kuda, T, Kimura, B. Use of commercially available antimicrobial compounds for prevention of *Listeria monocytogenes* growth in ready-to-eat minced tuna and salmon roe during shelf life. *J. Food Prot.* 2011 Jun;74(6):994-8.

[198] Palumbo, D;Iannaccone, M;Porta, A, Capparelli, R. Experimental antibacterial therapy with puroindolines, lactoferrin and lysozyme in *Listeria monocytogenes*-infected mice. *Microbes Infect.* 2010 Jul;12(7):538-45.

[199] Mastromatteo, M;Lucera, A;Sinigaglia, M, Corbo, MR. Synergic antimicrobial activity of lysozyme, nisin, and EDTA against *Listeria monocytogenes* in ostrich meat patties. *J Food Sci.* 2010 Sep;75(7):M422-9.

[200] Giannou, E;Kakouri, A;Matijasic, BB;Rogelj, I, Samelis, J. Fate of *Listeria monocytogenes* on fully ripened Greek Graviera cheese stored at 4, 12, or 25 degrees C in air or vacuum packages: in situ PCR detection of a cocktail of bacteriocins potentially contributing to pathogen inhibition. *J Food Prot.* 2009 Mar;72(3):531-8.

[201] Solomakos, N;Govaris, A;Koidis, P, Botsoglou, N. The antimicrobial effect of thyme essential oil, nisin, and their combination against *Listeria monocytogenes* in minced beef during refrigerated storage. *Food Microbiol.* 2008 Feb;25(1):120-7.

[202] Heng, NCK, Wescombe, Philip A., Burton, Jeremy P.,Jack, RWaT, John R. *The Diversity of Bacteriocins in Gram-Positive Bacteria.Chavan MARMA*, editor. Heidelberg Germany: Springer 2007.

[203] Lohans, CT, Vederas, JC. Development of Class IIa Bacteriocins as Therapeutic Agents. *Int J Microbiol.*2012:386410.

[204] Lawton, EM;Ross, RP;Hill, C, Cotter, PD. Two-peptide lantibiotics: a medical perspective. *Mini Rev Med Chem.* 2007 Dec;7(12):1236-47.

[205] Salvucci, E;Saavedra, L;Hebert, EM;Haro, C, Sesma, F. Enterocin CRL35 inhibits *Listeria monocytogenes* in a murine model. *Foodborne Pathog Dis.* Jan;9(1):68-74.

[206] Barrett, E;Hayes, M;O'Connor, P;Gardiner, G;Fitzgerald, GF;Stanton, C, et al. Salivaricin P, one of a family of two-component antilisterial bacteriocins produced by intestinal isolates of *Lactobacillus salivarius. Appl. Environ Microbiol.* 2007 Jun;73(11):3719-23.

[207] Drider, D;Fimland, G;Hechard, Y;McMullen, LM, Prevost, H. The continuing story of class IIa bacteriocins. *Microbiol Mol. Biol. Rev.* 2006 Jun;70(2):564-82.

[208] Castellano, P, Vignolo, G. Inhibition of *Listeria innocua* and *Brochothrix thermosphacta* in vacuum-packaged meat by addition of bacteriocinogenic *Lactobacillus curvatus* CRL705 and its bacteriocins. *Lett Appl. Microbiol.* 2006 Aug;43(2):194-9.

[209] Saavedra, L;Minahk, C;de Ruiz Holgado, AP, Sesma, F. Enhancement of the enterocin CRL35 activity by a synthetic peptide derived from the NH_2-terminal sequence. *Antimicrob Agents Chemother*. 2004 Jul;48(7):2778-81.

[210] Richard, C;Drider, D;Elmorjani, K;Marion, D, Prevost, H. Heterologous expression and purification of active divercin V41, a class IIa bacteriocin encoded by a synthetic gene in *Escherichia coli*. *J Bacteriol*. 2004 Jul;186(13):4276-84.

[211] Berjeaud, JM, Cenatiempo, Y. Purification of antilisterial bacteriocins. *Methods Mol. Biol*. 2004;268:225-33.

[212] Yamazaki, K;Suzuki, M;Kawai, Y;Inoue, N, Montville, TJ. Inhibition of *Listeria monocytogenes* in cold-smoked salmon by Carnobacterium piscicola CS526 isolated from frozen surimi. *J. Food Prot*. 2003 Aug;66(8):1420-5.

[213] Sabia, C;de Niederhausern, S;Messi, P;Manicardi, G, Bondi, M. Bacteriocin-producing *Enterococcus casseliflavus* IM 416K1, a natural antagonist for control of *Listeria monocytogenes* in Italian sausages ("cacciatore"). *Int J. Food Microbiol*. 2003 Oct 15;87(1-2):173-9.

[214] Saavedra, L;Taranto, MP;Sesma, F, de Valdez, GF. Homemade traditional cheeses for the isolation of probiotic *Enterococcus faecium* strains. *Int J. Food Microbiol*. 2003 Dec 1;88(2-3):241-5.

[215] Jones, E;Salin, V, Williams, G. *NISIN AND THE MARKET FOR COMMERICIAL BACTERIOCINS: Texas Agribusiness Market Research Center (TAMRC)2005. Report No.: CP-01-05*.

[216] Ravyts, F;Barbuti, S;Frustoli, MA;Parolari, G;Saccani, G;De Vuyst, L, et al. Competitiveness and antibacterial potential of bacteriocin-producing starter cultures in different types of fermented sausages. *J. Food Prot*. 2008 Sep;71(9):1817-27.

[217] Liu, L;O'Conner, P;Cotter, PD;Hill, C, Ross, RP. Controlling *Listeria monocytogenes* in Cottage cheese through heterologous production of enterocin A by *Lactococcus lactis*. *J Appl Microbiol*. 2008 Apr;104(4):1059-66.

[218] De Vuyst, L, Leroy, F. Bacteriocins from lactic acid bacteria: production, purification, and food applications. *J. Mol Microbiol Biotechnol*. 2007;13(4):194-9.

[219] Salvucci, E;Hebert, EM;Sesma, F, Saavedra, L. Combined effect of synthetic enterocin CRL35 with cell wall, membrane-acting antibiotics and muranolytic enzymes against *Listeria* cells. *Lett Appl. Microbiol*. Aug;51(2):191-5.

[220] Minahk, CJ;Dupuy, F, Morero, RD. Enhancement of antibiotic activity by sub-lethal concentrations of enterocin CRL35. *J Antimicrob Chemother*. 2004 Feb;53(2):240-6.

[221] Ingham, A;Ford, M;Moore, RJ, Tizard, M. The bacteriocin piscicolin 126 retains antilisterial activity *in vivo*. *J Antimicrob Chemother*. 2003 Jun;51(6):1365-71.

[222] Gardiner, GE;Rea, MC;O'Riordan, B;O'Connor, P;Morgan, SM;Lawlor, PG, et al. Fate of the two-component lantibiotic lacticin 3147 in the gastrointestinal tract. *Appl Environ Microbiol*. 2007 Nov;73(21):7103-9.

[223] Corr, SC;Li, Y;Riedel, CU;O'Toole, PW;Hill, C, Gahan, CG. Bacteriocin production as a mechanism for the antiinfective activity of Lactobacillus salivarius UCC118. *Proc Natl Acad Sci U S A*. 2007 May 1;104(18):7617-21.

[224] Bernbom, N;Licht, TR;Saadbye, P;Vogensen, FK, Norrung, B. Lactobacillus plantarum inhibits growth of *Listeria monocytogenes* in an in vitro continuous flow gut model, but promotes invasion of L. monocytogenes in the gut of gnotobiotic rats. *Int J. Food Microbiol*. 2006 Apr 15;108(1):10-4.

In: Listeria Infections   ISBN: 978-1-62081-639-4
Editors: A. Romano and C. F. Giordano   © 2012 Nova Science Publishers, Inc.

Chapter IV

Sublethal Damage in *Listeria monocytogenes* after Non-Thermal Treatments, and Implications for Food Safety

A. Silva[1], C. M. Belda-Galbis[2], S. F. Zanini[3],
D. Rodrigo[2], P. Martorell[1], and A. Martínez[2]

[1]Departamento de Biotecnología Agroalimentaria,
BIOPOLIS S.L., Valencia, Spain
[2]Departamento de Conservación y Calidad,
Instituto de Agroquímica y Tecnología de los Alimentos (IATA-CSIC),
Valencia, Spain
[3]Universidade Federal do Espirito Santo, Brazil

Abstract

The presence of microorganisms in foods during production, packaging, transport and storage is unavoidable. Since January 2005, Regulation 178/2002/EC or General Food Law requires the traceability of the food chain in all its stages (EU, 2002). This directive will enforce the introduction of security mechanisms and controls for foodstuffs. One of the microorganisms of concern, mainly for ready-to-eat foods, is *Listeria monocytogenes*. Between 2002 and 2006 there was a significant increase in reported cases of human listeriosis in Member States of the European Union (EU) (EFSA, 2007). In 2007 there were 1,639 reported cases, of which 1,635 were subsequently confirmed, in 29 countries. The rate of global reporting was 0.35 cases per 100,000 inhabitants. The proportion of samples exceeding the legal limit for *Listeria monocytogenes* in Member States was higher in ready-to-eat foods based on fish, followed by meat products and cheeses (EFSA and ECDC, 2011). Consequently, knowledge of microbial inactivation and growth behavior is very important for food safety and shelf-life assessment. Important aspects that should be considered as emerging risks are the changes that could take place after sublethal injury, i.e., changes in virulence. This review aims to evaluate

Listeria monocytogenes inactivation and growth in foodstuffs by simulating the supply chain in order to verify the relation existing between the various treatments that could be used by the industry to increase product lifetime without risk to consumers and sublethal damage.

Introduction

Listeria monocytogenes is a microorganism that has become one of the main pathogenic agents transmitted by foods. It is considered an opportunistic pathogen associated with mortality rates of 20–30% (Mead *et al.*, 1999; FAO/WHO, 2004). All strains of this species are considered pathogenic, although their virulence varies according to the susceptibility of the individuals infected.

The highest risk groups in the population are pregnant women, people over 65, infants (up to 4 weeks), and immunocompromised people (transplant patients, patients with leukemia, HIV carriers, dialysis patients, cancer patients, and those suffering from liver disease, diabetes, and alcoholism).

Between 1995 and 2009, 11 outbreaks of listeriosis associated with cheese consumption were identified all over the world. 545 people were affected, with estimated mortality rates between 14% and 30% and hospitalizations up to 100%. In the European Union (EU), between 2002 and 2006 there was a significant increase in reported cases of human listeriosis (EFSA, 2007). This trend continued until 2007, according to "The Community Summary Report on Trends and Sources of Zoonoses, Zoonotic Agents in the European Union" (EFSA, 2011). From 2004 to 2008, rates were estimated at 0.3 cases per 100,000 inhabitants, which is higher than the rate reported in previous years (0.17 per 100,000 inhabitants) (EC, 2002; Garvey and McKeown, 2004). In 2007, the highest number of cases was found among people over 65 (53.1%), at an estimated rate of 1 case/100,000 inhabitants, and among children under 5 (0.51 cases/100,000 inhabitants).

L. monocytogenes has some unique distinctive properties (FSAI, 2005; Luber *et al.*, 2011). Seeliger and Jones (1986) described *L. monocytogenes* as a bacterium that grows at temperatures between 1 °C and 45 °C. More recently, it has been assumed that this bacterium can grow at a minimum temperature between −0.4 °C and 0 °C in sterile food rich in nutrients and with neutral pH (ICMSF, 1996). Its ability to grow at cooling temperatures is particularly important since it can reproduce and reach critical levels in food stored at low temperatures. Several studies have been made in relation to the behavior of bacteria in various foods and under various storage conditions and they show that the bacterium not only survives but can increase its concentration in the product between 0.5 to 3.0-log during storage under refrigeration (Ikeda *et al.*, 2003). This allows it to remain viable inside or on the surface of foods that are stored at low temperatures.

L. monocytogenes is widespread throughout the environment, and is frequently found in food processing plants, contaminating surfaces in contact with food products and the products themselves. Thus, *L. monocytogenes* represents a major concern for both food business operators and regulatory agencies. It has been involved in sporadic cases following consumption of milk and milk-based products (cheese), meat, and vegetables. Currently, however, ready-to-eat foods (RTE foods) that are intended for direct human consumption without receiving any heat treatment during production, that support *L. monocytogenes* growth, and that may become contaminated by the factory environment are the major concern for regulatory authorities and the industry (EU, 2008), because they seem to be the kind of foods that contribute most to outbreaks of listeriosis. RTE foods are considered a heterogeneous group of foods with variations from country to country, depending on habits, cold chain availability, and current regulations that determine marketing temperature (FAO/WHO, 2004). Consequently, it is crucial that manufacturers of foods take appropriate measures to control both contamination by *L. monocytogenes* and its growth in a product until the end of its shelf-life. Accordingly, they need to have access to information and documents regarding the potential growth and inactivation of this microorganism in a particular food, which they should take into account when calculating a product's shelf-life (EU, 2008).

Effect of Treatments on *Listeria monocytogenes*

Measures for Reducing *Listeria monocytogenes* in Foods

Controlling concentration and growth of *L. monocytogenes* is an important challenge for food business operators because it is a ubiquitous, psychrotrophic, facultative anaerobic bacterium that grows in really hostile environments (Codex Alimentarius Commission, 2002; Gandhi and Chikindas, 2007; Mosqueda-Melgar *et al.*, 2008) and that forms biofilms on all the materials commonly used in industry (Møretrø and Langsrud, 2004; Zhu *et al.*, 2005).

In order to obtain safe, high-quality foods it is necessary to promote the monitoring of raw materials, the application of effective standardized cleaning and disinfection programs, the implementation of HACCP systems, and the use of preservation techniques that guarantee safety and quality, keeping market requirements in mind.

To reduce colonization, transmission, and cross-contamination by *L. monocytogenes*, the enforcement of good hygienic and manufacturing practices is crucial (Adzitey and Huda, 2010). Measures commonly applied to prevent establishment of *L. monocytogenes* on food-processing equipment include the use of chlorine-based disinfectants because of their effectiveness in removing *L. monocytogenes* biofilms (Kousta *et al.*, 2010), heat sterilization of critical areas (Autio *et al.*, 1999), and the addition of sodium benzoate to the lubricants that are used in food production machines because it prevents the spread of the microorganism (FSAI, 2005).

In any case, it is necessary to set up processing and environmental monitoring plans to verify the effectiveness of the preventive, corrective, and control measures applied. These plans must be specified in the company's HACCP program (Huss *et al.*, 2000; Adzitey and Huda, 2010), and must include analyses of samples taken from walls, floors, drains, cold rooms, processing equipment, raw materials, and processed foods to determine the source of contamination and prevent transmission if the presence of the pathogen is detected.

Nevertheless, total elimination of *L. monocytogenes* from the processing environment is impossible, and post-processing contamination is always more than likely (Huss *et al.*, 2000). Therefore foods should be submitted to treatments that guarantee their safety. Until now, the use of chemical preservatives, thermal processing, and/or refrigeration have been the main technologies used by the food industry to obtain microbiologically safe foods. In response to consumer demand for fresh, natural, minimally processed products (Raso and Barbosa-

Cánovas, 2003; Burt, 2004), nowadays foods are pasteurized or subjected to non-thermal treatments and stored at low temperatures because it is well known that *L. monocytogenes* growth depends strongly on temperature. It is able to grow under refrigeration conditions, but, as temperature decreases, the time needed for adaptation to the environment increases and the growth rate decreases, even though the reduction in temperature is small and the incubation temperature is close to the optimum (Belda-Galbis *et al.*, 2011).

Among non-thermal technologies that can be used to reduce the presence of pathogens on foods, high hydrostatic pressure (HHP) and the application of pulsed electric fields (PEF) stand out because they are both able to inactivate vegetative cells without altering product properties (Barbosa-Cánovas *et al.*, 2005 – cited by Saldaña *et al.*, 2010; Raso and Heinz, 2006 – cited by Saldaña *et al.*, 2010; Pina-Pérez *et al.*, 2009b). Their efficiency depends on treatment intensity, exposure time, temperature, pH, water activity, the composition of the media in which the bacteria are growing, and even on the type of microorganism at strain level (Alpas *et al.*, 1999; Saldaña *et al.*, 2010).

Both technologies have shown their effectiveness against *L. monocytogenes*. With HHP, Alpas *et al.* (1999) achieved a 5-log cycle reduction of *L. monocytogenes* in phosphate buffer, subjecting the samples to 375 MPa for 15 minutes. Higher reductions have been observed in food matrices. Chen and Hoover (2003) achieved more than an 8-log cycle reduction by subjecting inoculated milk samples to 500 MPa for 5 minutes. Working with PEF, Sepulveda *et al.* (2005) achieved a 6-log cycle reduction in buffered solution. The same result was achieved by McDonald *et al.* (2000) after subjecting inoculated orange juice samples to 6 pulses of 30 kV/cm, with a treatment time of 12 µs. Even so, the use of HHP as the sole post-processing treatment is not advisable if the consumer wants the food to retain its original properties, and it does not achieve reductions of 5 or more log cycles when applied on foods at intensities that do not alter product characteristics, keeping treatment temperature near or below ambient temperature (Carlez *et al.*, 1993; Ponce *et al.*, 1997; Simpson and Gilmour, 1997; Reina *et al.*, 1998; Fleischman *et al.*, 2004; Saldaña *et al.*, 2010). The best inactivation results have been obtained after subjecting samples to very long treatments, at high intensities and/or combined with mild thermal treatments. These processing conditions can cause undesirable effects on foods (Chen and Hoover, 2003; Tiwari *et al.*, 2009). An alternative is to combine these non-thermal technologies with natural ingredients that have bacteriostatic and/or bactericidal properties, because they can improve the effectiveness of these non-thermal processing techniques and prevent or modify bacterial growth if some cells remain viable in food after it is processed or if post-processing contamination occurs, maintaining or improving product characteristics and shelf-life (Aymerich *et al.*, 2005; Nguyen and Mittal, 2007; Ferrer *et al.*, 2009; Pina-Pérez *et al.*, 2009a; Pina-Pérez *et al.*, 2009b; Belda-Galbis *et al.*, 2010; Espinosa *et al.*, 2010; Belda-Galbis *et al.*, 2011).

Numerous studies have shown that there are many substances derived from plants, animals, and microorganisms with bactericidal or bacteriostatic effects on *L. monocytogenes*. Cranberry extracts and concentrates have been reported to be effective inhibitors for *L. monocytogenes in vitro* as well as in ground meat (Apostolidis *et al.*, 2008). Egg white lysozyme can also kill it and/or prevent its growth in cabbage, lettuce, corn, green beans, carrots, and cheese (Hughey *et al.*, 1989). The bacteriocin nisin, produced by certain *Lactococcus lactis* strains, inactivates *L. monocytogenes* in milk, meat, and poultry products, alone or combined with other substances of natural origin (Sivarooban *et al.*, 2007; Kim *et al.*, 2008a; Ruiz *et al.*, 2009; Ruiz *et al.*, 2010; Mohamed *et al.*, 2011).

Recently, we have shown that very low doses of carvacrol and citral can modify *L. monocytogenes* growth at low temperatures, even though the bacterium is growing at optimum temperature (Figure 1) (Belda-Galbis *et al.*, 2011).

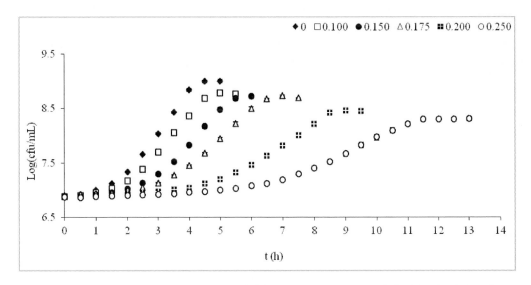

Figure 1. *L. innocua* growth in the presence of different concentrations of citral (μL/mL) in reference media at 37 °C. The variation coefficient is expressed by error bars.

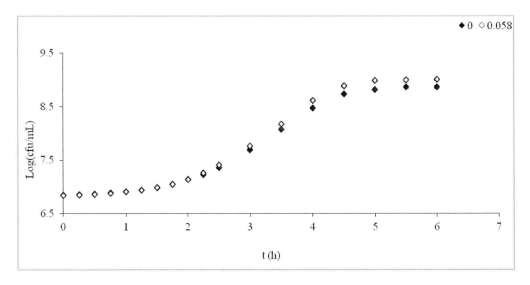

Figure 2. *L. innocua* growth in the presence of 0 and 0.058 mg/mL of lysozyme and lactoferrin (1:1) at 37 °C. The variation coefficient is expressed by error bars.

All of these results show that at least certain natural substances can be used alone, mixed, and/or combined with non-thermal technologies in order to obtain healthy, tasty, nutritious, safe foodstuffs in which the presence and growth of *L. monocytogenes* can be controlled.

Nevertheless, it is necessary to take into account that the effectiveness of any agent must be scientifically proven, since there are antimicrobial compounds that have no effect on

L. monocytogenes viability and growth, and its bacteriostatic or bactericidal activity can be influenced by the chemical composition and physical conditions of foods.

Together with researchers of Nofima, the Norwegian Institute of Food, Fisheries, and Aquaculture Research, we observed that, in the presence of lysozyme and lactoferrin (1:1), *L. innocua*, used as a non-pathogenic surrogate of *L. monocytogenes*, grows as well as or better than in their absence (Figures 2 and 3), although the combination of these two substances has bactericidal and bacteriostatic effects on many bacteria.

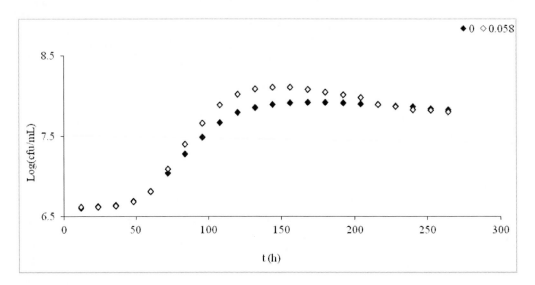

Figure 3. *L. innocua* growth in the presence of 0 and 0.058 mg/mL of lysozyme and lactoferrin (1:1) at 8 °C. The variation coefficient is expressed by error bars.

When considering the practical application of these compounds, it is also necessary to bear in mind the costs derived from obtaining them and adding them to foods or containers, their effect on the product's sensorial characteristics, their impact on its final price, and, especially, whether they are generally recognized as safe (GRAS), whether they can be used as additives, and whether the concentration that is needed to control *L. monocytogenes* exceeds the maximum permitted dose.

Sublethal Damage in *Listeria monocytogenes* after being Treated by Mild Technologies

Mild preservation treatments can produce a huge amount of damaged cells that may repair their injuries during the storage period. Consequently, sublethal injury is an important aspect that should be considered when evaluating the effectiveness of any food preservation method, because the presence of injured bacterial cells could place the food at risk. Under favorable conditions, injured cells can proliferate once their recovery has been completed. Studies have shown that sublethally injured pathogens could proliferate to microbiologically hazardous levels during the sprouting process where water and nutrients are plentiful (Busch and Donelly, 1992; Ariefdjohan *et al.*, 2004).

As indicated earlier, the use of natural antimicrobials is now gaining interest, but, as with non-thermal or mild thermal technologies, sublethal damage can be produced when they are used at sublethal concentrations or conditions. This situation can pose a risk to the consumer because changes that modify the behavior of microorganisms can occur during the repair process.

Studies conducted in our laboratory, working with 10^6 cfu/mL of *L. monocytogenes*, indicated that the lag phase duration (λ) and the maximum growth rate (μ_{max}) depend on the citral and carvacrol concentration ($p < 0.05$).

As the concentration of citral increased from 0.150 µL/mL to 0.250 µL/mL, we observed an increase in λ of 1.13 hours and a decrease in μ_{max} of 1.42 log(cfu/mL)/h ($p < 0.05$). This behavior was also reflected in the percentage of injured cells when treated *L. monocytogenes* was grown in a selective medium containing 5% of sodium chloride (Figures 4 and 5). Sublethal damage was observed in 20–25% of the cells after being treated by citral. Other authors have also shown the effect of citral on *E. coli*, *E. coli* O157:H7, and *S. typhimurium* (Kim *et al.*, 1995).

For carvacrol, the results obtained showed that, when the concentration of carvacrol increased from 0.100 µL/mL to 0.175 µL/mL, λ increased by 2.90 hours, whereas μ_{max} decreased by 0.13 log(cfu/mL)/h ($p < 0.05$). As in the case of citral, the contact of cells with carvacrol affected the percentage of injured cells, using 5% sodium chloride as selective medium (Figures 6 and 7). The percentage of damage by carvacrol that was observed ranged between 18 and 22% of the cells. Carvacrol has been found to possess *in vitro* antimicrobial activity against a broad spectrum of Gram-positive bacteria, including *L. monocytogenes* (Gaysinsky *et al.*, 2005; Di Pasqua *et al.*, 2006; Gill and Holley, 2006). Faleiro *et al.* (2005) reported that the minimum inhibitory concentration (MIC) of carvacrol ranged from 0.05 to 0.15 µL/mL and the minimum bactericidal concentration (MBC) was 0.25 µL/mL for *L. monocytogenes*. According to the reports of Shintani (2006), in the presence of injured cells there is an increase in λ in comparison with uninjured cells.

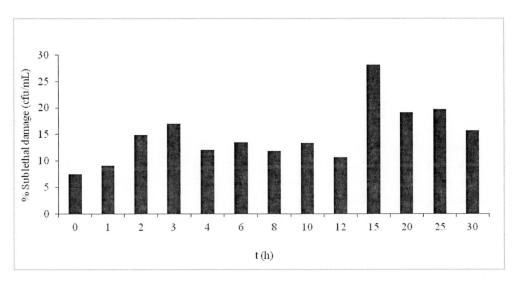

Figure 4. *L. monocytogenes* sublethal damage (cfu/mL) in the presence of a citral concentration of 0.150 µL/mL, with $N_0 = 10^6$ log(cfu/mL).

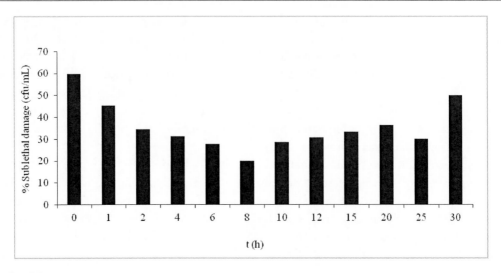

Figure 5. L. monocytogenes sublethal damage (cfu/mL) in the presence of a citral concentration of 0.250 µL/mL, with $N_0 = 10^6$ log(cfu/mL).

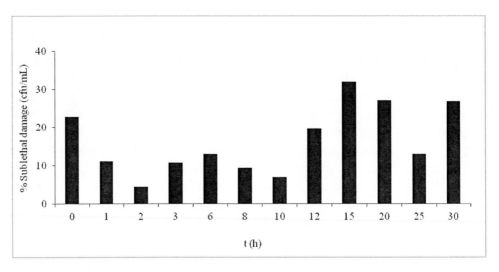

Figure 6. *L. monocytogenes* sublethal damage (cfu/mL) in the presence of a carvacrol concentration of 0.100 µL/mL, with $N_0 = 10^6$ log(cfu/mL).

This extension is required to repair the damage and synthesis of proteins and nucleic acids, necessary for the multiplication of microorganisms. Injury to pathogens eliminates their ability to cause disease, but once the cells are repaired pathogenicity is totally restored (Meyer and Donnelly, 1992).

Sublethal Injury and Changes in Virulence of Pathogens Surviving the Presence of the Antimicrobial Substances

During the repair process, sublethally damaged microorganisms can acquire new abilities and modify existing ones. This section describes an example of the effect produced when antimicrobial substances are used. Changes have been described in microbes resulting from repairs to damage (Busch and Donelly, 1992; Ariefdjohan *et al.*, 2004). They can be studied in various ways.

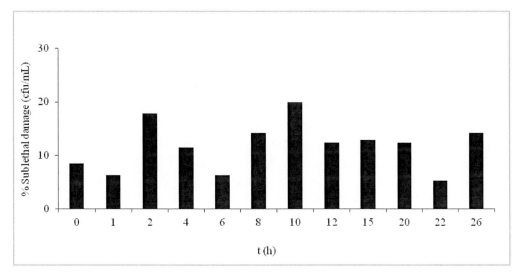

Figure 7. L. monocytogenes sublethal damage (cfu/mL) in the presence of a carvacrol concentration of 0.175 μL/mL, with $N_0 = 10^6$ log(cfu/mL).

In the literature there are examples where Caco-2 cells have been used to study the virulence of various microorganisms. In addition to *L. monocytogenes*, Caco-2 cells have been used to study the virulence of other pathogenic microorganisms, such as *E. coli* O157:H7 (Isumikawa *et al.*, 1998), *Campylobacter jejuni*, *Campylobacter coli* (Everest *et al.*, 1992), *Enterobacter sakazakii* (Kim and Loessner, 2008), and *Bacillus cereus* (Minnaard *et al.*, 2004). In comparison with animal models, this system can be considered as a rapid laboratory test.

Caco-2 cells were used in our laboratory in a preliminary study to assess the possible changes in the virulence of *L. monocytogenes*. The viability of the Caco-2 cells was analyzed by three different techniques: alamar blue, trypan blue exclusion, and flow cytometry.

Alamar blue is a test based on the ability of viable, metabolically active cells to reduce resazurin sodium to resorufin and dihydroresorufin, which is measurable by colorimetric methods. The data obtained after exposure to *L. innocua* and *L. monocytogenes* for 24 hours show that *Listeria* spp. are able to oxidize resazurin, giving rise to false positives. Therefore this technique cannot be used to study the virulence of *L. monocytogenes* after treatment with antimicrobials.

The trypan blue exclusion test is used to determine the number of viables, based on the principle that live cells possess intact cell membranes that exclude trypan blue, whereas dead cells do not. The data show the suitability of this technique for viability studies of Caco-2 cells exposed to *Listeria* spp. However, it is a subjective, arbitrary, and more time-consuming technique than flow cytometry, so it is only used as an auxiliary method to complete data obtained by other ways, such as the Annexin-FITC/IP double staining method.

Annexin V/PI double staining can be used to distinguish between viable [Annexin(−), PI(−)], necrotic [Annexin(−), PI(+)], and apoptotic cells [early: Annexin(+), PI(−); late:

Annexin(+), PI(+)]. Annexin V is a member of the family of calcium and phospholipid binding proteins with a high affinity for phosphatidylserine. The data obtained with this technique show that after 24 hours of exposure there were no significant differences between treatments with *L. innocua* and *L. monocytogenes*, with ratios of viability, apoptosis, and necrosis similar to those obtained in untreated samples. These results corroborate the findings of Pine *et al.* (1991), who indicated that Caco-2 virulence tests for *L. monocytogenes* may not reflect its relative virulence as determined by its mouse LD_{50}. Consequently, efforts have been made recently to find easier model systems to study the virulence of pathogenic microorganisms.

More recently, a new study model has appeared, based on *Caenorhabditis elegans*, which has shown its potential for conducting studies of this kind (Thomsen *et al.*, 2006; Forrester *et al.*, 2007). Previous works have demonstrated that many mammalian pathogenic bacteria and fungi can infect and cause disease in simple non-vertebrate hosts, such as *C. elegans* (Anderson *et al.*, 2006). *C. elegans* is a simple and economic invertebrate animal model that is increasingly used for the study of mechanisms of microbial pathogenesis, requiring very inexpensive, simple growth conditions because it grows on a layer of bacteria in an agar plate (Diard *et al.*, 2007). *C. elegans* provides the opportunity simultaneously to explore pathogen virulence and host defense, and to identify novel pathogen-encoded virulence factors and universal virulence factors that are relevant in mammalian pathogenesis and specialized human pathogens (Garsin *et al.*, 2001; Aballay and Ausubel, 2002; Ewbank, 2002; Costi *et al.*, 2005; Thomsen *et al.*, 2006; Forrester *et al.*, 2007; Jensen *et al.*, 2008b).

Various parameters can be studied using the nematode as a model: life span, egg laying, mobility, pharyngeal pumping rate, chemotaxis, and the production of new phenotypes. In our laboratory we studied life span, egg laying, mobility, food choice, and the production of new phenotypes. A preliminary study was conducted with *L. innocua* and *L. monocytogenes*, trying to find a parameter that would accurately account for the possible virulence changes that could take place in *Listeria* spp. after sublethal damage (Silva-Angulo *et al.*, 2011). In these investigations, *C. elegans* was used as a model to study sublethal damage and possible changes in virulence as a consequence of exposure of *L. monocytogenes* and *L. innocua* to various concentrations of carvacrol and citral. The percentage of sublethal damage produced after each treatment was determined in relation to antimicrobial concentration and exposure time. The percentage was calculated by the following equation (Busch and Donelly, 1992; Dykes, 1999):

[1 − (count on TSA-YE-NaCl/count on TSA)]*100

where TSA is the non-selective medium and TSA-YE-NaCl is the selective one.

The results obtained indicated that when *C. elegans* fed on a lawn of *L. monocytogenes* and *L. innocua* the mobility of the worm was reduced in both cases as compared with *E. coli* OP50 as negative control. The "bag of worms" phenotype was also observed when the worm was fed with *L. monocytogenes* and *L. innocua*, respectively. This phenotype was also observed by Thomsen *et al.* (2006) in *L. monocytogenes*. Both *L. innocua* and *L. mono-cytogenes* produced a reduction in egg-laying as compared with OP50. However, this effect was higher in *L. monocytogenes* than in *L. innocua*. These results are promising, indicating that this nematode could be a good model to study changes of virulence linked to sublethal damage in *L. monocytogenes*.

Conclusion

Sublethal injury should be considered as an emerging risk that can affect the development of safe preservation processes when non-thermal or mild thermal technologies are used alone or combined as a "hurdle" technology. Safety issues can arise after damaged bacterial cells repair the injury and the environmental conditions allow them to grow. During the repair process they can acquire new abilities or changes in their virulence can take place. To avoid this emerging risk an in-depth validation of minimal processes should be made, focusing on the number of injured cells produced. For this validation, tests carried out using animal models such as *C. elegans* could be a very useful tool.

Acknowledgments

The sublethal damage studies carried out were charged to the AGL2010-22206-CO2-01 project, sponsored by the Spanish Ministry of Science and Innovation. The authors are grateful to the Departamento de Biotecnología Agroalimentaria, BIOPOLIS S.L for its collaboration in the studies conducted with *C. elegans*. They also wish to thank NOFIMA, the Norwegian Institute of Food Fisheries and Aquaculture Research, for its collaboration in the study of the effects of lysozyme and lactoferrin on the growth of *L. innocua*.

References

Aballay, A; Ausubel, F. *Caenorhabditis elegans* as a host for the study of host-pathogen interactions. *Host-Microbe Interactions: Bacteria* 2002, 97-101.

Adzitey, F; Huda, N. *Listeria monocytogenes* in foods: Incidences and possible control measures. *African Journal of Microbiology Research* 2010 4 25, 2848-2855.

Alpas, H; Kalchayanand, N; Bozoglu, F; Sikes, A; Dunne, CP; Ray, B. Variation in resistance to hydrostatic pressure among strains of food-borne pathogens. *Applied and Environmental Microbiology* 1999 65 9, 4248-4251.

Anderson, G; Kenney, S; Millner, P; Beuchat, L; Williams, P. Shedding of foodborne pathogens by *Caenorhabditis elegans* in compost-amended and unamended soil. *Food Microbiology* 2006 23, 146-153.

Apostolidis, E; Kwon YI; Shetty, K. Inhibition of *Listeria monocytogenes* by oregano, cranberry and sodium lactate combination in broth and cooked ground beef systems and likely mode of action through proline metabolism. *International Journal of Food Microbiology* 2008 128, 317-324.

Ariefdjohan, M; Nelson, P; Singh, R; Bhunia, K; Balasubramaniam, M; Singh, N. Efficacy of high hydrostatic pressure treatment in reducing *Escherichia coli* O157:H7 and *Listeria monocytogenes* in alfalfa seeds. *Food Microbiology and Safety* 2004 5 69, 117-120.

Autio, T; Hielm, S; Miettinen, M; Sjöberg, AM; Aarnisalo, K; Björkroth, J; Sandholm, TM; Korkeala, H. Sources of *Listeria monocytogenes* contamination in a cold-smoked rainbow trout processing plant detected by pulsed-field gel electrophoresis typing. *Applied Environmental Microbiology* 1999 65, 150-155.

Aymerich, T; Jofré, A; Garriga, M; Hugas, M. Inhibition of *Listeria monocytogenes* and *Salmonella* by natural antimicrobials and high hydrostatic pressure in sliced cooked ham. *Journal of Food Protection* 2005 68 1, 173-177.

Belda-Galbis, CM; Martínez, A; Rodrigo, D. Antimicrobial effect of carvacrol on *Escherichia coli* K12 growth at different temperatures. In: Mendez-Vilas A, editor. *Science and Technology Against Microbial Pathogens: Research, Development and Evaluation. Proceedings of the International Conference on Antimicrobial Research (ICAR2010)*. Singapore: World Scientific Publishing; 2010; 80-84.

Belda-Galbis, CM; Martínez, A; Rodrigo, D. Seguridad032C: Evaluación *in vitro* de la actividad antimicrobiana del citral sobre *Listeria innocua* a distintas temperaturas. In: *Proceedings of the VI Congreso Nacional de Ciencia y Tecnología de los Alimentos*. Spain; Universitat Politècnica de València; 2011.

Burt S. Essential oils: Their antibacterial properties and potential applications in food - A review. *International Journal of Food Microbiology* 2004 94, 223-253.

Busch, S; Donnelly, C. Development of a repair-enrichment broth for resuscitation of heat-injured *Listeria monocytogenes* and *Listeria innocua*. *Applied and Environmental Microbiology* 1992 1 58, 14-20.

Carlez, A; Rosec, JP; Richard, N; Cheftel, J. High pressure inactivation of *Citrobacter freundii*, *Pseudomonas fluorescens* and *Listeria innocua* in inoculated minced beef. *Lebensmittel-Wissenschaft & Technologie* 1993 26, 48-54.

Chen, H; Hoover, DG. Modeling the combined effect of high hydrostatic pressure and mild heat on the inactivation kinetics of *Listeria monocytogenes* Scott A in whole milk. *Innovative Food Science and Emerging Technologies* 2003 4, 25-34.

Codex Alimentarius Commission. Proposed draft guidelines for the control of *Listeria monocytogenes* in foods. Report nr. CX/FH 03//8. USA 2002.

Costi, S; Begun, J; Ausubel, F. Review: The worm has turned – microbial virulence modeled in *Caenorhabditis elegans*. *Trends in Microbiology* 2005 3 13, 119-127.

Di Pasqua, R; Hoskins, N; Betts, G; Mauriello, G. Changes in membrane fatty acids composition of microbial cells induced by addiction of thymol, carvacrol, limonene, cinnamaldehyde and eugenol in the growing media. *Journal of Agricultural and Food Chemistry* 2006 54, 2745-2749.

Diard, M; Baeriswyl, S; Clermont, O; Gouriou, S; Picard, B; Taddei, F; Denamur, E; Matic, I. *Caenorhabditis elegans* as a simple model to study phenotypic and genetic virulence determinants of extraintestinal pathogenic *Escherichia coli*. *Microbes and Infection* 2007 9, 214-223.

Dykes, G. Physical and metabolic causes of sub-lethal damage in *Listeria monocytogenes* after long-term chilled storage at 4 °C. *Journal of Applied Microbiology* 1999 87, 915-922.

EC [European Commission]. Report on trends and sources of zoonotic agents in the European Union and Norway. Health and Consumer Protection Directorate-General 2002.

EFSA [European Food Safety Authority]. Request for updating the former SCVPH opinion on *Listeria monocytogenes* risk related to ready-to-eat foods and scientific advice on different levels of *Listeria monocytogenes* in ready-to-eat foods and the related risk for human illness. *The EFSA Journal* 2007 599, 1-42.

EFSA [European Food Safety Authority]; ECDC [European Centre for Disease Prevention and Control]. The European Union summary report on trends and sources of zoonoses, zoonotic agents and food-borne outbreaks in 2009. EFSA Journal 2011 9 3, 2090.

Espinosa, J; Marco, A; Rodrigo, D; Martínez, A. Antimicrobial activity of *Stevia rebaudiana*. In: Fito P; Toldrá F, editors. *International Conference on Food Innovation – FoodInnova 2010: Book of Abstracts.* Spain: Universitat Politècnica de València; 2010; 237-237.

EU [European Union]. Regulation (EC) No 178/2002 of the European Parliament and of the Council of 28 January 2002 laying down the general principles and requirements of food law, establishing the European Food Safety Authority and laying down procedures in matters of food safety 2002.

EU [European Union]. Guidance document on *Listeria monocytogenes* shelf-life studies for ready-to-eat foods, under Regulation (EC) No 2073/2005 of 15 November 2005 on microbiological criteria for foodstuffs 2008. Available on: http://ec.europa.eu/food /food/biosafety/salmonella/docs/guidoc_listeria_monocytogenes_en.pdf   [Accessed: January 21, 2012].

Everest, P; Goossens, H; Butzler, J; Lloyd, D; Knutton, S; Ketley, J; Williams, P. Differentiated Caco-2 cells as a model for enteric invasion by *Campylobacter jejuni* and *C. coli. Journal of Medical Microbiology* 1992 37, 319-325.

Ewbank, J. Tackling both sides of the host-pathogen equation with *Caenorhabditis elegans. Microbes and Infection* 2002 4, 247-256.

Faleiro, L; Miguel, G; Gomes, S; Costa, L; Venâncio, F; Teixeira, A; Figueiredo, AC; Barroso, JG; Pedro, LG. Antibacterial and antioxidant activities of essential oils isolated from *Thymbra capitata* L. (Cav.) and *Origanum vulgare* L. *Journal of Agricultural and Food Chemistry* 2005 53, 8162-8168.

FAO/WHO [Agriculture Organization of the United Nation/World Health Organization]. Risk assessment of *Listeria monocytogenes* in ready-to-eat foods. Technical report. Microbiological risk assessment series 5. Rome, Italy 2004,269.

Ferrer, C; Ramón, D; Muguerza, B; Marco, A; Martínez, A. Effect of olive powder on the growth and inhibition of *Bacillus cereus. Foodborne Pathogens and Disease* 2009 6 1, 33-37.

Fleischman, GJ; Ravishankar, S; Balasubramaniam, VM. The inactivation of *Listeria monocytogenes* by pulsed electric field (PEF) treatment in a static chamber. *Food Microbiology* 2004 21, 91-95.

Forrester, S; Milillo, S; Hoose, W; Wiedmann, M; Schwab, U. Evaluation of the pathogenicity of *Listeria* spp. in *Caenorhabditis elegans. Foodborne Pathogens and Disease* 2007 1 4, 67- 73.

FSAI [Food Safety Authority of Ireland]. General pathogen control for food processing. In: *The control and management of Listeria monocytogenes contamination of food.* Dublin: Food Safety Authority of Ireland; 2005; 11-21. ISBN: 1-904465-29-3.

Gandhi, M; Chikindas, ML. *Listeria*: A foodborne pathogen that knows how to survive. *International Journal of Food Microbiology* 2007 113, 1-15.

Garsin, D; Sifri, C; Mylonakis, E; Qin, X; Singh, K, Murray, B; Calderwood, S; Ausubel, F. A simple model host for identifying Gram-positive virulence factors. *PNAS* 2001 19, 10892-10897.

Garvey, P; McKeown, P. Human listeriosis in Ireland. EPI-Insight (Disease Surveillance Report of NDSC, Ireland) 2004 5, 4.

Gaysinsky, S; Davidson, PM; Bruce, BD; Weiss, J. Growth inhibition of *E. coli* O157:H7 and *Listeria monocytogenes* by carvacrol and eugenol encapsulated in surfactant micelles. *Journal of Food Protection* 2005 68, 2559-2566.

Gill, AO; Holley, RA. Disruption of *Escherichia coli, Listeria monocytogenes* and *Lactobacillus sakei* cellular membranes by plant oil aromatics. *International Journal of Food Microbiology* 2006 108, 1-9.

Hughey, VL; Wilger, PA; Johnson, EA. Antibacterial activity of hen egg white lysozyme against *Listeria monocytogenes* Scott A in foods. *Applied and Environmental Microbiology* 1989 55 3, 631-638.

Huss, HH; Jørgensen LV; Vogel BF. Control options for *Listeria monocytogenes* in seafoods. *International Journal of Food Microbiology* 2000 62, 267-274.

ICMSF [International Commission on Microbiological Specifications for Foods]. *Microorganismos de los Alimentos: Características de los Patógenos Microbianos.* España: Acribia; 1996; 255-330.

Ikeda, JS; Samelis, J; Kendall, PA; Smith, GC; Sofos, JN. Acid adaptation does not promote survival or growth of *Listeria monocytogenes* on fresh beef following acid and nonacid decontamination treatments. *Journal of Food Protection* 2003 66, 985-992.

Isumikawa, K; Hirakata, Y; Yamaguchi, T; Takemura, H; Maesaki, S; Tomono, K; Igimi, S; Kafu, M; Yamada, Y; Kohno, S; Kamihira, S. *Escherichia coli* O157 interactions with human intestinal Caco-2 cells and the influence of fosfomycin. *Journal of Antimicrobial Chemotherapy* 1998 42, 341-347.

Jensen, A; Thomsen, L; Jorgensen, R; Larsen, M; Roldgaard, B; Christensen, B; Vogel, B; Gram, L; Ingmer, H. Processing plant persistent strains of *Listeria monocytogenes* appear to have a lower virulence potential than clinical strains in selected virulence models. *International Journal of Food Microbiology* 2008b 123, 254-261.

Kim, EL; Choi, NH; Bajpai, VK; Kang, SC. Synergistic effect of nisin and garlic shoot juice against *Listeria monocytogenes* in milk. *Food Chemistry* 2008a 110, 375-382.

Kim, JM; Marshall, MR; Cornell, JA; Preston III, IF; Wei, CI. Antibacterial activity of carvacrol, citral and geraniol against *Salmonella typhimurium* in culture medium and on fish cubes. *Journal of Food Science* 1995 60, 1364-1368.

Kim, K; Loessner, M. *Enterobacter sakazakii* invasion in human intestinal Caco-2 cells requires the host cell cytoskeleton and is enhanced by disruption of tight junction. *Infection and Immunity* 2008b 2 76, 562-570.

Kousta, M; Mataragas, M; Skandamis, P; Drosinos, EH. Prevalence and sources of cheese contamination with pathogens at farm and processing levels. *Food Control* 2010 21, 805-8015.

Luber, P; Scott, C; Christophe, D; Jeff, F; Atin, D; Ewen, CDT. Controlling *Listeria monocytogenes* in ready-to-eat foods: Working towards global scientific consensus and harmonization. Recommendations for improved prevention and control. *Food Control* 2011 22, 1535-1549.

Mead, PS; Slutsker, L; Dietz, V; McCaig, LF; Breese, JS; Shapiro, C; Griffin, PM; Tauxe, RV. Food-related illness and death in the United Stated. *Emerging Infectious Diseases* 1999 5 5, 607-625.

McDonald, CJ; Lloyd, SW; Vitale, MA; Petersson, K; Inning, F. Effects of pulsed electric fields on microorganisms in orange juice using electric field strengths of 30 and 50 kV/cm. *Journal of Food Science* 2000 65, 984-989.

Meyer, DH; Donnelly, CW. Effect of incubation temperature on repair of heat-injured *Listeria* in milk. *Journal of Food Protection* 1992 55, 579-582.

Minnaard, J; Moal, V; Coconnier, M; Servin, A; Pérez, P. Disassembly of F-Actin cytoskeleton after interaction of *Bacillus cereus* with fully differentiated human intestinal Caco-2 cells. *Infection and Immunity* 2004 5 72, 3106-3112.

Mohamed, HMH; Elnawawi, FA; Yousef, AE. Nisin treatment to enhance the efficacy of gamma radiation against *Listeria monocytogenes* on meat. *Journal of Food Protection* 2011 74 2, 193-199.

Møretrø, T; Langsrud S. *Listeria monocytogenes*: Biofilm formation and persistence in food-processing environments. *Biofilms* 2004 1 2, 107-121.

Mosqueda-Melgar, J; Elez-Martínez, P; Raybaudi-Massilia, RM; Martín-Belloso, O. Effects of pulsed electric fields on pathogenic microorganisms of major concern in fluid foods: A review. *Critical Reviews in Food Science and Nutrition* 2008 48, 747-759.

Nguyen, P; Mittal, GS. Inactivation of naturally occurring microorganisms in tomato juice using pulsed electric field (PEF) with and without antimicrobials. *Chemical Engineering and Processing* 2007 46, 360-365.

Pina-Pérez, MC; Silva-Angulo, AB; Muguerza-Marquínez, B; Rodrigo Aliaga, D; Martínez López, A. Synergistic effect of high hydrostatic pressure and natural antimicrobials on inactivation kinetics of *Bacillus cereus* in a liquid whole egg and skim milk mixed beverage. *Foodborne Pathogens and Disease* 2009b 6 6, 649-656.

Pina-Pérez, MC; Silva-Angulo, AB; Rodrigo, D; Martínez-López A. Synergistic effect of pulsed electric fields and CocoanOX 12% on the inactivation kinetics of *Bacillus cereus* in a mixed beverage of liquid whole egg and skim milk. *International Journal of Food Microbiology* 2009a 130, 196-204.

Pine, L; Kathariou, S; Quinn, F; George, V; Wenger, J; Weaver, R. Cytopathogenic effects in enterocytelike Caco-2 cells differentiate virulent from avirulent *Listeria* strains. *Journal of Clinical Microbiology* 1991 5, 990-996.

Ponce, E; Pla, R; Mon-Mur, R; Gervilla, R; Guamis, B. Inactivation of *Listeria innocua* inoculated in liquid whole egg by high hydrostatic pressure. *Journal of Food Protection* 1997 61, 119-122.

Raso, J; Barbosa-Cánovas GV. Nonthermal preservation of foods using combined processing techniques. *Critical Reviews in Food Science and Nutrition* 2003 43 3, 265-285.

Reina, LD; Jin, ZT; Zhang, QH; Yousef, AE. Inactivation of *Listeria monocytogenes* in milk by pulsed electric field. *Journal of Food Protection* 1998 61, 1203-1206.

Ruiz, A; Williams, SK; Djeri, N; Hinton Jr, A, Rodrick, GE. Nisin, rosemary, and ethylenediaminetetraacetic acid affect the growth of *Listeria monocytogenes* on ready-to-eat turkey ham stored at four degrees Celsius for sixty-three days. *Poultry Science* 2009 88, 1765-1772.

Ruiz, A; Williams, SK; Djeri, N; Hinton Jr, A, Rodrick, GE. Nisin affects the growth of *Listeria monocytogenes* on ready-to-eat turkey ham stored at four degrees Celsius for sixty-three days. *Poultry Science* 2010 89, 353-358.

Saldaña, G; Puértolas, E; Condón, S; Álvarez, I; Raso, J. Inactivation kinetics of pulsed electric field-resistant strains of *Listeria monocytogenes* and *Staphylococcus aureus* in media of different pH. *Food Microbiology* 2010 27, 550-558.

Seeliger, HPR; Jones, D. Genus Listeria Pirie. In: Sncath PHA; Mair NS; Sharpe ME; Holt JG, editors *Bergey's Manual of Systematic Bacteriology*, Baltimore: Williams and Wilkins; 1986; 1235-1245.

Sepulveda, DR; Góngora-Nieto, MM; San-Martín, MF; Barbosa-Cánovas, GV. Influence of treatment temperature on the inactivation of *Listeria innocua* by pulsed electric fields. *Lebensmittel-Wissenschaft & Technologie* 2005 38, 167-172.

Shintani, H. Importance of considering injured microorganisms in sterilization validation. *Biocontrol Science* 2006 11, 91-106.

Silva-Angulo, A; Rodrigo, M; Martínez, A; Martorell P. Studies for selecting a simple model for analyses of virulence in *Listeria monocytogenes* 2011. In: 1st CIGR Workshop Food Safety: Advances and Trends. 14th and 15th April, Dijon, France.

Simpson, RK; Gilmour, A. The resistance of *Listeria monocytogenes* to high hydrostatic pressure in foods. *Food Microbiology* 1997 14, 567-573.

Sivarooban, T; Hettiarachchy, NS; Johnson, MG. Inhibition of *Listeria monocytogenes* using nisin with grape seed extract on turkey frankfurters stored at 4 and 10°C. *Journal of Food Protection* 2007 70 4, 1017-1020.

Thomsen, L; Slutz, S; Tan, M; Ingmer, H. *Caenorhabditis elegans* is a model host for *Listeria monocytogenes*. *Applied and Environmental Microbiology* 2006 2. 72, 1700-1701.

Tiwari, BK; Valdramidis, VP; O'Donnell CP; Muthukumarappan, K; Bourke, P; Cullen, PJ. Application of natural antimicrobials for food preservation. *Journal of Agricultural and Food Chemistry* 2009 57, 5987-6000.

Zhu, M; Du, M; Cordray, J; Ahn, DU. Control of *Listeria monocytogenes* contamination in ready-to-eat meat products. *Comprehensive Reviews in Food Science and Food Safety* 2005 4, 34-42.

In: Listeria Infections
Editors: A. Romano and C. F. Giordano

ISBN: 978-1-62081-639-4
© 2012 Nova Science Publishers, Inc.

Chapter V

Listeria Infections Review: Epidemiology, Pathogenesis and Treatment

Karina Pellicer

Facultad de Ciencias Veterinarias, Universidad Nacional de La Plata,
La Plata; Provincia de Buenos Aires, República Argentina

Listeria monocytogenes is a pathogen that affects animals and human beings; it can produce potentially fatal infections in susceptible individuals. This bacterium can cause miscarriages in pregnant women and meningitis in newborns, children and adults who are immunosuppressed. Most cases of Listeriosis are sporadic; although outbreaks have been described due to food consumption. The ability of *L. monocytogenes* to resist stressful enviro-nmental conditions makes this pathogen a food industry concern.

Listeria monocytogenes

The genus Listeria includes short rods, with an average of 0.4-0.5 μm in diameter and 0.5 to 2 μm in length, gram positives, which do not produce spores. Cells occur singly, or arranged in short chains with each other forming a "V" or in groups arranged in parallel along an axis (Seeliger and Jones, 1986).

Listeria spp. does not form a capsule (Seeliger and Jones, 1986). It is motile by means of 2-3 peritrichous flagella (rarely more than 5 by the usual techniques of color) and does best at 20-25°C in semisolid media where it develops 3-5 mm below the surface in the form of inverted umbrella. At 37 °C it loses mobility because it does not develop flagella.

Listeria is catalase positive, oxidase negative. It is aerobic or facultatively anaerobic; physocrotrophic and regarded as mesophilic, it can also develop at refrigeration temperature. Its optimum temperature for development is between 30 to 37°C. According to the Manual of Sistematic Bacteriology Bergey, *L. monocytogenes* develops in the pH range of 6 to 9.

Generally considered that low pH is inhibitory and even lethal to the bacteria, it is however indicated that it tolerates acidity to pH 4.4 (Pellicer *et al.*, 2009; Giannuzzi and Zaritzky, 1996; Buchanan and Klawitter, 1990; Conner *et al.*, 1986).

There are now seven known species of Listeria, including *L. monocytogenes*, *L. innocua*, *L. seeligeri*, *L. welshimeri*, *L. ivanovii* who have between them a closer relationship than there are with *L. grayi* and *L. murrayi*.

The genus Listeria contains beta-hemolytic species. *L. monocytogenes* is beta hemolytic, while *L. ivanovii* produce a large area or multiples areas of hemolysis on blood agar. If the reaction is weak or inconclusive betahemolysis can be solved by CAMP test (Christie, Atkins, Munch-Petersen in Lovett 1988) which relies on the enhancement of the hemolytic activity of the metabolites of *Staphylococcus aureus* and *Rhodococcus equi* in blood agar plate (Lovett, 1988).

On nutrient agar colonies are 0.5 to 1.5 mm in diameter, round, translucent, low convex and net margins. They are gray with a bluish and greenish blue glow with obliquely transmitted light. The newly isolated strains show colonies circular, smooth ("S" shape), white with a shiny surface.

Listeria spp. possesses somatic (O) and flagellar (H) antigens, which allow their classification into serotypes, the main pathogenic species, *L. monocytogenes* is classified into 13 serotypes: 1/2a, 1/2b, 1/2c, 3a, 3b, 3c, 4a, 4ab, 4b, 4c, 4d, 4e, 7 (Seeliger and Höhne, 1979), which are all producers of Listeriosis. Most human isolates correspond to serotypes 4b, 1/2a and 1/2b. As for the food-borne isolates, they are also the most frequent.

Listeriosis

Listeria monocytogenes

Since the early 1980s, foodborne transmission has been recognized as a major source of human Listeriosis. Listeriosis can cause stillbirths, miscarriages, meningitis, or sepsis in immunocompromised hosts. Case-fatality rates as high as 40% have been reported during outbreaks (Scuchat, Swaminatan and Broome, 1991).

Listeria monocytogenes is a pathogen which causes miscarriages (Smith *et al.*, 1995) and mastitis (Gitter *et al.*, 1980) in animals whereas in human beings, it can produce potentially fatal infections in susceptible individuals. This bacterium can cause miscarriages in pregnant women and meningitis in newborns, children and adults who are immunosuppressed (Donelly, 1994; Seeliger, 1961).

Human Listeriosis can occur as epidemics or as sporadic cases, and is primarily an opportunistic infection primarily affecting pregnant women, newborns, elderly and immunocompromised adults, including the HIV-infected.

L. monocytogenes infections in healthy adults are usually asymptomatic or in some cases produce symptoms similar to influenza infection. In other cases, less common, is presented with diarrhea and abdominal discomfort. In fact, *L. monocytogenes* is transported in the gastrointestinal tract of 5 to 10 % of asymptomatic population.

L. monocytogenes is one of the few bacteria that can cross the placenta, which acts as an effective barrier to prevent seepage of pathogen infection of the fetus via the bloodstream. In pregnant women who get Listeriosis, the bacteria can (not always) infect the fetus resulting in stillborns, premature births or birth of infants with systemic infection by *L. monocytogenes* (Saylers and Whitt, 2005; Smith *et al.,* 2009). Neonatal Listeriosis could be septicemic, also known as early-onset disease (less than 5 days old) due to transplacental infection, or appear mainly as meningitis after 5 days of age (late-onset disease) due to infection during birth or immediately before birth. Some infections may be the result of acquisition of the organism during passage through the birth canal, although late-onset disease can occur following cesarean delivery. However, several nosocomial clusters of neonatal Listeriosis have been reported (Schuchart, Swaminathan and Broome, 1991).

Most cases of Listeriosis are often associated with meningitis (80 % of cases) or septicemia. A great majority of affected individuals have some form of immunodeficiency such as cancer, alcoholism, diabetes, transplantation, chronic hemodialysis and old age.

It actually has shown a wide range of manifestations including meningoencephalitis, septicemia, pneumonia, endocarditis, localized abscesses, skin lesions, conjunctivitis, osteitis, endocarditis, arthritis, cholangitis, conjunctivitis, etc. (ANLIS/INEI, 1999 (Argentina's National Laboratory and Health Institutes Administration / National Institute of Infectious Diseases)).

In the era of transplantation, immunosuppression induced increased cases of *Listeria monocytogenes* meningitis in adults, especially in renal transplant patients; it could be considered an opportunistic infection of endogenous origin (ANLIS/INEI, 1999).

Listeriosis is one of the less common opportunistic infections in patients with AIDS (Acquired Immunodeficiency Syndrome), but so far it is 300 times more frequent than in the population that does not have this syndrome.

Pathogenesis

Pathogenesis of *Listeria monocytogenes* infection's was well described (Lopez *et al.*, 2006). Listeria is a facultative intracellular pathogen and uses the host's cells to survive, multiply and cause disease. To produce infection, Listeria needs to recognize that it is inside the body, activating virulence genes in response, including Hpt protein (a membrane transporter that allows the bacteria to uptake glucose phosphate, in order to nourish and multiply quickly in host tissues). *L. monocytogenes* is one of the few bacteria that can cross placenta, an effective filtration barrier to prevent fetal infection through blood circulation.

Factors that may influence whether invasive disease will occur include the virulence of the infection organism, the susceptibility of the host, and the size of the inoculum.

Listeria monocytogenes is acquired by ingestion and must find and adhere to the intestinal mucosa. In humans and animals, *Listeria monocytogenes* is a clearly invasive organism that leaves the intestine and crosses the mucosa to reach underlying tissue. *Listeria monocytogenes* infection begins with adhesion to intestinal epithelial cells surface, due to adhesion by means of a 80 kDa membrane protein called internalin as Inl A to intestinal cells (Inl B and other internalins have been identified) (Pizarro-Cerda and Cossart, 2006). Invasion of the host cell includes other proteins such as autolysins, a fibronectin-binding protein and proteins involved in later stages of the intracellular cycle such as ActA (Suarez *et al,* 2001) and listeriolysin O (LLO) (Dussurget, Pizzarro-Cerda and Cossart, 2004; Lopez *et al.*, 2006; Ramaswamy *et al.,* 2007).

In the eukariotic cell, the bacteria are phagocytized. Once in the phagosome it secretes a hemolysin called LLO that acts on the cholesterol membrane forming pores with subsequent lysis of the phagosome, giving to *L. monocytogenes* the ability to escape from the phagocytic vesicle to the host cell cytosol (Kayal and Charbit, 2006). It was proposed that the survival of *Listeria monocytogenes* in macrophages could be due to its ability to escape the phagosome before phagolysosomal fusion occurs. *Listeria monocytogenes* also produce catalase and superoxide dismutase, two enzymes that could help protect it from the oxidative burst in the phagolysosome (Salyers and Whitt, 1994). Listeria moves from phagocytic vacuoles to the cytoplasm, where replication is improved by more-favorable growth conditions.

Listeria monocytogenes produces at least two other hemolysins besides LLO, that includes the secretion of two phospholipases C that damage cell membranes by hydrolyzing membrane lipids, they are PI-PLC whose substrate is phosphatidylinositol and that might aid intracellular spread of Listeria; while PC-PLC is a lecitinase which hidrolyzes phosphatidilcholine, phosphatidilserine and phosphatidiletanolamine (Vázquez-Boland *et al.,* 1992).

Glucose acts a repressor of the virulence genes of *Listeria monocytogenes*. Glucose-1-phosphate (G1P), the precursor metabolite and primary degradation product of glycogen in mammalian cells, and it has been shown that is essential for the intracellular growth of *L. monocytogenes* (Ripio *et al.,* 1997a). In the host cell cytoplasm, *Listeria monocytogenes* multiplies rapidly. It has been estimated that the bacteria inside a host cell divide once every 50 minutes, a high rate of growth for an intracellular pathogen.

Intracellular multiplication of Listeria needs hexosaphosphate conveyor (Hpt), a counterpart of eukaryotic cell´s glucose transporter-6-phosphate (G6P) responsible for entry into the endoplasmic reticulum G6P from the cytosol (Chico-Calero *et al.,* 2002; Goetz *et al.,* 2001). This protein (Hpt) is also responsible for entry of fosfomycin inside the bacteria cell, which explains their sensitivity *in vivo* associated with resistance *in vitro* (Scortti *et al.,* 2006). At 37°C, production of flagella is much decreased, and it is likely that motility due to flagella is not important as a virulence factor. Another type of motility is clearly important for virulence, the ability of the bacteria to use host cell actin to move themselves within and between host cells. Intracellular movement of Listeria occurs by a directional assembly of actin monomers in a host cell to the poles of the bacterium, apparently a led by ActA surface protein (Suarez *et al.,* 2001). *Listeria monocytogenes* can move as rapidly as 1.5 µm/sec using this model of locomotion.

In the end, most bacteria reach the periphery of the infected cell, in contact with cell membrane, forming protuberances adjacent to the cell cytoplasmic evaginations shaped at its end containing a bacterium. These structures are invasive bacteria phagocytosed and enclosed in a double-membrane phagosome, in whose rupture lecithinase (PC-PLC) seems to play a key role. As a mechanism that allows the spread of bacteria through the host tissue without contact with the humoral effectors of the immune system, this phenomenon of direct passage from cell to cell is crucial in the pathogenesis of infection caused by *L. monocytogenes* (Cossart and Mengaud, 1989; López et al., 2006). Most Listeriosis occurs in persons with impaired cell-mediated immunity due to disease process, medications or pregnancy.

In addition, the local placental suppression of cell mediated immunity necessary to prevent maternal rejection of the placenta may contribute to susceptibility of the fetus to infection with Listeriosis (Redline and Lu, 1987; Schuchart, Swaminathan and Broome, 1991). In the same way, the depressed cell-mediated immunity, deficiencies in immuno-globulin M and complement activity associated with the neonatal state may contribute to susceptibility of this host to Listeriosis (Schuchart, Swaminathan and Broome, 1991). Most of the genes encoding virulence factors are present in all strains of *L. monocytogenes*, but there are numerous specific sequences of the major genetic groups in this species (divisions or lineages) and the different serotypes (Doumith *et al.,* 2004). Virulence genes of *L. monocytogenes* are organized into genetic units known as Pathogenicity Island, which are acquired by the bacteria by horizontal transfer mechanism, sometimes as part of a mobile genetic element, important in bacterial evolution. Many of the virulence genes are, however, clustered in the same region of the *L. monocytogenes* chromosome.

The regulatory protein PrfA is absolutely essential for the expression of virulence in Listeria (Ripio *et al.,* 1997b). The expression of the virulence regulon by PrfA is dependent on various environmental signs, including high temperature (37°C), stress conditions and modifications of components of the cell, and catabolite repression (Gray, Freitag and Boor, 2006; Sokolovic *et al.,* 1993). New virulence factors have been discovered, including new surface proteins of the type internalin, the SrtA and SrtB sortases (transpeptidases that bind to different cell wall surface proteins such as internalin), and a bile salt hidrolase (BSH) present in *L. monocytogenes*, which allows the bacteria to survive in the intestine (Dussurget, Pizarro-Cerda and Cossart, 2004; López *et al.,* 2006). In animal models infected with *L. monocytogenes,* the bacteria first appear in the macrophages and then invade hepatocytes. Most of their replication probably occurs in the liver. Because *L. monocytogenes* is an intracellular pathogen, a cell-mediated host response that kills infected cells is important for eliminating the microorganism. A failure of the host's cell-mediated response to control *L. monocytogenes* allows the bacteria to spread systematically.

Epidemiology

Listeriosis has become a serious public health problem considering that, although it presents low mortality rates depending on the susceptibility of the host, its mortality is high in inmunosupressed persons (20 to 30%) and has a long incubation period (5 days-5 weeks) (Chhabra *et al.,* 1999; Donelly, 1994). The minimum infective dose of L. monocytogenes has not been established yet (FDA Bad Bug Book) although it has been indicated that the intake of up to 100 cells does not affect the health of healthy consumers (Jay, 1994; Golnazarian *et al.,* 1989). Most the cases of Listeriosis are sporadic; though outbreaks have been described due to food consumption. The ability of *L. monocytogenes* to resist stressful environmental conditions makes this pathogen a food industry concern.

Distribution in the Environment

Listeria monocytogenes is a cosmopolitan microorganism (Welshimer and Donker-Voet, 1971). It is found in soil, water and dust. It has been isolated from a variety of domestic and wild animals. Listeria fecal excretion typically occurs in 1% of a healthy population, in 4.8 %

of refrigerated abattoir workers and in 26 % of people in contact with Listeriosis patients (Pape y Jhonson, 1986).

Listeria has been isolated from soil with a pH range from 4.8 to 7.6, while in soils with pH below 3.5 the incidence is very low (Weis and Seeliger, 1975). Plants are also a source of Listeria, intervening in many infections. *L. monocytogenes* has been isolated from soy, decomposing corn, wild grass and shrub leaves. In plant silos its incidence is high (Fenlon, 1986; Nicolett, 1986), especially those of poor quality with high pH and can resist them for 10 to 12 years (Durst, 1975). Many animal Listeriosis cases are attributed to silos as a source of infection (Fenlon, 1986; Gray, 1960; Gronstol, 1979).

Many animals can serve as host of *L. monocytogenes*. It is often associated with the intestinal tract or subclinical infections in domestically animals and humans. Farm animals are identified as germ reservoir, with a great importance in the epidemiology of Listeriosis. It can be also isolated from amphibians, fish and insects, with lower epidemiological significance.

L. monocytogenes has been isolated in water and wastewater (Watkins and Slealth, 1981; Al-Ghazali and Al-Azawi, 1986); as well as effluent poultry slaughterhouse (Watkins and Slealth, 1981).

Transmission of Listeriosis

Investigations of large outbreaks of human Listeriosis finally provided epidemiologic and laboratory support to confirm the suspicion that Listeriosis was a foodborne disease (Schuchat, Swaminathan, and Broome, 1991). It is evident that the presence of *L. monocytogenes* in foods is one of the sources of Listeriosis in humans and is a threat to Public Health. However, is difficult to assess their presence in the environment. Possible transmission routes are shown in Figure 1 (Jay, 1994).

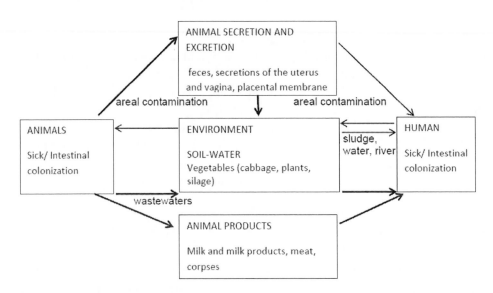

Figure 1. Schematic of the modes of spread of *Listeria monocytogenes* in the environment, animals, foods and people.

Gray and Killinger (1966) suggested that the fecal-oral route either directly or indirectly causes disease in humans and animals. The use of wastewater as fertilizer or irrigation increases the risk of transmitting Listeriosis (Watkins and Slealth, 1981).

Food handlers with latent infection of Listeria were considered a likely source of infection (Ralovich, 1974; 1984). Similarly, the presence of bacteria in the soil or decaying vegetation directly and indirectly contributes to food contamination (Gray, 1960). Soil is a natural reservoir of this organism and therefore it is more likely that vegetables are contaminated (Mitscherlich and Marth, 1984). Livestock manure can contaminate soil and this, in turn, contaminates a crop (Schlech, 1984).

L. monocytogenes has been isolated from cattle, pigs, sheep, turkeys, ducks, and a variety of other species (Seeliger, 1961; Schuchat, Swaminathan, and Broome, 1991). Because infected and sometimes healthy animals often eliminate fecal Listeria, Listeriosis was considered as zoonosis. Human disease was thought to be due to illness occurring in animals, and the animal host was considered the primary reservoir for the organism (Bojsen-Moller, 1972).The fecal-oral route favors direct transmission between humans.

The direct transmission of sick animals to humans was documented in 1961 by Seeliger.

Foods as Source of Infection

L. monocytogenes can develop at low temperatures in a wide pH range, with a high concentration of sodium chloride and reduced water activity (Kallipolitis and Higmer, 2001; Ko *et al.,* 1994). Hence, it can survive and multiply in a great variety of food products (Cole, Jones and Holyoak, 1990; Begot, Lebert and Lebert, 1997, Bergey's 1986; Copes *et al.,* 2000a; Copes *et al.,* 2000b; Monge and Arias-Echandi, 1999; Pellicer *et al.,* 2011). Listeria has been involved in a large number of food-borne outbreaks transmitted through food all over the world.

The most hazardous products are those "ready to eat" which are stored at room temperature for long periods of time (Pellicer *et al.,* 2002a; Pellicer *et al.,* 2002b). *Listeria spp.* has been found in a great variety of meats and meat products, even in sausages (Jonson, Doyle, Cassens, 1990; Encinas *et al.,* 1999).

L. monocytogenes and *L. innocua* are the most frequently isolated strains in food processing plants. However, most of the cases of listeriosis transmitted through food are due to the contamination of raw or cooked foods with *L. monocytogenes* (Cox *et. al.,* 1989; WHO, 1988). Most of the human and food-borne isolates correspond to serotypes 4b, 1/2a y 1/2b.

Treatment and Prevention

Antibiotic therapy of pregnant women or immunocompromised people who have eaten food contaminated by *L. monocytogenes* can prevent the most serious consequences of disease if it is diagnosed in time, but usually it is not diagnosed early. *Listeria monocytogenes* responds poorly to antibiotics currently used in treatment since they hardly penetrate to sites of infection, mainly the brain. This helps explain the high mortality rate of Listeriosis (20 to 30%) of hospitalized patients.

Penicillin or ampicillin, alone or in combination with gentamicin is recommended for treatment; although there have been reports of treatment failure with these antibiotics, this combination therapy is considered the treatment of choice. Although duration of treatment for Listeriosis has not been standardized, 2 weeks of therapy for uncomplicated sepsis or meningitis and 4 to 6 weeks for an immunocompromised host is recommended (Schuchart, Swaminathan and Broome, 1991). In serious diseases such as cerebritis, meningitis or gran-ulomatosis infantiseptica, early initiation of treatment is essential for infection control. In vitro studies have demonstrated the efficacy of ampicillin and penicillin with aminoglycosides. The combination of trimethoprim and sulfamethoxazole has been used successfully in patients allergic to penicillins, and is currently considered as alternative therapy in this circumstance.

Recent studies "*in vivo*" suggest that Listeria incorporates fosfomycin in the cells through Hpt protein, a membrane transporter that enables bacteria to steal glucose phosphate to feed and multiply rapidly in the tissues of animal or human hosts; which could introduce an improvement in the combined antibiotic therapy against *Listeria monocytogenes* (Scortti *et al.,* 2006).

Tests to determine if an antibiotic is active or not against one microorganism are performed in vitro, but the bacteria are in contact with living cells; Listeria lacks Hpt and thus appears as fosfomycin resistant. However, since Hpt comes into operation when the bacterium is inside cells, fosfomycin is actually effective against Listeria during infection (Universia, 2006).

The first signs of an outbreak are cases of stillbirths or serious infections in susceptible individuals. Although the most publicized cases of Listeriosis are those that involved large outbreaks, sporadic cases of Listeriosis also occur. Since Listeriosis is frequently associated with contaminated food consumption, avoiding contamination of foods in the first place would be the ideal solution. Refrigeration is not as effective in preventing growth of *L. monocytogenes* in food as it is for most other pathogens. It is easy to imagine why this germ is a food's processors nightmare, due to the fact that at least 5% to 10% of the adults are asymptomatic carriers of *L. monocytogenes*.

Moreover, prevention is also in the hands of food consumers, mainly pregnant women and immunocompromised individuals. They should avoid unpasteurized milk products and raw eggs, cook all meats, and rinse thoroughly all raw vegetables and fruits before being eaten. Separate uncooked meats and poultry from vegetables, cooked foods, and ready-to-eat foods. Wash hands, knives, countertops, and cutting boards after handling and preparing uncooked foods. Use precooked or ready-to-eat food as soon as possible. Prepare foods without cross-contamination between raw and cooked foods. Do not store the product in the refrigerator beyond the use-by date (CDC's Listeriosis webpage).

A low initial inoculum of Listeria in a food at the time of manufacturing can turn into a big dose of Listeria for consumers, in relation to shelf life and handling of each product, so the potential of transmission of Listeriosis should be considered (Schuchat, Swaminathan and Broome, 1991). In order to prevent the food contamination with *Listeria spp.*, implementation of assurance quality systems and the manufacturing practice in which the early detection of the microorganism constitutes the main tool, are required for food industry.

Given that *Listeria monocytogenes* is transmitted by food consumption, mainly ready to eat products including meat products, some strategies are proposed in order to prevent the development of Listeria in those products using the hurdle theory (Leitsner and Gorris, 1995;

Pellicer *et al.*, 2011). During fermentation and drying of sausage, *L. monocytogenes* tends to decrease substantially, however, this organism, which is ubiquitous, psychrotrophic and relatively resistant to curing ingredients, may survive (Ingham, Beuge, Dropp, Losinski, 2004; Juntilla *et al.*, 1989; Jonson, Doyle, Cassens, 1990). It has been reported that the undissociated lactic acid inhibits the growth of microorganisms and is frequently used to extend the shelf life of foods (Barbuddhe, Malik and Bhilegaonkar, 1999). Lactic acid is effective to inhibit the development of *L. monocytogenes* when at pH values of 4.5 and 4.6 (Ahmad and Marth, 1990; Ariyapitipun, Mustapha and Clarke, 2000; Sorrels, Engil, Hatfield, 1989). Sodium nitrite when applied individually did not present antimicrobial effects. However, an enhancement of the bactericidal effect with the combination of lactic acid with sodium nitrite was observed. Bacteriocins are increasingly used to control the growth of *L. monocytogenes;* among them, nisin is an antimicrobial agent that can be used in meat products (Brandt *et. al.*, 2010; Breukink, Krujiff, 1999), in combination with pH reduction and the addition of NaCI (Bouttefroy *et al.*, 2000). Nisin is an antimicrobial peptide which acts against *L. monocytogenes* as well as other Gram-positive bacteria. Its use is permitted in dairy products (FAO Nutrition Meeting Report Series N° 45 A (1969) but still does not have approval for its application in meat products in South America; some countries such as Australia and New Zealand are trying to use it, proposing the inclusion of a limit for the use of nisin in meat products (Food Standards Agency of Australia and New Zealand; October 2007 (A565)).; Directive 95/2/CE ratified by the Commission of European Communities FAO/WHO, 2007; FDA, 2006). Its potential application is high, especially to avoid the deterioration caused by Gram-positive bacteria in processed meat such as sausage and meat paste in which the homogenization of the product allows the better distribution of nisin (Gonalves and Massaguer, 1999; Ariyapitipun, Mustapha and Clarke, 2000; FDA, 1988; Pellicer *et al.*, 2011). An enhancement of the bactericidal effect of lactic acid with the addition of nisin has been demonstrated.

   L. monocytogenes and other species of Listeria can be isolated from foods and food industry, but these other organisms don´t hold the same pathogenic potential as *L. monocytogenes*. Molecular methods may facilitate rapid detection of all these organisms in the food industry, and for this reason, they are an important area of research.

References

Administración Nacional de Laboratorios e Institutos de Salud. Instituto Nacional de Enfermedades Infecciosas. ANLIS/INEI Dr. Carlos G. Malbrán. Departamento de Bacteriología, Servicio de Bacteriología Especial. Detección de *Listeria monocytogenes*. Vigilancia de Listeriosis. Noviembre de 1999.

Ahmad, N; Marth, E. (1990) Acid-injury of *Listeria monocytogenes*. *Journal of Food Protection* 53: 26-29.

Al-Ghazali, M R; Al-Azawi, S K. (1986) Detection and enumeration of *Listeria monocytogenes* in a sawage treatment plant in Iraq. *Journal of Applied Microbiology* 60: 251-254.

Ariyapitipun, T; Mustapha, A; Clarke, A D. (2000) Inhibition of *Listeria monocytogenes* Scott A on vacuum-packaged raw beef treated with polylactic acid, lactic acid and nisin. *Journal of Food Protection* 63: 131-136

Barbuddhe, S B; Malik, S V S; Bhilegaonkar, K N. (1999) Growth inhibition of *Listeria monocytogenes* by commercial nisin and lactic acid in raw buffalo meat mince. *Journal of Food Science Technology* 36: 320-324.

Begot, L; Lebert, I; Lebert, A. (1997) Variability of the response of 66 *Listeria monocytogenes* and *Listeria innocua* strains to different growth conditions. *Food Microbiology* 14: 403-412.

Bergey's Manual of Systematic Bacteriology (1986*). Volume 2. Baltimore:* Williams and Wilkins.

Bojsen-Moller, J. (1972) Human Listeriosis: diagnostic, epidemiologic and clinical studies. *Acta Pathologica, Microbiologica et Inmunologica Scandinávica. Sect. B Suppl.* 229: 72-92.

Bouttefroy, A; Mansour, M; Linder, M; Millière, J B. (2000) Short communication: Inhibitory combinations of nisin, sodium chloride, and pH on *Listeria monocytogenes* ATCC 15313 in broth by an experimental design approach. *International Journal of Food Microbiology* 54: 109-115.

Brandt, A. L., Castillo, A., Harris, K. B., Keeton, J. T., Hardin, M. D., Taylor, T. M. (2010) Inhibition of *Listeria monocytogenes* by Food Antimicrobials Applied Singly and in Combination. *Journal of Food Science* 75: M557-M563.

Breukink Eefjan; Kruijff Ben de. (1999) The lantibiotic nisin, a special case or not? *Biochimica et Biophysica Acta* 1462: 223-234.

Buchanan, R L; Klawitter, L A. (1990) Research note: Effects of temperature and oxygen on the growth of *Listeria monocytogenes* at pH 4.5. *Journal of Food Science* 55: 1754-1756.

CDC. Center for Disease Control and Prevention. http://www. CDC.gov/ listeria.

Cole, M B; Jones, M V; Holyoak, C. (1990) The effect of pH, salt concentration and temperature on the survival and growth of *Listeria monocytogenes. Journal of Applied Bacteriology* 69: 63-72.

Conner, D E; Brackett, R E; Beuchat, L R. (1986) Effect of temperature, sodium chloride and pH on growth of *Listeria monocytogenes* in cabbage juice. *Applied and Environmental Microbiology* 52: 59-63.

Copes, J; Pellicer, K; Malvestiti, L; Stanchi, N. (2000) a. Sobrevivencia en tablas de cocina de madera y plástico inoculadas experimentalmente con *Listeria monocytogenes. Analecta Veterinaria* 20: 47-50.

Copes, J; Pellicer, K; Echeverria, G; Stanchi, N; Martinez, C; Leardini, N. (2000) b. Investigación de *Listeria monocytogenes* en quesos de pasta blanda. *Revista Argentina de Microbiología* 32: 49-52.

Cossart P, Mengaud L. (1989) *Listeria monocytogenes.* A model system for the study of intracelular parasitism. *Molecular Biology & Medicine* 6: 463-474.

Cox, L J; Kleiss, T; Cordier, J L; Cordellana, C; Kondel, P; Perazzini, C; Beumer, R; Siebenga, A. (1989) *Listeria spp.* in food processing, non-food and domestic environments. *Food Microbiology* 6: 49-61.

Chhabra, A T; Carter, W H; Linton, R H; Cousin, M A. (1999) A predictive model to determine the effects of pH, milkfat, and temperature on thermal inactivation of *Listeria monocytogenes*. *Journal of Food Protection* 62: 1143-1149.

Chico-Calero I, Suarez M, Gonzalez-Zorn B, Scortti M, Slaughuis J, Goebel W, *et al*. Hpt, a bacterial homolog of the microsomal glucose-6-phosphate translocase, mediates rapid intracellular proliferation in Listeria. *Proceeding National Academy Science USA* 2002; 99: 431-436.

Donelly, C W. (1994) *Listeria monocytogenes*, p. 215-252. *In* Y H Hui; J R Gorham; K D Murrell; D O Cliver (ed.), *Foodborne disease handbook.* Marcel Dekker, Neww York.

Doumith M, Cazalet C, Simoes N, Frangeul L, Jacquet C, Kunst F, *et al*. (2004) New aspects regarding evolution and virulence of *Listeria monocytogenes* revealed by comparative genomics and DNA arrays. *Infection and Immunity* 72: 1072-1083.

Durst, J. (1975) The role of temperature factors in epidemiology of Listeriosis. *Zentralbl Bakteriol Microbiol Hyg* I., 223:72-81.

Dussurget O, Pizzarro-Cerda J, Cossart P. (2004) Molecular determinants of *Listeria monocytogenes* virulence. *Annual Reviews Microbiology* 58: 587-610.

Encinas, J P; Sanz, J J; García-López, M L; Otero, A. (1999) Short communication: Behaviour of *Listeria spp*. in naturally contaminated chorizo (Spanish fermented sausage). *International Journal of Food* Microbiology 46: 167-171.

FAO. Nutrition Meeting Report. Series N° 45.A (1969): http://www.fao. org/docrep/ w4601e/ w4601e03.htm.

FAO/OMS (2007) Directiva 95/2/CE: http://eur-lex.europa.eu/LexUriServ/LexUri Serv.do?uri=COM:2007:0418:FIN:ES:PDF.

FDA 1988: http://www.accessdata.fda.gov/scripts/fcn/gras_notices/grn 0065.pdf.

FDA: Bad Bug Book http://www.fda.gov/food/foodsafety/foodborneillness/foodborneillness foodbornepathogensnaturaltoxins/badbugbook/ucm070064.htm

FDA 2006: aditivos http://www.fda.gov/Food/FoodIngredientsPackaging/ FoodAdditives /ucm073015.htm.

Fenlon, DR. (1986) Rapid quantitative assesment of the distributionof Listeria in silage implicated in a suspected outbreak of Listeriosis in calves. *Veterinary Record* 118: 240-242.

Gianuzzi, L; Zaritzky, N. (1996) Effect of ascorbic acid in Comparison to citric and lactic acid on *Listeria monocytogenes* inhibition at refrigeration temperatures. *Lebensmittel-Wissenschaft Und Technologie* 29: 1-8.

Gitter, M; Bradley, R; Blampied, PH. (1980) *Listeria monocytogenes* infection in bovine mastitis. *Veterinary Record* 107: 390-393.

Goetz M, Bubert A, Wang G, Chico-Calero I, Vazquez-Boland JA, Beck M, *et al*. (2001) Microinjectionand growth of bacteria in the cytosol of mammalians host cells. *Proceeding National Academy Science USA* 98: 12221-12226.

Gonalzarian, CA; Donelly, CW; Pintauro SJ, and Howard DB. (1989) Comparison of infectious dose of Listeria monocytogenes F5817 as determined for normal versus compromised C57B1/6J mice. *Journal of Food Protection* 52: 696-701

Gonalves, J D; Massaguer, P R. (1999) The effect of antimicrobials in vacuum-packaged hot dog sausage. *IFT'99 Annual Meeting.*

Gray, M L. (1960) A possible link in the relationship between silage feeding and Listeriosis. *Journal of American Veterinary Medical Association.* 136:205-208.

Gray MJ, Freitag NE, Boor KJ. (2006) How the bacterial pathogen *Listeria monocytogenes* mediates the switch fron environmental Dr. Jekyll to pathogenic Mr. Hyde. *Infection and Immunity* 74: 2505-2512.

Gray, M L; Killinger, A H. (1966) *Listeria monocytogenes* and listeric infections. *Bacteriology Reviews.* 30: 309-382.

Gronstol, H. (1979) Listeriosis in sheep. Isolation of *Listeria monocytogenes* from grass silage. *Acta Veterinaria Scandinavica* 20:492-497.

Ingham, S. C., Beuge, D. R., Dropp, B. K., Losinski, J. A. (2004) Survival of *Listeria monocytogenes* during storage of ready-to-eat meat products processed by drying, fermentation, and/or smoking. *Journal of Food Protection* 67: 2698-2702.

Jay, J M. (1994) *Microbiología moderna de los Alimentos,* 3º edición Wayne State University. Editorial acribia S.A. Zaragoza.

Jay, J M. (2000) *Modern Food Microbiology*, sixth ed. Aspen Publishers, Inc., Gaithersburg, MD, p 679.

Jonson, J L; Doyle, M P; Cassens, R G. (1990) *Listeria monocytogenes* and other *Listeria spp.* in meat and meat products. A review. *Journal of Food Protection* 53: 81-91.

Juntilla, J; Him, J; Hill, P; Nurmi, E. (1989) Effect of different levels of nitrite and nitrate on the survival of *Listeria monocytogenes* during the manufacture of fermented sausage. *Journal of Food Protection* 52: 158-161.

Kallipolitis, R M; Higmer, H. (2001) *Listeria monocytogenes* response regulators important for stress tolerance and pathogenesis. *FEMS Microbiology* Letters 204: 111-115.

Kayal S, Charbit A. (2006) Listeriolysin O: a key protein of *Listeria monocytogenes* with multiple functions. *FEMS Microbiology Reviews* 30: 514-529.

Ko, R; Tombras Smith, L; Smith, GM. (1994) Glycine Betaine Confers Enhanced Osmotolerance and Cryotolerance on *Listeria monocytogenes*. *Journal of Bacteriology* 176: 426-431.

López V, Suárez M, Chico-Calero I, Navas J, Martinez-Suárez JV. (2006) *Listeria monocytogenes* en alimentos: ¿son todos los aislamientos igual de virulentos? *Revista Argentina de Microbiología* 38: 224-234.

Lovett, J. (1988) Isolation and Identification of *Listeria monocytogenes* in dairy products. *Journal of Association of Official Analytical Chemists* 71: 658-660.

Mitscherlich, E; Marth, E H. (1984) Microbial Survival in the Environment: *Bacteria and Rickettsiiae Important in Human and Animal Health.* Springer Verlag Berlin.

Monge, Rafael; Arias-Echandi, María L. (1999) Presence of *Listeria monocytogenes* in fresh salad vegetables. *Revista Biomedica* 10: 29-30.

Nicolet, Jacques. (1986) *Compendio de Bacteriología Médica y Veterinaria.* Ed. Acribia. S. A. Zaragoza, España.

Organismo de Normas Alimentarias de Australia y Nueva Zelanda (2007) (A565): http://www.bis.org.in/sf/aug2007/gtbtn07AUS57.doc.

Pape; Johnson. (1986) *Medicina Interna* T. II. Jy H. Stein. Ed. Salvat. P. 1403.

Pellicer, K; Copes, J; Malvestiti, L; Echeverria, G; Nosetto, E; Stanchi, N. (2002) a. Ready to eat salads an análisis of health and safety conditions. *Analecta Veterinaria* 22: 4-6.

Pellicer, K; Copes, J; Malvestiti, L; Lanfranchi, M; Stanchi, N; Echeverria, G; Nosetto, E. (2002) b. Aislamiento e Identificación de *Listeria monocytogenes* y *Listeria spp.* en embutidos secos obtenidos en mercados de la ciudad de La Plata, Argentina. *Revista Argentina de Microbiología* 34: 219-221.

Pellicer, K; del Hoyo, G; Brocardo, MS; Aliverti, V; Aliverti, F y Copes, J. (2009) Efecto del ácido clorhídrico y ácido láctico sobre el desarrollo de treinta cepas de *Listeria spp.* aisladas de alimentos. *Revista de la Facultad de Ciencias Veteterinarias UCV*. 50: 19-22.

Pellicer, K, Copes, J, Giannuzzi, L, Zaritzky, N. (2011) Behavior of *Listeria monocytogenes* type1 355/98 (85) in meat emulsions as affected by temperature, pH, water activity, fat and microbial preservatives. *Food Control*. 22: 1573-1581.

Pizarro-Cerda J, Cossart P. (2006) Subversion of cellular functions by *Listeria monocytogenes*. *Journal of Pathology* 208: 215-223.

Ralovich, B. (1974) *Listeriosis Research. Present Situation and Perspective*. Akademiai Kiado, Budapest.

Ralovich, B. (1984). What is the role of food-stuffs in transportation of Listeria. In *"Microbial Associations and Interactions in Food"* ed. I. Kiss, T. Deàk, and K. Incze, p. 99. Akademiai Kiads. Budapest.

Ramaswamy V, Cressence VM, Rejitha JS, Lekshmi MU, Dharsana KS, Prasad SP, Vijila HM. (2007) *Listeria*- review of epidemiology and pathogenesis. *Journal of Microbiology, Immunology and Infection* 40: 4-13.

Redline RW and Lu CY. (1987) Role of local immunosuppression in murine fetoplacental Listeriosis. *Journal of Clinical Investigation* 79: 1234-1241.

Ripio MT, Brehm K, Lara M, Suarez M, Vazquez-Boland JA. (1997)a A Glucose-1-phosphate utilization by *Listeria monocytogenes* is PrfA dependent and coordinately expressed with virulence factors. *Journal of Bacteriology* 179: 7174-7180.

Ripio MT, Dominguez-Bernal G, Lara M, Suárez M, Vazquez-Boland JA. (1997)b A Gly 145Ser substitution in the transcriptional activator PrfA causes constitutive overexpression of virulence factors in *Listeria monocytogenes*. *Journal of Bacteriology* 179: 1533-1540.

Saylers, A A; Whitt D D. (1994) *Bacterial Pathogenesis. A molecular approach*. ASM Press, Washington DC.

Saylers, A A; Whitt, D D. (2005) *Revenge of the Microbes: How Bacterial Resistance is undermining the Antibiotic Miracle*. ASM Press, Washington DC.

Scortti M, Lacharme-LoraL, Wagner M, Chico-Calero I, Losito P, Vazquez-Boland JA. (2006) Coexpression of virulence and fosomycin susceptibility in Listeria: molecular basis of an antimicrobial *in vitro-in vivo* paradox. *Nature Medicine* 12: 515-517.

Schlech, W F III. (1984) New Perspectives on the gastrointestinal mode of transmission in invasive *Listeria monocytogenes* infection. *Clinical & Investigative Medicine* 7: 321-326.

Schuchat A, Swaminathan B, Broome CV. (1991) Epidemiology of human listeriosis. *Clinical Microbiology Reviews* 4:169-83.

Seeliger, H P R. (1961) *Listeriosis*. New York: Hafner.

Seeliger, H P R; Jones, D. (1986) Genus Listeria. En: P.H.A. Sneath, (ed), *Bergey's Manual of Systematic Bacteriology. vol 2*. The Williams and Wilkins, Baltimore. MD.

Smith, G A; Marques, H; Jones, S; Johnston, N C; Portnoy, D A; Goldfine, H. (1995) The two distinct phospholipases C of *Listeria monocytogenes* have overlapping roles in escape from a vacuole and cell-to-cell spread. *Infection and Immunity* 63: 4231-4237.

Smith, B; Kemp, M; Ethelberg, S; Schiellemp, P; Bruun, B G; Gerner-Smidt, P; Christensen, J J. (2009) *Listeria monocytogenes*: Maternal-faetal infections in Denmark 1994-2005. *Scandinavian Journal of Infectious Diseases* 41: 21-25.

Sokolovic Z, Riedel J, Wuenscher M, Goebel W. (1993) Surface-associated, PrfA-regulated proteins of *Listeria monocytogenes* synthesized under stress conditions. *Molecular Microbiology* 8: 219-227.

Sorrels, K M; Engil, D C; Hatfield, J R. (1989) Effect of pH, acidulate, time, and temperature on the growth and survival of *Listeria monocytogenes*. *Journal of Food Protection* 52: 571-573.

Suarez M, Gonzalez-Zorn B, Vega Y, Chico-Calero I, Vazquez-Boland JA. (2001) A role for Act A in epitelial cell invasión by *Listeria monocytogenes*. *Cell Microbiology* 3: 853-864.

Universia 2006. http://noticias.universia.es/ciencia-nn-tt/noticia/2006/05/17/ 666286/ nuevo-tratamiento-listeriosis.html.

Vázquez-Boland JA, Kocks C, Dramsi S, Ohayon H, Geoffroy C, Mengaud J, *et al.* (1992) Nucleotide sequence of the lechitinase operon of *Listeria monocytogenes* and possible role of lechitinase in cell-to-cell spread. *Infection and Immunity 60*:219-230.

Watkins, J; Slealth, K P. (1981) Isolation and enumeration of *Listeria monocytogenes* from sewage, sewage sludge and river water. *Journal of Applied Bacteriology.* 50: 1-7.

Weis, J; Seeliger, H P R. (1975) Incidence of *Listeria monocytogenes* in nature. *Applied Microbiology* 3:29-32.

Welshimer, H J; Donker-Voet, J. (1971) *Listeria monocytogenes* in nature. *Applied Microbiology* 30:29-32.

WHO (1988) Working group on Foodborne Listeriosis. Foodborne listeriosis. Document N° WHO/WHE/FOS/88.5. *World Health Organization,* Geneva, Switzerland.

In: Listeria Infections
Editors: A. Romano and C. F. Giordano

ISBN: 978-1-62081-639-4
© 2012 Nova Science Publishers, Inc.

Chapter VI

Epidemiology of *Listeria monocytogenes* in RTE Fermented Meat and Smoked Fish Products

D. Meloni, A. Mureddu, F. Piras, R. Mazza, S. Lamon,
S. G. Consolati, F. Fois, and R. Mazzette
Department of Veterinary Medicine, University of Sassari,
Sassari, Italy

Introduction

Listeria monocytogenes is an ubiquitous organism, widely distributed in the environment. The principal reservoirs are soil, forage and water. Other reservoirs include healthy humans and animals (ILSI, 2005) or infected domestic and wild animals (EFSA, 2011). *L.monocytogenes* is also the etiologic agent of listeriosis, which occurs in humans and animals. Since the beginning of the 1980's *L. monocytogenes* has been recognized as an emerging food-borne pathogen after several sporadic and epidemic cases of listeriosis occurred in Europe and the USA (Kathariou, 2002). Recently the incidence of sporadic cases rose again in Europe (Gillespie et al., 2006; Goulet et al., 2008; Cairns and Payne, 2009). Two main forms of listeriosis have been described in humans: febrile gastroenteritis in healthy individuals and life-threatening invasive infections in susceptible individuals, with the latter posing a serious problem to public health. In fact, invasive human listeriosis is a rare but severe infection, typically causing septicemia, encephalitis and meningitis (Vazquez-Boland et al., 2001; Swaminathan and Gerner-Smidt, 2007) in defined high-risk groups: young, old, pregnant and immune-compromised, the so called "YOPI" (De Cesare et al., 2007). Listeriosis is the fifth most common zoonotic disease in Europe, less common than other diseases (eg. by *Escherichia coli* 0157:H7, *Campylobacter jejuni* or *Salmonella* spp.). It has an incidence of 3.3 cases per 1.000.000 population per year (Zunabovic et al., 2011), an estimated case fatality rate of 20 up to 30% (Swaminathan and Gerner-Smidt, 2007) and the highest hospitalization rate (90%) of all food -borne pathogens with additional long term sequelae in some patients (Manfreda et al., 2005; Jemmi and Stephan, 2006). In Europe, 55.6% of all human listeriosis cases are reported in patients aged above 60 years, approximately 2.5 times higher than those reported in any other age group (Denny and McLauchlin, 2008). Therefore, although this disease continues to occur in association with pregnancy, it is now predominantly an infection of immune-compromised individuals amongst the older sections of the populations (Orsi et al., 2011). Data on listeriosis in USA show a similar marked reduction-trend (Voetsch et al., 2007). The majority (99%) of the infections caused by *L.monocytogenes* are thought to be foodborne (Swaminathan and Gerner-Smidt, 2007). The pathogen is able to survive at a broad range of temperature (from 0 to 45°C) and pH (from 4.5 to 9.0), high salt concentrations (10%) and low water activity values (0.92) (Ryser and Marth, 2007). These properties, together with the severity of human listeriosis infections, make *L. monocytogenes* of particular concern for manufacturers of cold stored "ready to eat" (RTE) foods (Romanova et al., 2002; Van Coillie et al., 2004; Shen et al., 2006). RTE food is a large, heterogeneous category of foodstuffs and can be subdivided in many different ways. According to the Codex definition, RTE include any food that is normally consumed in its raw state or any food handled, processed, mixed, cooked or otherwise prepared into a form in which it is normally consumed without further processing (CAC, 1999). *L.monocytogenes* has been isolated from a wide variety of RTE products capable of supporting its growth (McLauchlin, 1996) and is responsible for numerous outbreaks associated with the consumption of RTE meat, poultry, dairy, fish and vegetable products (U.S. FDA/USDA/CDC, 2003). Seafood products have been reported to be contaminated with *L.monocytogenes* and several reports of outbreaks or sporadic cases have been linked to these products (Johansson et al., 1999; Medrala et al., 2003) in particular with cold or hot-smoked salmon, "gravad" salmon, shrimps, mussels, fermented fish, fish and seafood salads (Ben Embarek, 1994; Rocourt et al., 2000; Gombas et al., 2003). Concerning RTE meat products, a large outbreak occurred in 2008 in Canada causing 22 deaths and 57 confirmed cases (PHAC, 2009). Although fermented pork meat RTE products as dry and semi-dry sausages have been rarely implicated in food poisoning, more risks should be linked to the consumption of these products because mainly in the manufacturing of traditional products, an empirical application of the hurdles technology often occurs. In the following, through an up-to-date review of (personal and non) published data, the epidemiology of *L.monocytogenes* in two selected RTE food categories will be discussed: fermented meat and smoked fish products. Fermented meat products are often contaminated and are produced without any lethal processing step while smoked fish products (in particular cold smoked ones) are frequently contaminated, have no lethal processing steps and permits growth during an extended storage period.

Listeria monocytogenes in RTE Fermented Meat Products

Processed meat products may be contaminated by *L.monocytogenes* at several stages: either raw materials are contaminated and the manufacturing process is not sufficient to sterilize the final product or by contact with contaminated unprocessed raw materials, unclean surfaces or people (Chasseignaux et al., 2001; Thevenot et al., 2006). At present, the information on the occurrence of *L.monocytogenes* in processed pork meat products, are sporadic, nevertheless several studies have documented the prevalence of the pathogen in processed raw pork meat products as RTE fermented sausages. Fermentation is one of the oldest methods of meat preservation and is widely used in making fermented sausages. Fermented sausages are characterised by their relatively longer shelf life, which is brought about by production of lactic acid in the fermentation process. According to the length of the ripening period, fermented sausages are generally classified into dry and semi-dry (Essien, 2000). The manufacturing of fermented sausages utilises curing ingredients, spices and starter cultures in a fermentation process and at the end of the process they come out as cured meat products. Traditionally, fermented sausages are made using acid bacteria naturally present in the meat or with the inoculation of the new batch with an old batch. The introduction of microflora occurs at the chopping step of the technological process: the mixture is filled in natural or artificial casings and left to ferment and then dried (Essien, 2000). Generally, in fermented sausages the development of pathogenic bacteria as *L.monocytogenes* is inhibited by a sequence of hurdles which leads to stable and safe products consumed without heat treatment. The "hurdle technology" concept includes several hurdles, essential in different stages of the fermentation or ripening process (Barbuti and Parolari, 2002). In the early stages of the ripening process, the main hurdles are nitrite and salt because they inhibit bacteria as pseudomonads and other Gram-negative oxidative bacteria (Leistner and Gould, 2002). Other bacteria are able to multiply, use up the oxygen and cause the decrease of the redox potential. This in turn favors the selection of lactic acid bacteria, the competitive flora which flourish by metabolizing the added sugars causing a decrease in pH value: this is of particular importance for the microbial stability of quick-ripened fermented sausages, which are not greatly dried (Leistner and Gould, 2002). Only the water activity hurdle is strengthened with time, and this hurdle is largely responsible for the stability of long-ripened raw sausages (Leistner, 1987). After drying, the water activity of fermented sausages is <0.90, which inhibit bacterial growth (Tyopponen et al., 2003). Fermented meat products have moderate rates of consumption and serving sizes in many countries and have rarely been implicated in food poisoning: the risk per serving is low (2.1×10^{-12}) and the global number of annual cases per 100,000 people was calculated to be only 0.0000055 (FAO/WHO, 2004). However, mostly in the manufacturing of traditional RTE fermented products marketed locally or regionally, an empirical application of the hurdles technology often occurs and these products are regularly contaminated with *L.monocytogenes*. Previous surveys carried out on traditional fermented products at the end of ripening showed a prevalence of 10% in France (Thevenot et al., 2005), 10.6% in Chile (Cordano and Rocourt, 2001) and between 15.2 and 40% in Italy (De Cesare et al., 2007; Meloni et al., 2009; Meloni et al., 2012). Some manufacturers tend to reduce drying times of the traditional fermented sausages in order to increase profitability. Insufficiently dried products may have water activity levels (0.92) which permit the growth of *L.monocytogenes* (AFSSA, 2000). Moreover, the pathogen may survive during the processing of the fermented meat products due to its high tolerance to low pH conditions (between 4.6 and 9.6) and high salt concentrations (up to 10% NaCl) with contamination levels always lower than 100 cfu/g (Farber and Peterkin, 1991). The latter is true because *L.monocytogenes* cannot compete well with lactic acid bacteria which prevail in fermented sausages. However, without competitive microflora the pathogen is able to multiply and reach high levels of contamination presenting a major public health concern (Thevenot et al., 2006). In conclusion, it has been shown that *L. monocytogenes* poses a microbiological risk in fermented meat products. The pathogen is able to survive during sausage fermentation, overcoming the hurdles encountered during the manufacturing process. To decrease the presence of *L.monocytogenes* in the traditional fermented sausages at the end of ripening, food business operators should adhere to accurate application of hurdle technologies. Products can also become contaminated through contact with work surfaces and equipment, therefore special care must be taken to ensure that cleaning and disinfecting procedures are applied correctly. General preventive measures such as Good Hygiene Practices and Good Manufacturing Practices will help limit the risk of spread *L.monocytogenes*. HACCP principles should be applied to each food-processing plant in order to identify and control sources of *L. monocytogenes* contamination and dissemination (Thevenot et al., 2006).

Listeria monocytogenes in RTE Smoked Fish Products

In recent years epidemiological evidence has indicated that listeriosis is often associated with RTE seafood products (Ben Embarek, 1994; Rocourt et al., 2000; Gombas et al., 2003; McLauchlin et al., 2004) and in particular with cold or hot-smoked salmon. This product, normally vacuum packed, with a refrigerated shelf-life of 3-8 weeks, is considered a risk product for human listeriosis: several studies demonstrated that is an excellent substrate for *L. monocytogenes* (Farber, 1991; Nilsson, Huss, and Gram, 1997; Rørvik, 2000). The growth of this microorganism in smoked salmon has been reported most of all during the storage period (Gonzalez-Rodriguez et al., 2002), suggesting that the stress applied during the technological processes may extend the lag phase or reduce the growth rate, but is not able to affect the vitality of the cells (Serio et al., 2011). *L.monocytogenes* can contaminate smoked fish at many levels of the manufacturing chain (Vogel et al., 2001[a]). Contamination depends on many factors such as the cleaning and processing procedures, microbiological status of the raw fish and the existence of the surface persistent *L.monocytogenes* in the processing plant (Autio et al., 1999; Rørvik, 2000). Sources and contamination patterns have been often traced back to the fish processing plants, but the primary origin of the contamination has not been determined (Katzav et al., 2006). Several authors have reported the colonisation of some subtypes of *L.monocytogenes* in fish processing plants, equipment, utensils and brine causing persistent contamination for months or even years (Rørvik, Caugant and Yndestad, 1995; López et al., 2008). Numerous studies showed that in-house *L. monocytogenes* flora contaminates smoked salmon during processing (Vogel et al., 2001[b] ; Autio et al., 2003; Miettinen & Wirtanen, 2005). The ability of some strains to attach to surfaces forming biofilm may enable these bacteria to persist for long periods in processing plants (Di Bonaventura et al., 2008). Apart from the processing environment, the raw fish itself has been regarded as a source of contamination (Gudmundsdottir et al., 2005). There are indications that *L. monocytogenes* present in the raw material can proliferate and contaminate the final products, especially those that are not heat-treated before consumption (Vogel et al., 2001[b]; Eklund et al., 2004; Miettinen and Wirtanen, 2005). Although the bacterium has been isolated from several different environments, it is insufficient to understand the overall ecology of the transmission dynamics of *L.monocytogenes*. The prime objective of fish smoking in most part of the world is still preservation. This may be preservation for very long periods or the addition of an extra day or two on the expected shelf-life of fresh fish to allow it to be distributed to remote markets or to keep slightly longer on retail displays. Even when the process has been greatly reduced, with the aim of attracting new consumers to a subtle taste difference, or increasing the yield of finished product from raw material, extended shelf-life still appears to be expected by manufacturers, retailers and consumers alike (Horner, 1991). The production of smoked salmon includes several technological steps, such as filleting, salting (dry-salting or brine microinjection), drying, smoking, trimming and packaging, that require a lot of handling by workers (Rørvik, 2000). There are two general methods of smoking fish: hot-smoking and cold-smoking. In these products, both hot and cold smoking are usually not capable of preventing the growth of the pathogen to high numbers, posing an increased risk of causing listeriosis.

1. Hot Smoked Fish Products

Hot-smoked fish products are widely consumed in the United States and Europe. In the European seafood market in particular, hot-smoked products belonging to various families such as *Gadidae*, *Salmonidae* and *Clupeidae* are present most frequently (Civera and Manzoni, 1993). These products are classified as mildly heat-preserved seafood products as they are hot smoked at temperatures > 60° C (Arcangeli, Baldrati and Pirazzoli, 2003). In a 1992 survey, Jemmi and Keush have shown that after experimental inoculation of *L. monocytogenes* in fresh fish destined to be hot-smoked, the organism did not survive the process. It was therefore advanced the hypothesis that contamination of the hot smoked fish could be related mainly to post-process contamination. The temperatures used for hot-smoking of fish may vary, however, the most common combinations of time and temperature reported in the literature are 65°C for 20' and 60° C for 45' (Heintz and Johnson, 1998). Since the hot-smoking treatment alone is not able to guarantee the safety of the product or to ensure a satisfactory shelf-life period, it is necessary to submit the products to a pre-treatment of salting and to strictly respect the cold chain management during the shelf life. Salting is normally carried out by immersion of the product in a brine solution at 80° salinometers (21.1 g NaCl/100 ml of brine) for a time varying depending on the species, size and degree of grooming (whole fish, gutted or threaded). This salt concentration is an indicative compromise to prevent a possible recrystallization of the salt on the surface of the product after cooking and smoking, and reach the desired salinity in an acceptable time. The sodium chloride concentration in the aqueous phase of the finished product must also be sufficient to inhibit the growth of spore-forming bacteria that can withstand the hot smoking process, such as *Clostridium botulinum* (Arcangeli, Baldrati and Pirazzoli, 2003). At the end of the process, before being packed, the fish are cooled to about 0°C. However, if the fish should be vacuum packed and stored under freezing, it is advisable to bagging at room temperature. This is to avoid condensation inside the packages and the inevitable "snow effect" (Arcangeli, Baldrati and Pirazzoli, 2003). In hot-smoked fish products, the prevalence of *L. monocytogenes* never exceed 9.12% (Jemmi and Keush, 1992; Ben Embarek, 1994, Jorgensen et al. 1998; Rørvik, 2000). In general, the contamination level is between 100 and 1000 cfu / g, but in several studies higher levels of contamination, up to 132,000 cfu/g have been reported (Loncarevic et al., 1996, Cortesi et al., 1997, Jorgensen et al., 1998).

2. Cold Smoked Fish Products

Cold-smoking is the most frequently used method in the preservation of a wide variety of fish products (fish, molluscs and crustaceans). Vacuum packed cold-smoked salmons obtained from the species *Salmo salar* and from other species of the genus *Onchorynchus*, are certainly the predominant products. These products, classified as lightly preserved seafood products, are widely consumed in the United States and Europe and thus are of considerable economic importance for the seafood market in particular in Northern Europe (Hoffmann et al., 2003; Cardinal et al., 2004). Cold smoked salmon is usually consumed without any further cooking (Eklund et al., 1995; Gudmundsdóttir et al., 2005). In addition, salmon has a high lipid content which may protect microorganisms from a possible thermal treatment or from freezing and cold-smoking below 20°C, cannot be considered a listericidal treatment. Moreover, physical and chemical parameters of smoked salmon are usually within values permitting the growth of *L.monocytogenes*. In general, the consumed amount of this product is rather moderate (about 60 g per serving) and the estimated listeriosis risk related to the number of meals served yearly is very high (5.3 cases per 10^8 × number of served meals). Overall, given the moderate frequency of consumption of these products (1-18 meals per year) the annual rate of listeriosis cases is moderate (0.016 cases per 100,000 inhabitants) (FAO / WHO, 2004). In the North-European countries, where the consumed amounts are higher, the estimated listeriosis risk related to the number of meals served is quite similar, however the annual rate of cases of listeriosis per 100,000 inhabitants is much higher. The raw materials are often contaminated at negligible levels, while a massive contamination of the finished products often occurs (Eklund et al., 1995). The prevalence of *L.monocytogenes* in smoked fish products has been documented repeatedly (Katzav et al., 2006): varies from zero (Ben Embarek et al., 1997) to about 30% (Hoffman et al., 2003; Miettinen and Wirtanen, 2005) in raw fish and between 10% and 40% in freshly produced cold-smoked salmon (Jemmi and Keusch, 1992; Rørvik et al., 2000; Vogel et al., 2001[a]; Dauphin et al., 2001; Aguado et al., 2001; Autio et al., 2003; Nakamura et al., 2004; Azevedo et al., 2005; Miettinen and Wirtanen, 2005). In recent studies performed in Italy, Di Pinto et al. (2010) reported a prevalence of 34%, Mureddu et al. (2011) of 12% while Gambarin et al. (2011) of 16%. The high prevalence of *L.monocytogenes* in these products could be due to the low smoking temperature (20 °C) applied during the cold-salmon processing, as this condition would be ideal for the proliferation of *L.monocytogenes*. As reported above, the characteristics of the product should allow the growth of the pathogen at levels dangerous to humans (Gombas et al., 2003, Cornu et al., 2006). When the refrigeration temperatures are observed throughout the storage period, the development of *L. monocytogenes* is generally moderate (<100 cfu / g), however the long period of shelf life may allow a significant increase in the level of contamination, because of the absence of competitive microflora (Johansson et al., 1999). The ability of *L. monocytogenes* to grow to a significant level also at refrigeration temperature, given sufficient time must be taken into account (Little et al., 2007). Temperature abuse may be a factor in growth to high numbers unless prolonged storage has occurred (ILSI, 2005). Although it is rather uncommon, contamination levels up to 10^4 cfu/g have been reported in samples stored at temperatures of thermal abuse between 8 and 10°C (Loncarevic et al., 1996, Cortesi et al., 1997, Jorgensen et al. 1998; Gnanou-Besse et al. 2004). Two of the major episodes of febrile gastroenteritis (Sweden 1997 and Finland 1999) have been associated with consumption of cold-smoked fishery products contaminated at high levels. In particular, in the Finnish outbreak, the contamination level was 190,000 cfu/g. Subsequent investigations proved that the product, manufactured about 20 days earlier, had been stored at inappropriate temperatures for commercial resale (around 10°C, above the range of 0-3° C recommended by the manufacturer), allowing the organism to reach very high levels of contamination (Ericson et al., 1997, Miettinen et al., 1999). Cold smoked fish confirms itself as one of the most perishable food products: cold smoking processing does not eliminate the possibility of contamination of raw materials and refrigeration or vacuum storage are not able to prevent the growth of *L. monocytogenes* (Duffes, 1999). For these reasons, consumer education to keep cold chain management during the shelf life becomes very important to minimize the growth of the pathogen. Shortening of the best-before date is sometimes useful to reduce the risk of causing food-borne listeriosis (Marklinder et al. 2004; ILSI, 2005; Garrido, 2008) and to respect the food safety criteria provided by the Commission Regulation (EC) N° 2073/2005 on microbiological criteria for foodstuffs.

References

Agence Française de Sécurité Sanitaire des Aliments (2000). Rapport de la Commission d'étude des risques liés à *Listeria monocytogenes*. http://www.afssa.fr

Aguado V., Vitas A.I., García-Jalón I. (2001). Random amplified polymorphic DNA typing applied to the study of cross-contamination by *Listeria monocytogenes* in processed food products. *Journal of Food Protection,* 64, 716–720.

Arcangeli G., Baldrati G., Pirazzoli P. (2003). La trasformazione dei prodotti della pesca: tecnologia, controllo e igiene di lavorazione. Ed. Stazione Sperimentale per l'Industria delle Conserve Alimentari, Litografica Faenza, 2003.

Autio T. (1999). Sources of *Listeria monocytytogenes* contamination in a cold-smoked rainbow trout procesing plant detected by pulsed-field gel electrrophoresis typing. *Applied Environmental Microbiology* 65:150-155.

Autio T., Keto-Timonen R., Biorkroth J. and Korkeala H. (2003). Characterization of persistent and sporadic *Listeria monocytogenes* strains by pulsed-field gel electrophoresis (PFGE) and amplified fragment length polymorphism (AFLP). *Systematic and Applied Microbiology* 26, (4), 539.

Azevedo I., Regalo M., Mena C., Almeida G., Carneiro L., Teixeira P., Hogg T., Gibbs P. (2005). Incidence of *Listeria* spp. in domestic refrigerators in *Portugal Food Control,* 16:121-4.

Barbuti S., Parolari G. (2002). Validation of manufacturing process to control pathogenic bacteria in typical dry fermented products. *Meat Science* 62, (3), 323.

Ben Embarek P.K. (1994). Presence, detection and growth of *Listeria monocytogenes* in seafoods: a review. *International Journal of Food Microbiology* 23: 17.

Ben Embarek P.K., Hansen L.T., Enger O. and Huss H.H. (1997). Occurrence of *Listeria spp.* in farmed salmon and during subsequent slaughter: comparison of Listertestk Lift and the USDA method. *Food Microbiology* 14: 39.

Cairns B.J., Payne R.J.H. (2009). Sudden increases in listeriosis rates in England and Wales, 2001 and 2003. *Emerging Infectious Diseases* 15(3): 465-468.

Cardinal M., Gunnlaugsdottir H., Bjoernevik M., Ouisse A., Vallet J.L. (2004). Sensory characteristics of cold-smoked Atlantic salmon (Salmo salar) from European market and relationships with chemical, physical and microbiological measurements. *Food Research International* 37, 181-93.

Chasseignaux E., Toquin M., Ragimbeau C., Salvat G., Colin P. and Ermel G. (2001). Molecular epidemiology of *Listeria monocytogenes* isolates collected from the environment, raw meat and raw products in two poultry and pork processing plants. *Journal of Applied Microbiology* 91, (5), 888.

Civera P., Manzoni P. (1993). Lezioni di Igiene e Controllo dei prodotti della pesca, Ed. CLU, Torino 1993.

Codex Alimentarius Commission (1999). Report of the 32nd session of the Codex Committee on Food Hygiene. Washington, DC, 29 November - 4 December 1999.

Cordano A.M. and Rocourt J. (2001). Occurrence of *Listeria monocytogenes* in food in Chile. *International Journal of Food Microbiology* 70, (1-2), 175.

Cornu M., Beaufort A., Rudelle S., Laloux L., Bergis H., Miconnet N., Serot T., Ignette-Muller M.L. (2006). Effect of temperature, water-phase salt and phenolic contents on *Listeria monocytogenes* growth rates on cold-smoked salmon and evaluation of secondary models. *International Journal of Food Microbiology,* 106,159–168.

Cortesi M.L., Sarli T., Santoro A., Murru N., Pepe T. (1997). Distribution and behavior of *Listeria monocytogenes* in three lots of naturally-contaminated vacuum-packed smoked salmon stored at 2 and 10°C. *International Journal of Food Microbiology,* 37, 209–214.

Dauphin, G., Ragimbeau, C., Malle, P. (2001). Use of PFGE typing for tracing contamination with *Listeria monocytogenes* in three cold-smoked salmon processing plants. *International Journal of Food Microbiology* 64, 51-61.

De Cesare A., Mioni R. and Manfreda G. (2007). Prevalence of *Listeria monocytogenes* in fresh and fermented sausages and ribotyping of contaminating strains. *International Journal of Food Microbiology* 120, (1-2), 124.

Denny J., McLauchlin J. (2008). Human *Listeria monocytogenes* infections in Europe – an opportunity for improved European Surveillance. *Eurosurveillance* 13 (13).

Di Bonaventura, G., Piccolomini, R., Paludi, D., D'Orio, V., Vergara, A., Conter, M., Ianieri, A. (2008). Influence of temperature on biofilm formation by *Listeria monocytogenes* on various food-contact surfaces: relationship with motility and cell surface hydrophobicity. *Journal of Applied Microbiology* 104, 1552–1561.

Di Pinto A., Novello L., Montemurro F., Bonerba E., Tantillo G. (2010). Occurrence of *Listeria monocytogenes* in ready-to-eat foods from supermarkets in Southern Italy. *New Microbiologica*, 33, 249-252.

Duffes F. (1999). Improving the control of *Listeria monocytogenes* in cold smoked salmon. *Trends in Food Science and Technology* 10: 211.

Ericsson I.L., Eklow A., Danielsson-Tham M.L., Loncarevic S., Mentzing O., Persson I., Unnerstad H., Tham W. (1997). An outbreak of listeriosis suspected to have been caused by rainbow trout. *Journal of Clinical Microbiology,* Nov (1997), 2904–290

Essen E. (2000). *Sausage manufacture: principles and practice*. CRC Press, Woodhead Publishing Limited.

European Commission (EC) 2005. Regulation (EC) No 2073/2005 of 15 November 2005 on microbiological criteria for foodstuffs. *Off. J. Eur.* Union L 338:1.

European Food Safety Authority, European Centre for Disease Prevention and Control; The European Union Summary Report on Trends and Sources of Zoonoses, Zoonotic Agents and Food-borne Outbreaks in 2009. 2011. *EFSA Journal 2011*; 9 (3):2090. doi:10.2903/j.efsa.2011.2090. Available online: www.efsa.europa.eu/efsajournal.

Eklund, M. W., Poysky, F. T., Paranjpye, R. N., Lashbrook, L. C., Peterson, M. E., & Pelroy, G. A. (1995). Incidence and sources of *Listeria monocytogenes* in cold smoked fishery products and processing plants. *Journal of Food Protection,* 58, 502-508.

FAO/WHO (2004). Risk assessment of *Listeria monocytogenes* in ready-to-eat foods: interpretative summary. *FAO/WHO Microbiological risk* assessment series n.4.

Farber J.M., Peterkin P. (1991). *Listeria monocytogenes*, a food-borne pathogen. *Microbiology and Molecular Biology Reviews* 55, (3), 476.

Farber J. M. (1991). *Listeria monocytogenes* in fish products. *Journal of Food Protection,* 54, 922-924.

Gambarin P., Magnabosco C., Arcangeli G., Losio M., Pavoni E. (2011). *Listeria monocytogenes* in semiconserve ittiche e potenziali rischi per il consumatore. *Industrie Alimentari,* 19-27.

Garrido V., Torroba L., García-Jalón I., Vitas A.I. (2008). Surveillance of listeriosis in Navarre, Spain, 1995-2005--epidemiological patterns and characterisation of clinical and food isolates. *Euro Surveillance Dec* 4;13(49). pii: 19058.

Gillespie, I.A., Mc Lauchlin, J., Grant, K., Little, C.L., Mithani V., Penman C., Lane X.C., Regan, M. (2006). Changing pattern of human listerios, England and Wales, 2001-2004. *Emerging Infectious Diseases,* 12 (9), 1361-1366.

Gnanou Besse N., Audinet N., Beaufort A., Colin P., Cornu M., Lombard B. (2004). A contribution to the improvement of *Listeria monocytogenes* enumeration in cold-smoked salmon. *International Journal of Food Microbiology* 91:119.

Gombas D.E., Chen Y., Clavero R.S., Scott V.N. (2003). Survey of *Listeria monocytogenes* in ready-to-eat foods. *Journal of Food Protection* 66:559.

Gonzalez-Rodriguez, M. N., Sanza, J. J., Santos, J. A., Otero, A., Garcia-Lopez, M. L. (2002). Numbers and types of microorganisms in vacuum-packed cold-smoked freshwater fish at the retail level. *International Journal of Food Microbiology,* 77, 161-168.

Goulet, V., Hedberg, C., Le Monnier, A., de Valk, H. (2008). Increasing incidence of listeriosis in France and other European countries. *Emerging Infectious Diseases* 14, 734–740.

Gudmundsdóttir, S., Gudbjörnsdóttir, B., Lauzon, H.L., Einarsson, H., Kristinsson, K.G., Kristjánsson, M. (2005). Tracing *Listeria monocytogenes* isolates from cold-smoked salmon and its processing environment in Iceland using pulsed-field gel electrophoresis. *International Journal of Food Microbiology* 101, 41-51.

Heintz M.L., Johnson J.M. (1998). The incidence of *Listeria spp.*, *Salmonella spp* and *Clostridium botulinum* in smoked fish and shellfish. *Journal of Food Protection,* 61 (3), 318-323.

Hoffman A., Gall K.L., Norton D.M. and Wiedmann M. (2003). *Listeria monocytogenes* contamination patterns for the smoked fish processing environment and for raw fish. *Journal of Food Protection* 66:52.

Horner W.F.A. (1991). Water sorption and shelf life of dry cured cod muscle in humid environments. M. *Phil. Thesis,* Loughborough University of Technology.

Kathariou S. (2002). *Listeria monocytogenes* virulence and pathogenicity, a food safety perspective. *Journal of Food Protection* 65:1811.

Ilsi Research Foundation-Risk Science Institute - Expert Panel on *Listeria monocytogenes* in foods, Achieving continuous improvement in reductions in foodborne listeriosis - a risk-based approach. (2005). *Journal of Food Protection* 68, (9), 1932.

Jemmi T., Keusch A., (1992). Behaviour of *Listeria monocytogenes* during processing and storage of experimentally contaminated hot-smoked trout. *International Journal of Food Microbiology,* 15, 339–346.

Jemmi, T., Stephan, R., (2006). *Listeria monocytogenes*: food-borne pathogen and hygiene indicator. *Revue Scientifique et technique de l'Office International des Epizoozies,* 25 (2):571-580.

Johansson T., Rantala L., Palmu L., Honkanen-Buzalski T. (1999). Occurrence and typing *of Listeria monocytogenes* strains in retail vacuum packed fish products and in a production plant. *International Journal of Food Microbiology* 47:111.

Jørgensen L.V., Huss H.H. (1998). Prevalence and growth of *Listeria monocytogenes* in naturally contaminated seafood. *International Journal of Food Microbiology,* 42, 127–131.

Katzav, M., Hyvönen, P., Muje, P., Rantala, L., von Wright A. (2006). Pulsed-Field Gel Electrophoresis typing of *Listeria monocytogenes* isolated in two Finnish fish farms. *Journal of Food Protection* 69, 1443-1447.

Leistner L. (1987). Shelf-stable products and intermediate moisture foods based on meat. *Water activity: theory and applications to food*, Marcel Dekker Inc. New York.

Leistner L., Gould G., (2002). Hurdle technologies: combination treatments for food stability, safety and quality. Kluwer Academic/Plenum Publishers, Food Engineering Series.

Little C.L., Taylor F.C., Sagoo S.K., Gillespie I.A., Grant K. and McLauchlin J. (2007). Prevalence and level of *Listeria monocytogenes* and other *Listeria* species in retail pre-packaged mixed vegetable salads in the UK. *Food Microbiology* 24:711.

Loncarevic S., Tham W., Danielsson-Tham M.L. (1996). Prevalence of *Listeria monocytogenes* and *Listeria spp.* in smoked and «gravad» fish. *Acta Veterinaria Scandinava,* 37, 13–18.

López V., Villator D., Oertiz S., López P., Navas J., Dávila J.C. and Martínez-Suarez J.V. (2008). Molecular tracking of *Listeria monocytogenes* in an Iberian pig abattoir and processing plant. *Meat Science* 78, (1-2), 130.

Manfreda, G., De Cesare, A., Stella, S., Cozzi, M., Cantoni, C., (2005). Occurrence and ribotypes of *Listeria monocytogenes* in Gorgonzola cheeses. *International Journal of Food Microbiology,* 34, 45-49.

Marklinder I.M., Lindblad M., Eriksson L.M., Finnson A.M., Lindqvist R. (2004). Home storage temperatures and consumer handling of refrigerated foods in Sweden. *Journal of Food Protection*, 67, 2570–2577.

McLauchlin, J., (1996). The relationship between *Listeria* and listeriosis. *Food Control* 7, 4/4: 187-193.

McLauchlin, J., Mitchell, R. T., Smerdon, W. J., Jewell, K. (2004). *Listeria monocytogenes* and listeriosis: a review of hazard characterisation for use in microbiological risk assessment of foods. *International Journal of Food Microbiology,* 92, 15, 33.

Medrala D., Dabrowski W., Czekajlo-Kolodziej U., Daczkowska-Kozon E., Koronkiewicz A., Augustynowicz E., Manzano M. (2003). Persistence of *Listeria monocytogenes* strains isolated from products in a Polish fish processing plant over a 1-year period. *Food Microbiology,* 20:715.

Meloni D., Galluzzo P., Mureddu A., Piras F., Griffiths M., Mazzette R. (2009). *Listeria monocytogenes* in RTE foods marketed in Italy: prevalence and automated EcoRI ribotyping of the isolates. *International Journal of Food Microbiology* 129, (2), 166.

Meloni D., Piras F., Mureddu A., Mazza R., Nucera D., Mazzette R. (2012). Sources of *Listeria monocytogenes* contamination in traditional fermented sausage processing plants in Italy. *Italian Journal of Food Science, accepted, in press.*

Miettinen M.K., Björkroth K., Korkeala H.J. (1999). Characterization of *Listeria monocytogenes* from an ice cream plant by serotyping and pulsed-field gel electrophoresis. *International Journal of Food Microbiology,* 46, 187–192.

Miettinen H., Wirtanen G. (2005). Prevalence and location of *Listeria monocytogenes* in farmed rainbow trout. *International Journal of Food Microbiology* 104:135.

Nakamura, H., Hatanaka, M., Ochi, K., Nagao, M., Ogasawar, J., Hase, A., Kitase, T., Haruki, K., Nishikawa, Y. (2004). *Listeria monocytogenes* isolated from cold-smoked fish products in Osaka City, Japan. *International Journal of Food Microbiology* 94, 323-8.

Mureddu A., Conter M., Meloni D., Piras F., Ianieri A., Mazzette R. (2011). Molecular characterization of *L.monocytogenes* isolated from ready to eat seafood in Italy. *Italian Journal of Food Science,* 23, 106-117.

Nilsson, L., Huss, H. H., & Gram, L. (1997). Inhibition of *Listeria monocytogenes* on cold-smoked salmon by nisin and carbon dioxide atmosphere. *International Journal of Food Microbiology,* 38, 217-227.

Orsi R.H., den Bakker H.C., Wiedmann M. (2011). *Listeria monocytogenes* lineages: Genomics, evolution, ecology, and phenotypic characteristics. *International Journal of Medical Microbiology* 301, 79–96.

Public Health Agency Canada, Lessons Learned Report: The Canadian Food Inspection Agency's Recall Response to the 2008 Listeriosis Outbreak. (2009). Available online: http://www.phac-aspc.gc.ca/fs-sa/listeria/2008-lessons-lecons-eng.php .

Rocourt J., Jacquet C., Relly A. (2000). Epidemiology of human listeriosis and seafoods. *International Journal of Food Microbiology* 62:197.

Romanova, N., Favrin, S., Griffiths, M. W. (2002). Sensitivity of *Listeria monocytogenes* to sanitizers used in the meat processing industry. *Applied and Environmental Microbiology* 68: 6405–6409.

Rørvik, L.M., Caugant, D., Yndestad, M. (1995). Contamination pattern of Listeria *monocytogenes* and other *Listeria spp.* in a salmon slaughterhouse and smoked salmon processing plant. *International Journal of Food Microbiology* 25, 19-27.

Rørvik, L. M. (2000). *Listeria monocytogenes* in the smoked salmon industry. *International Journal of Food Microbiology,* 62, 183-190.

Ryser E.T., Marth E.H. (2007). *Listeria*, listeriosis and food safety, (3rd ed.). CRC Press, Boca Raton, FL.

Serio A., Chaves-López C., Paparella A. (2011). *Listeria monocytogenes* isolated from the smoked salmon industry: Growth potential under different environmental conditions. *Food Control* 22 (2011) 2071-2075.

Shen, Y., Liu, Y., Zhang, Y., Cripe, J., Conway, W., Meng, J., Hall, G., Bhagwat, A.A., (2006). Isolation and Characterization of *Listeria monocytogenes* Isolates from Ready-To-Eat Foods in Florida. *Applied and Environmental Microbiology,* 72, 7, 5073-5076.

Swaminathan B., Gerner-Smidt P. (2007). The epidemiology of human listeriosis. *Microbes Infection* 9:1236.

Thévenot D., Delignette-Muller M.L., Christieans S. and Vernozy-Roland C. (2005). Prevalence of *Listeria monocytogenes* in 13 dried sausage processing plants and their products. *International Journal of Food Microbiology* 102, (1), 85.

Thévenot D., Dernburg A., Christieans S., Vernozy-Roland C. (2006). An updated review of *Listeria monocytogenes* in the pork meat industry and its products. *Journal of Applied Microbiology*, 101, 7.

Tyopponen S., Petaja E., Mattila-Sndholm T. (2003). Bioprotectives and probiotics for dry sausages. *International Journal of Food Microbiology* 83, 233-244.

United States Food and Drug Administration /United States Department of Agriculture /CDC, (2003). Quantitative assessment of the relative risk to public health from foodborne *Listeria monocytogenes* among selected categories of ready-to-eat foods. Available from: http://www.foodsafety.gov/~dms/lmr2-toc.html.

Van Coillie, E., Werbrouck, H., Heyndrickx, M., Herman, L., Rjipens, N., (2004). Prevalence and typing of *Listeria monocytogenes* in Ready-to Eat food products on the Belgian market. *Journal of Food Protection* 67, 2480-2487.

Vazquez-Boland J.A., Kuhn M., Berche P., Chakraborty T., Domingues-Bernal G., Goebel W., Gonzalez-Zorn B., Wehlamd J. and Kreft J. (2001). *Listeria* pathogenesis and molecular virulence determinants. *Clinical Microbiolical Review* 14, (3), 584.

Voetsch, A.C., Angulo, F.J., Jones, T.F., Moore, M.R., Nadon, C., McCarthy, P., Shiferaw, B., Megginson, M.B., Hurd, S., Anderson, B.J., Cronquist, A., Vugia, D.J., Medus, C., Segler, S., Graves, L.M., Hoekstra R.M., Griffin P.M. (2007). Reduction in the incidence of invasive listeriosis in foodborne diseases active surveillance network sites, 1996-2003. *Clinical Infectious Diseases,* 44, (4), 513-520.

Vogel, B. F., Huss, H. H., Ojneiyi, B., Ahrens, P., & Gram, L. (2001[a]). Elucidation of *Listeria monocytogenes* contamination routes in cold-smoked salmon processing plants detected by DNA-based typing methods. *Applied and Environmental Microbiology,* 67, 2586-2595.

Vogel, B.F., Jorgensen, L.V., Ojeniyi, B., Huss. H.H., Gram, L. (2001[b]). Diversity of *Listeria monocytogenes* isolates from cold-smoked salmon produced in different smokehouses as assessed by Random Amplified Polymorphic DNA analyses. *International Journal of Food Microbiology* 65, 83-92.

Zunabovic M., Domig K.J., Kneifel W. 2011. Practical relevance of methodologies for detecting and tracing of *Listeria monocytogenes* in ready-to-eat foods and manufacture environments –A review. *LWT – Food Science and Technology* 44, 351-362.

In: Listeria Infections
Editors: A. Romano and C. F. Giordano

ISBN: 978-1-62081-639-4
© 2012 Nova Science Publishers, Inc.

Chapter VII

Epidemiology of Invasive Listeriosis in Clinical Cases in Navarra (Spain): Comparison between 1995-2005 and 2006-2011

V. Garrido[*1], *A. I. Vitas*[2], *I. García-Jalón*[2],
L. Torroba[3], *and A. Navascués*[4]
[1]Animal Health, Instituto de Agrobiotecnología
(CSIC-UPNA-Gobierno de Navarra), Pamplona, Spain
[2]Microbiology and Parasitology Department,
University of Navarra, Pamplona, Spain
[3]Navarra Hospital Center, Pamplona, Spain
[4]Reina Sofía Hospital, Tudela, Spain

Abstract

The incidence of human listeriosis in Navarra (Spain) was monitored during two different periods of time (1995-2005 and 2006-2011) by active surveillance in collaboration with the main hospitals within this region. A total of 72 cases of invasive listeriosis were detected, with an average incidence rate of 0.75/100,000 inhabitants. The incident rate shows a tendency to increase, as the first period (40 cases within 11 years) showed a rate of 0.65/100,000 while the second period (32 cases within 6 years) showed a rate of 0.86/100,000. Over the whole period studied, 44.4% of the cases were diagnosed among aged population (32 cases out 72), the group most affected by listeriosis, while case fatality (including fetal death) was 57.9% in pregnant women (n=11 out of 19 pregnancy-associated cases). Most of the isolated strains belonged to serotype

* Corresponding author: Ph.D. Victoria Garrido. Instituto de Agrobiotecnología (IdAB). Universidad Pública de Navarra (UPNA). Carretera de Mutilva s/n, 31192, Mutilva, Navarra (Spain). Mail: victoria.garrido@unavarra .es; phone: +34 948168022; fax: +34 948232191.

4b (n=38 out of 65 strains; 58.5%), but a significant increase of 1/2a serotype has been observed in recent years ($P \leq 0.05$). In addition, serotype 1/2c was isolated from a clinical case, and to the best of our knowledge, it is the first clinical isolation of this serotype in the region. In this chapter, the epidemiology of human listeriosis and how to improve the current Spanish surveillance system will be discussed.

Keywords: *L. monocytogenes*, listeriosis, surveillance, serotypes

1. Introduction

Listeria monocytogenes (*L. monocytogenes*) has been recognized as a serious food-borne pathogen due to the severity of its symptoms (sepsis, meningitis, meningoencefalitis, rhomboencephalitis, perinatal infections, abortions or death), occuring in persons with recognized underlying diseases, and the elderly, pregnant women and in some cases, even in healthy population. It is the seventh zoonoses in the EU with 1,645 confirmed cases in 2009, but with regard to its high fatality rate, it is the first zoonoses [1]. Moreover, listeriosis is considered the third most frequent cause of bacterial meningitis, after *Streptococcus pneumoniae* and *Neisseria meningitidis* [2] and although listeriosis has been mainly diagnosed in immunocompromised patients, elderly or newborns, healthy adults can also be affected by this pathogen [3].

Despite the severity of their symptoms and their public health impact on developed countries, listeriosis notification is not mandatory in several countries (including Spain), and as a result, surveillance of the disease is based on voluntary reports. Currently, there is a statutory obligation in the EU to report cases of human outbreaks of listeriosis as part of the Zoonoses Directive2003/99/EC [4] (for epidemiological surveillance purposes, but sporadic cases of listeriosis are usually not investigated and they could be linked to unnoticed outbreaks [3]. Even in countries with compulsory notification of listeriosis and efficient surveillance systems, such as PulseNet in the United States, the number of cases could be greater than reported [5] due to the occurrence of many sporadic cases and spontaneous miscarriages which are not investigated. Numerous countries had already established surveillance programs of listeriosis years ago, such as Finland (1995) or France (2001). In Spain, the current surveillance of listeriosis is based on voluntary reporting of the cases to the National System of Microbiology but it is not included in the list of communicable diseases. A total of 121 listeriosis cases were reported in 2009, covering 25% of all of Spain [1]. Due to the inexistence of a surveillance system for this disease in Spain, low incidence rates have been reported. However, when active surveillance methodology is carried out, a large number of diagnosed cases occurs, as in the case of Italy [6]. In compliance with decision No. 2119/98/EC of the European Parliament and of the Council [7], Navarra, a community of northern Spain, has a statutory report of cases since 2008 [8], setting up a network for the epidemiological surveillance and control of communicable diseases. Our research team started to monitor this disease in Navarra, a small region in northern Spain, in 1995. The population of this community increased from 532,493 inhabitants in 1995 to 641,293 inhabitants in 2011 [9].

The purpose of this study was to compare the incidence of listeriosis cases in Navarra in two different periods (1995-2005 and 2006-2011), by applying an active surveillance method, in order to have reliable data regarding the evolution of the disease rates. The study includes the characterization of isolated strains and a description of the groups that have been affected the most, in order to develop the most suitable preventive programs for populations with the highest risk.

2. Material and Methods

2.1. Established Protocol for Active Surveillance of Listeriosis in Navarra (Spain)

Since 1995, the principal hospitals of Navarra have actively notified our laboratory of the cases of human listeriosis. Confirmed cases were reported by physicians, using a standardized form for documenting the clinical information, disease presentation, underlying conditions and disease outcome. Information regarding sex, age of the patient, clinical symptoms, immunosuppressive treatment or underlying disease and evolution of the patient was reported when available. It is important to point out that our team was notified on the very same day that a listeriosis case was confirmed.

A case was defined by isolation of *L. monocytogenes* from a normally sterile site in a patient with a clinically compatible illness. A perinatal case was considered when an infected pregnant women, miscarriage, stillbirth or newborn less than one month old was detected. When the pathogen was isolated from both the pregnant women and her newborn, the event was considered as a single case. If a patient had more than one underlying disease, the case was assigned to the condition considered to be the most immunosuppressive. Age was categorized into 4 age-groups between 1 and ≥ 60 years old (mother ages were considered in pregnancy-associated cases). The evolution of listeriosis in the perinatal cases was reported in terms of recovery of affected women and fetus or newborn evolution.

Risk factors were categorized as known risk factor of listeriosis or not at risk people (healthy). Known risk factors were defined as malignancies (solid or hematological malignancies and solid organ transplant), chronic diseases (immunosuppressive treatment, inflammatory diseases such as colitis or Crohn's disease, diabetes mellitus, alcohol addiction or corticosteroid theraphy) and pregnant women.

The incidence rate by year was calculated as the ratio between confirmed cases and Navarra population reported on the first of January of each year [9]. The incidence rates were expressed per 100,000 inhabitants or per different population groups such as aged population (number of listeriosis cases in aged persons vs. population of this group) or pregnant women. Pregnancy associated cases were referred to as the total number of births in each year and the incidence rate was expressed per 1,000 births.

2.2. Collection of *L. monocytogenes* Strains

The main hospitals of Navarra were asked to send the documentation (information given on the forms) and the isolated strains to our research group (Department of Microbiology of the University of Navarra) in order to perform the complete characterization of each clinical case.

From the 72 confirmed listeriosis cases that were detected between 1995 and 2011, only 65 strains were isolated and stored. One colony per patient was isolated and subsequently characterized (it was assumed that only one serotype and/or macrorestriction pattern would be found per patient). Strains were confirmed by biochemical methods: characteristic growth in Aloa Agar (AES, Cedex, France), catalase production, positive Henry illumination, rhamnose and xylose fermentation (Scharlau, Barcelona, Spain), positive *B*-hemolysis and Christie Atkins Munch-Petersen test (CAMP versus *S. aureus*) in 5% Sheep Blood Agar (Biomerieux, Marcy l'Etoile, France). All biochemical tests were performed and interpreted as described in the standardized method for the isolation of *L. monocytogenes* NF ISO EN 11290-1/A1 [10]. Strain controls used in each experiment were *L. monocytogenes* ATCC 35152, *L. innocua* ATCC 33090, *L. welshimeri* ATCC 35897, *L. ivanovii* ATCC 19118, *S. aureus* ATCC 25923 and *R. equi* ATCC 6939. The collection of *L. monocytogenes* isolates was stored in 10% sterilized skimmed milk at -80°C.

2.3. Serotyping

Serotyping of *L. monocytogenes*, based on antibodies that specifically react with somatic (O antigens) and flagellar (H antigens) antigens, was performed using commercial *Listeria* antisera (Denka, Seiken Co., Ldt., Tokyo, Japan) by following the manufacturer's instructions. Strains were pre-cultured at 37°C/18 h in Sheep Blood Agar (Biomerieux), then one colony was streaked in Tryptose Soy Agar supplemented with 0.6 % Yeast extract (TSAY, Biomerieux) and cultured at 37°C/18 h. Fresh cultures were suspended with NaCl 0.2% and heat denatured. This suspension was used for the detection of somatic antigens (O antigens).

Agglutination of each strain was carried out with antisera anti-O (O-I/II), O V/VI, O-I, O-II, O-VI, O-VII, O-VIII, O-IX). For detection of flagella (H antigens), at least 3 consecutive cultures at 25°C/48 h in Motility Agar (Difco, Detroit, USA) were needed. Next, each strain was grown in Brain Heart Infusion (Microkit, Madrid, Spain) at 25°C/24 h and fixed with formaldehyde 1% (Panreac, Barcelona, Spain) for 48 h at 25°C. Agglutination was carried out with the anti-H (H-A, H-AB, H-C, H-D) mixing 1:1 (V/V) on a microtiter plate and incubating at 52°C/2 h. A collection of *L. monocytogenes* was used as control strains: ATCC 35152 (1/2a), CECT 936 (1/2b), ATCC 19112 (1/2c), ATCC 19113 (3a), CECT 937 (3b), CECT 938 (3c), ATCC 19114 (4a), ATCC 13932 (4b), ATCC 19116 (4c), ATCC 19117 (4d). Strains were classified according to the scheme established by Seeliger and Höhne [11], and then grouped in 1/2 serogroup (1/2 a, 1/2 b and 1/2c serotypes) and 4 serogroup (3 and 4 serotypes).

2.4. Statistical Analysis

All the statistical analyses were performed with SPSS 16.0 software package. Pearson´s Chi-Square (X^2) test was used for categorical variables. Statistical significance was considered when the probability was equal to or less than 0.05 (*P*≤0.05).

3. Results

3.1. Incidence of Listeriosis in Navarra (Spain)

A total of 72 cases of invasive listeriosis have been confirmed in Navarra over 17 years of surveillance (1995 to 2011), with an average incidence rate of 0.75/100,000 inhabitants. The mean annual incidence in the first period of time (1995 to 2005) was 0.65/100,000 [3], while 0.86/100,000 was detected in the second period (2006 to 2011), showing a tendency to increase but no statistical differences were detected ($P>0.05$, X^2) between the two analyzed periods.

However, a significant increase of the disease has been observed among the elderly in recent years, with an incidence rate of 2.38/100,000 in the second period vs. 0.87/100,000 in the first one. Years 2007 and 2009 were especially dramatic among this group at risk, with 3.6 and 4.2 cases per 100,000 elderly inhabitants, respectively (Figure 1). The mean annual incidence in the elderly group was 1.4/100,000 inhabitants in the whole study.

As can be observed in Figure 2, the group corresponding to pregnant women was the second most affected group at risk. Although a low incidence rate per 1,000 births was detected for the entire study, the number of cases ranged from 0.15 in the first period to 0.65 in the second period.

Interestingly, a high number of cases were detected from 2003 to 2005, showing an incidence from 0.49 to 0.65/1,000 births, when 10 out of the 19 total pregnancy cases (52.6%) were diagnosed. Despite the fact that all the affected women recovered, the high fatality outcome of fetus or newborn detected (57.9%), showed the severity of this disease among pregnant women.

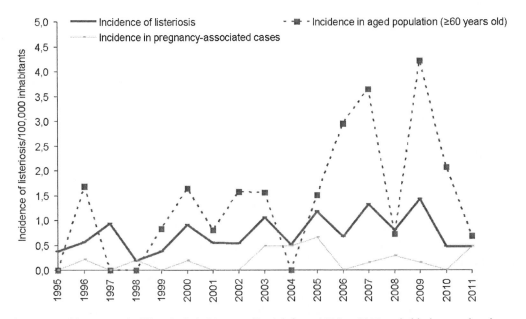

Figure 1. Incidence trend of listeriosis in Navarra (Spain) from 1995 to 2011 and elderly associated cases.

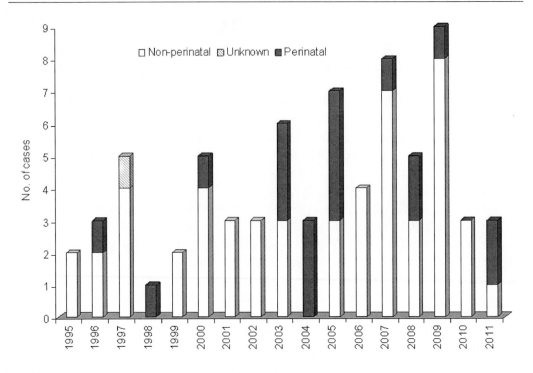

Figure 2. Incidence trend of listeriosis in Navarra (Spain) from 1995 to 2011 and pregnancy-associated cases.

3.2. Clinical and Epidemiological Data

Table 1 shows the epidemiological information of 72 reported listeriosis cases, comparing the data in both studied periods. A total of 40 cases (55.6%) were diagnosed within the first period, while 32 (44.4%) were detected from 2006 to 2011. The case fatality rate detected for the entire study was quite high (41.7%). From the total reported cases, 90.2% of them (65 out of 72) had an underlying risk factor, with a fatal outcome of 40.2%. Patients with an underlying disease were mainly aged persons (n=32). A total of 50 patients (69.4%) were grouped into the non-perinatal group (known listeriosis risk factors and non-predisposition risk factors detected), while 19 perinatal infections (pregnant women and/or newborns) were reported (26.4%).

3.2.1. Non-Perinatal and Perinatal Population

Among the non-perinatal group, the elderly population represented 64.0% of the cases (32 out of 50 non-perinatal cases), showing other associated predisposition risk factors due to age and a fatal outcome of 32.5% (12 out of 32). Despite a significant increase (P=0.01) in the number of cases related to aged population observed between the two analyzed periods (30% and 62.5%, respectively), the fatality rate in this group decreased (P=0.01) in the second period (66.6% to 20%, respectively). This fact is the reason for the global decrease in the fatality rate among the two studied periods, from 52.5% to 28.2% (P=0.037, X^2).

Non-elderly population with risk factors to listeriosis was also reported for the entire study (18 out of 72 cases; 25.0%). This means that 36% of the non-perinatal group (18 out of 50) belonged to this group.

With regard to pregnant women, no significant decrease has been detected in the number of cases between the two analyzed periods (32.5% to 18.8%; $P=0.22$), although 10 out of 19 pregnancy-associated cases (52.6%) were diagnosed in the years 2003 to 2005. Despite the fact that all the pregnant women recovered after receiving treatment, the case fatality rate among this group was very high (11 cases out of 19; 57.9%). Clinical information showed that deaths reported in this group were associated to the high fatality rate of the fetus, resulting in miscarriages, stillbirths or infant deaths within 24 to 48 hours of birth. Fatality rate of pregnancy associated cases for each of the two periods of time analyzed was similar ($P=0.633$).

3.2.2. Risk Factors

As can be observed in Table 1, data regarding elderly people (44.4% of cases) has not been included in the section of "risk factors". In this section, age is not considered the main cause of underlying disease when a chronic or acute disease has been diagnosed. Having taken into account this consideration, 90.3 % of the diagnosed cases were included in one of the three identified risk groups (malignancies, chronic diseases and pregnancy).

Solid tumors were detected in 10 patients, while other underlying diseases such liver disease or alcoholic habits (n=7), solid organ transplant (n=7), diabetes mellitus (n=6), Crohn's disease or ulcerative colitis (n=3), hematologic malignancy (leukemia n=2) corticosteroid therapy (n=2) or chronic kidney disease (n=1) and other diseases (n=9) were also observed in listeriosis patients in this study carried out in Navarra. In addition, one pregnant woman from the first period (included in the group of risk of pregnancy associated cases) also had HIV infection.

There is a clear decrease in the fatality outcome of the cases in the risk group between the first and second period of time (58.8% to 29.0%; $P=0.016$). A decrease in the number of deaths is noticeable in the risk group associated to chronic diseases (Crohn's disease or ulcerative colitis, diabetes mellitus or corticosteroid therapy) with a decrease from 67.7% to 14.3% ($P=0.019$) in the two periods analyzed.

Finally, it should be pointed out that of the total cases of listeriosis, only 6 of them (8.3%) were diagnosed in healthy people: 3 of them were approximately 50 years old, 2 were younger (<20 years old) and the remaining case was a 32-year-old non-pregnant women . Only 1 case resulted in fatal outcome (1 out of 6; 16.7%).

3.2.3. Clinical Symptoms of Listeriosis

The most common clinical presentations were related to the central nervous system (n=16; 22.2%), with cases of meningitis (n=9), meningoencephalitis (n=2), brain abscess (n=2), encephalitis (n=1), rhomboencephalitis (n=1) and ictus (n=1). Septicemia was the second most frequent presentation in patients with listeriosis (n=15; 20.8%). Other symptoms were fever, flu-like, vomiting, miscarriage or premature birth (n=15; 20.8%). With regard to problems associated with organs (11.1%), there were heart diseases (n=4), kidney failure (n=2), lung (n=1) and liver disease (n=1). Local infections (6.9%) included colitis (n=3), osteomyelitis or arthritis (n=2). In the remaining group, there were hormonal disorders or unknown (n=13, not available data).

Table 1. Epidemiological information of listeriosis cases reported in Navarra over 17 years of surveillance

Epidemiological data		First period (1995-2005)			Second period (2006-2011)			Total (%)[H]	
		No. of cases (%)[A]	No. of deaths	% Fatal outcome[B]	No. of cases (%)[A]	No. of deaths	% Fatal outcome[B]		
Clinical form									
	Non-perinatal	26 (65.0)	13	(50.0)	24 (75.0)	6	(25.0)	50	(69.4)
	Perinatal	13 (32.5)	8	[C] (61.5)	6 (18.8)	3	[C] (50.0)	19	(26.4)
	Unknown	1 (2.5)	0	-[D]	2 (6.2)	0	-[D]	3	(4.2)
Risk factors									
Type or risk factors	Malignancies[E]	15 (37.5)	8	(53.3)	11 (34.4)	4	(36.4)	26	(36.1)
	Chronic diseases[F]	6 (15.0)	4	(66.7)	14 (43.8)	2	(14.3)	20	(27.8)
	Pregnancy-associated	13 (32.5)	8	[C] (61.5)	6 (18.8)	3	[C] (50.0)	19	(26.4)
	Total cases at risk	34 (85.0)	20	(58.8)	31 (96.8)	9	(29.0)	65	(90.3)
Not at risk people		5 (12.5)	1	(20.0)	1 (3.1)	0	-[D]	6	(8.3)
Unknown		1 (2.5)	0	-[D]	0 -[D]	0	-[D]	1	(1.4)
Age group[G]									
	1-19	2 (5.0)	1	(50.0)	1 (3.1)	0	-[D]	3	(4.2)
	20-39	13 (32.5)	0	-[D]	7 (21.9)	0	-[D]	20	(27.8)
	40-59	8 (20.0)	2	(25.0)	4 (12.5)	2	(50.0)	12	(16.7)
	≥60	12 (30.0)	8	(66.7)	20 (62.5)	4	(20.0)	32	(44.4)
	Unknown	5 (12.5)	2	(40.0)	0 -[D]	D	-[D]	5	(6.9)
Total number of cases		40 (55.6)	21	(52.5)	32 (44.4)	9	(28.1)	72	-[D]

A. % of the total number of cases per period (n=40 and n=32 respectively). B. % of the number of cases detected each period in each group. C. Patient considered: newborn (pregnant women recovered). D. Not applicable (-). E. Solid or hematological malignancies and solid organ transplant. F. Other diseases: chronic diseases, inflammatory diseases (ulcerative colitis or Crohn's disease), diabetes mellitus or corticosteroid therapy. G. Age of the pregnant women only (data of newborn death not included). H. Percentage based on the total number of cases (n=72).

3.3. Serotypes Distribution

A total of 6 serotypes belonging to 2 different serogroups were detected among the 65 available strains, as shown in Table 2. Serotype 4b was the overall predominant serotype in the entire study (n=38, 58.5%), followed by serotype 1/2a (n=20; 30.7%). A significant increase in the number of serogroup 1 strains has been observed in the second time period (P=0.004).

Table 2. Serotype distribution of *L. monocytogenes* isolated from diagnosed cases in Navarra (Spain) from 1995 to 2011

Period of time	Serotypes No.						Serogroup %		Total strains
	1/2a	1/2b	1/2c	3b	4b	4d	I	IV	
1995-2005	6	1	0	1	25	0	21.0	79.0	33
2006-2011	14	3	1	0	13	1	56.0	44.0	32
Total	20	4	1	1	38	1	38.5	61.5	65

3.3.1. Distribution of Serotypes among Groups at Risk and Healthy Population

Four different serotypes were detected within the 30 strains isolated from the 32 diagnosed cases among elderly population. The most frequent serotype was 4b (n=16) followed by 1/2a (n=12), 1/2b and 4d (n=1, respectively). Most of isolated strains in the first period belonged to 4b serotype (4b n=8; 1/2a n=2; 2 strains not available), while the remaining serotypes were detected in the second time period.

From the strains available from pregnant women (n=16 out of 19 diagnosed cases), 4 different serotypes were detected (4b n=10; 1/2a n=4; 1/2b n=1; 1/2c n=1). The serotype 1/2c was isolated from meconium of a premature baby in 2009. Both, pregnant woman and the baby recovered.

Four serotypes were detected in the known group of risk (n=14) other than pregnant women and aged population (4b n= 7; 1/2a n=3; 1/2b n=2; 3b n=1 and 1 case not available - NA-). The underlying conditions of the 4b serotype were alcoholic habits and or cirrhosis (n=4), Crohn's disease (n=1), cancer (n=1) and a diabetes patient with heart problems (n=1). Underlying conditions for serotype 1/2a included heart transplant (n=1), breast cancer (n=1) and Crohn's disease (n=1).

Two serotypes were detected among the cases diagnosed in healthy people: 4b (n=5) and 1/2a (n=1).

3.3.2. Fatality Rate ad Serotypes

Further analysis was carried out to relate the fatality rate and the serotype of the isolated strains (data available for both variables in 27 out of 30 cases with fatal outcome). Figure 3 shows that the majority of fatal outcomes were related with serotype 4b (n=22 out 38 4b; 57.9%). Significant differences were observed in the fatal outcomes of patients infected with serotype 4b *versus* 1/2a (*P*=0.011). The fatality rate of clinical patients infected with 4b serotype, do not decrease along the two periods analyzed *P*=0.112).

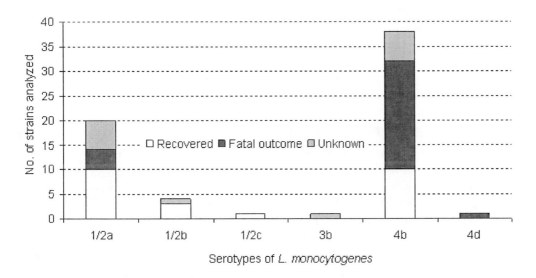

Figure 3. Serotype distribution of *L. monocytogenes* isolated in clinical cases in Navarra Spain from 1995 to 2011.

4. Discussion

Based on the average incidence of the entire study, the frequency of listeriosis is relatively low in Navarra, although a tendency to increase was observed in the last few years, similar to that which was reported in several European countries (EU) [12-15]. In 2009, the 26 Member States of the EU reported 1,645 cases of confirmed listeriosis human cases, meaning an increase of 19% (n=264) when compared to 2008. The overall incidence rate was 0.4 cases per 100,000 inhabitants. One of the highest notification rates came from Spain, as a result of adjusting notification rates with the population coverage in the Spanish surveillance system (25%). Within each country, a statistically significant increasing trend was noted in listeriosis rates from 2005 to 2009 in Austria, Denmark, Hungary, Italy, Spain and Sweden, while statistically significant decreasing trends were noted in the Netherlands [1].

Human listeriosis notification in the EU in 2007 led to an incidence rate of 0.3/100,000 population, with the highest notification rates reported in Denmark (1.1), Finland (0.8), Sweden (0.6) and Luxembourg (0.6), with a total of 1558 cases of listeriosis reported from 27 Member States of the EU [16]. Spain reported 81 cases, with an incidence rate of 0.2/100,000, while for the same year a rate of 1.3/100,000 was confirmed in Navarra and also observed in a study carried out in Madrid in 2007 [17]. Considering that the likelihood of listeriosis in Navarra is similar to the whole country (similar distribution of groups at risk and similar food intake habits among Spain communities), the reason for the high rates in Navarra could be the active surveillance system developed that has been carried out in Navarra since 1995, with the notification of all sporadic listeriosis cases. It is important to point out that the same procedures have been used during the entire 17 years of surveillance, so the increase of disease in the past few years is a reality and can not be attributed to methodological changes in listeriosis diagnosis. We believe that our incidence rate is more reliable than the official one mentioned in the EFSA report, because several communities of Spain do not notify sporadic cases to the National Surveillance System (and afterwards to EFSA), due to the characteristic of non-mandatory disease. Similar annual average of listeriosis (0.76/100,000 inhabitants) have been observed in Madrid during a 22-year study [17].

Likewise, the active surveillance performed in Italy which involved distribution of clinical and food questionnaires to hospitals, combined with the characterization of the isolated strains, resulted in a higher number of listeriosis cases than those reported by notifications [6].

Coinciding with that which was observed in this study, the most affected population group within the EU in 2009 was the elderly [1]. As in previous years, the elderly were especially affected by listeriosis (58.5%; aged >65 years) and the overall case fatality rate was 16.6%, showing a slight decrease with respect to that which was observed in 2008. In the retrospective study carried out in Madrid (Spain) during 22-years study a significant increase among the elderly population was observed in agreement with our results [17]. As 91.7% of listeriosis cases were detected in "risk groups" they should be warned regarding the specific risks when exposed to the pathogen due to consumption of contaminated food products.

Ingestion of *L. monocytogenes* is usually quite common and given the ubiquitous distribution of this bacteria and the high frequency of contamination of raw and industrially processed foods, high exposure to the population would be expected [18]. Food products are mainly contaminated with serogroup 1/2 (this includes 1/2a, 1/2b and 1/2c), or serotype 4b as observed in several studies [19-20]. It is well known that the population is exposed to the pathogen by ingestion of contaminated food products due to an inadequate treatment for destroying the pathogen and/or a cross contamination after processing at industry, market or home level. Delicatessen turkey or ham products and other types of ready-to-eat products (RTE) such as cheeses, sausages or salads among others, have been linked to listeriosis outbreaks. Therefore, the increase of serogroup 1 among listeriosis cases in the most recently studied period (56% vs. 21%) suggests that further studies should be carried out with regard to periodic surveillance of *L. monocytogenes* in food products at risk, in order to compare clinical and food isolated strains (by serotyping and molecular methods). A previous survey of *L. monocytogenes* in selected ready-to-eat products carried out in Navarra [19], showed that smoked fish products were highly contaminated with serotype 4b followed by 1/2a, while predominant serotypes in sliced cooked ham were 1/2a and 1/2c [19], and the majority of clinical cases were 4b [3]. However, the increase in serotype 1/2a clinical isolates reported in this chapter has also been observed by other researchers [6, 21]. Strikingly, few cases of reported listeriosis have being caused by serotype 1/2c [21] and to the best of our knowledge this is the first time that a clinical case belonging to serotype 1/2c was isolated in Navarra. It should also be pointed out that characterization of food and clinical isolates in Navarra [3] by serological and genetically techniques (Pulsed-field electrophoresis, PFGE) helped us to relate sporadic listeriosis cases, allowing the detection of possible outbreaks that perhaps would remain unnoticed when just a few cases are involved (isolated strains of smoked salmon in 2004 and 10 clinical cases detected since 2002 to 2005). Therefore, we consider the isolation and rapid characterization of clinical strains by serotyping and PFGE to be essential for listeriosis surveillance. Despite the fact that this method is laborious and time-consuming, it is considered to be the most sensitive technique for strain discrimination, and has become the standard subtyping method for detecting listeriosis outbreaks and for relating sporadic cases [3, 22-24]. In addition to these procedures, more investigations regarding the virulence of *L. monocytogenes* strains are needed, taking into account the decrease in the fatality rate within recent years (28.1% in the second period vs. 52.5% in the first one), and the decrease of serotype 4b among isolated clinical strains.

In order to assure the protection of public health in Spain, statutory notification of listeriosis should be established on a National level due to the severity of this disease and its high fatality rate. The overall case fatality rate for human listeriosis in Europe in 2009 was 16.6%(270 human deaths), being the first cause of death in the EU followed by *Salmonella* (90 deaths) and *Campylobacter* (40 deaths) [1]. Food safety criteria for *L. monocytogenes* in RTE foods have been established by the European Comission [25-27]. Absence of the pathogen is established in 25 g of RTE products capable of supporting growth (once the product leaves the industry) and RTE for medical purposes or food for infants, being less than 100 CFU/g for all products (capable or incapable of supporting the growth) at the end of their shelf-life. We believe that this legislation is sufficient for maintaining the incidence of listeriosis at low levels, but collaboration on the part of Industry and consumers is also required. Hygienic measures at the industrial level should be maintained in order to assure microbiological safety and more specific instructions regarding storage and recommendations for consumers should be included on the product labels, including special warnings for people at risk. Consumers play an important role in listeriosis control, especially if they apply correct hygienic measures and store food products at the correct temperature [28] so as to prevent *L. monocytogenes* growth.

Conclusion

The harmonization of listeriosis surveillance in Spain could be improved by reporting all sporadic cases throughout the different communities (in addition to suspicious outbreaks), recovering epidemiological data (clinical information and food habits consumption) and isolating and characterizing the strain responsible in each case. In addition, all miscarriages or stillbirth cases should be investigated in search for the possible origin of *L. monocytogenes* infection.

Active surveillance of listeriosis on a national level is the only way to determine the real prevalence of disease for further comparison with the other Member States of the EU or other countries. Finally, in order to reduce the increasing trend of listeriosis observed, risk groups should be warned regarding their specific risks when exposed to the pathogen through educational programs established for this purpose.

Acknowledgments

The contract for V. Garrido, Ph.D., was funded by UPNA (Postdoctoral Fellowship). We would like to express our appreciation to the following institutions for their close collaboration: Complejo Hospitalario de Navarra (CHN), Clínica Universitaria de Navarra (CUN) and Hospital Reina Sofía. We would also like to express our gratitude to José Leiva, Ph.D. and Jose Luís del Pozo, Ph.D. (Clínica Universitaria de Navarra, CUN). In addition, we would like to thank Laura Stokes for revising this manuscript.

Transparency Declaration

The authors have no conflict of interest.

References

[1]   EFSA & ECDPC.(2011). The European Union Summary Report on Trends and Sources of Zoonoses, Zoonotic Agents and Food-borne Outbreaks in 2009. *The EFSA Journal*, *9*,2090.

[2]   Van de Beek, D., de Gans, J., Spanjaard, L., Weisfelt, M., Reitsma, J. B. & Vermeulen, M. (2004). Clinical features and prognostic factors in adults with bacterial meningitis. *New England Journal of Medicine*,*351*,1849-1859.

[3]   Garrido, V., Torroba, L., Garcia-Jalon, I. & Vitas, A. I. (2008). Surveillance of listeriosis in Navarre, Spain, 1995-2005-epidemiological patterns and characterisation of clinical and food isolates. *EuroSurveillance,13*. Available from: *http://www.eiss.org/images/dynamic/EE/V13N49/art19058.pdf*.

[4]   EC (2003) Directive 2003/99/EC of the European Parlament of the Council of 17 November 2003 on the monitoring of zoonoses and zoonotic agents, amending Council

Decision 90/424/EC and repealing Council Directive 92/117/EEC. Law 325. *Official Journal of the European Union*, 31-40.

[5]   Swaminathan, B., Barrett, T. J., Hunter, S. B. & Tauxe, R. V. (2001). PulseNet: the molecular subtyping network for foodborne bacterial disease surveillance, United States. *Emerging Infectious Diseases, 7*, 382-389.

[6]   Gianfranceschi, M.V., Gattuso, A., D'Ottavio, M. C., Fokas, S. & Aureli, P. (2007). Results of a 12-month long enhanced surveillance of listeriosis in Italy. *EuroSurveillance, 12*, E7-8.

[7]   EC. (1998). Decision No 2119/98/EC of the European Parliament and of the Council of 24 September 1998 setting up a network for the epidemiological surveillance and control of communicable diseases in the Community.*Official Journal* L 268, 03/10/1998.

[8]   BON, Boletín Oficial de Navarra. (2008). *Orden Foral 19/2008, de 15 de Feberero, de la consejera de salud, por la que se modifican las enfermedades incluidas en el Sistema de Vigilancia Epidemiológica de Navarra.* 28, 2641-2642.

[9]   INE (Instituto Nacional de Estadística). [Population of Spain since 1995 to 2011]. 2012 [cited 2011 January 30]. Available from: *www. ine.es.*

[10] AFNOR. (2005). *Microbiology of food and animal feeding stuffs - Horizontal method for the detection and enumeration of Listeria monocytogenes.* Part 1: Detection method - Amendment 1: Modification of the isolation media of the haemolysis test and inclusion of precision data. International Standard ISO 11290:1:1997/Amd 1: 2005. International Organization for Standardization, Geneva.

[11] Seeliger, H. & Höhne. K. (1979). Serotyping of *Listeria monocytogenes* and related species. In Norris, T. (Eds.), *Methods in Microbiology* (pp. 31-49). New York: Academic Press.

[12] Denny, J. & McLauchlin, J.(2008). Human *Listeria monocytogenes* infections in Europe-an opportunity for improved European surveillance. EuroSurveillance13.

[13] Cairns, B.J. & Payne, R.J. (2009). Sudden increases in listeriosis rates in England and Wales, 2001 and 2003. *Emerging Infectious Diseases, 15*, 465-468.

[14] Goulet, V., Hedberg, C. Le Monnier, A. & de Valk, H. (2008). Increasing incidence of listeriosis in France and other European countries. *Emerging Infectious Diseases, 14*, 734-740.

[15] Kasper, S., Huhulescu, S., Auer, B., Heller, I., Karner, F.,Wurzner, R., Wagner, M. & Allerberger, F. (2009). Epidemiology of listeriosis in Austria. *Wien Klin Wochenschr, 121*, 113-119.

[16] EFSA. (2009).The Community Summary Report on Trends and Sources of Zoonoses and Zoonotic Agents in the European Union in 2007. *The EFSA Journal, 223.*

[17] Munoz, P., Rojas, L., Bunsow, E., Saez, E., Sanchez-Cambronero, L., Alcala, L., Rodriguez-Creixems, M. & Bouza, E. (2012). Listeriosis: An emerging public health problem especially among the elderly. *Journal of Infection, 64*, 19-33.

[18] Garrido, V., A.I. Vitas & Garcia-Jalon, I. (2010) The problem of Listeriosis and ready-to-eat products: Prevalence and persistence. In A. Mendez Vilas (Eds.), *Current Research, Technology and Education Topics in Applied Microbiology and Microbial Biotechnology* (pp. 1182-1189). Badajoz (Spain): Formatex Reseach Center.

[19] Garrido, V., Vitas, A.I. & García-Jalón, I. (2009). Survey of *Listeria monocytogenes* in ready-to-eat products: Prevalence by brands and retail establishments for exposure assessment of listeriosis in Northern Spain. *Food Control*, *20*, 986-991.

[20] Vitas, A.I., Aguado, V. &. Garcia-Jalon, I. (2004). Occurrence of *Listeria monocytogenes* in fresh and processed foods in Navarra (Spain). *International Journal of Food Microbiology*, *90*, 349-356.

[21] Gilbreth, S.E., Call, J. E., Wallace, F. M., Scott, V. N., Chen, Y. & Luchansky, J. B. (2005). Relatedness of *Listeria monocytogenes* isolates recovered from selected ready-to-eat foods and listeriosis patients in the United States. *Applied and Environmental Microbiology*, *71*, 8115-8122.

[22] Nucera, D., Lomonaco, S., Bianchi, D. M., Decastelli, L., Grassi, M. A., Bottero, M. T. & Civera, T. (2010). A five year surveillance report on PFGE types of *Listeria monocytogenes* isolated in Italy from food and food related environments. *International Journal of Food Microbiology*, *140*, 271-276.

[23] Graves, L.M. & Swaminathan, B. (2001). PulseNet standardized protocol for subtyping *Listeria monocytogenes* by macrorestriction and pulsed-field gel electrophoresis. *International Journal of Food Microbiology*, *65*, 55-62.

[24] CDC. (2010). Outbreak of invasive listeriosis associated with the consumption of hog head cheese-Louisiana. *Morbidity and Mortality Weekly Report*, *60*, 401-405.

[25] EC (2005). Comission Regulation (EC) No. 2073/2005 of 15 of November 2005 on microbiological criteria for foodstuffs. Law 338. *Official Journal of the European Union*.

[26] EC, (2007). Comission Regulation (EC) No. 1441/2007 of 5 December 2007 amending Regulation (EC) No. 2073/2005 on microbiological criteria for foodstuffs Law 322/12. *Official Journal of the European Union*.

[27] EC. (2010). Comission Regulation (EC) No. 365/2010 of 28 April 2010 amending Regulation (EC) No. 2073/2005 on microbiological criteria for foodstuffs as regards *Enterobacteriaceae* in pasteruised milk and other pasteurised liquid dairy products and *Listeria monocytogenes* in food grade sal. Law 107/9. *Official Journal of the European Union*.

[28] Garrido, V., García-Jalón, I. & Vitas, A. I. (2010). Temperature distribution in Spanish domestic refrigerators and its effect on *Listeria monocytogenes* growth in sliced ready-to-eat ham. *Food Control*, *21*, 896-901.

In: Listeria Infections   ISBN: 978-1-62081-639-4
Editors: A. Romano and C. F. Giordano   © 2012 Nova Science Publishers, Inc.

Chapter VIII

Listeria Infections: Epidemiology, Pathogenesis and Treatment

Imane Saleh[1], Nisreen Alwan[2], Elie Barbour[3],
Esam Azhar[4][5], and Steve Harakeh[5]
[1]Dubai, United Arab Emirates
[2]Department of Biology, American University of Beirut, Beirut, Lebanon
[3] Department of Animal and Veterinary Sciences,
American University of Beirut, Beirut, Lebanon
[4]Medical Laboratory Technology Department,
Faculty of Applied Medical Sciences,
King Fahad Medical Research Center,
King Abdulaziz University, Jeddah, Saudi Arabia
[5]Special Infectious Agents Unit
King Fahad MedicalResearch Center, King Abdulaziz University,
Jeddah, Saudi Arabia

Abstract

Listeria is a motile, Gram-positive, rod-shaped coccobacillus. It is a non-sporeforming, facultatively anaerobic bacterium that can cause a life-threatening disease to both humans and animals known as Listeriosis. Listeria can frequently be isolated from soil, water, food products and vegetation. It is a major food-borne pathogen worldwide, accounting for about 28% of food-related deaths in the USA alone. In 2006, Listeriosis was reported in 23 European Union Member States and it ranked fifth among the most common zoonotic infections in Europe after Campylobacter, Salmonella, Yersinia and Verotoxin-Producing *Escherichia coli* (VTEC) infections.

The most pathogenic species of Listeria is *Listeria monocytogenes* that often causes food-borne infections in immuno-compromised hosts, including newborns and the elderly. As a facultative intracellular parasitic bacterium, *L. monocytogenes* invades a variety of host cells, such as hepatocytes, fibroblasts and epithelial cells, multiplying in the cytoplasm of these cells. This pathogen is one of the reasons of meningoencephalitis and abortion in ruminants. In neonates, it is the third most common cause of bacterial meningitis after *E. coli* and *Streptococcus agalactiae*.

In most Listeria infections cases, the symptoms spontaneously clear in about seven days. However, patients at high risk such as pregnant women require antimicrobial treatment to prevent halt and development of more severe diseases. The duration of antimicrobial treatment depends on the severity of the infection. In Listeriosis treatment, the initial choice of antimicrobials is usually Ampicillin. Some studies also reported a successful treatment using the synergism present in the Trimethoprim-sulfamethoxazole preparations.

Introduction

Listeria are either rod shaped or coccobacilli ranging in size between 1-2 μm in length and are present either individually or in small groups consisting of short chains, palisades or filaments (Singh *et al.*, 2003). They are Gram-positive, non-sporeforming, facultatively anaerobic and ubiquitous bacteria (Cocolin *et al.*, 2002).

They belong to the Clostridium-Lactobacillus-Bacillus branch of bacteria (Troxler *et al.*, 2000). They have peritrichous flagella and are motile however their motility is affected by temperature. They show "tumbling motility" when grown at 20-25°C but not at 35°C (Pearson and Marth, 1990).

Six species are included within the listeria genus*: L. grayi, L. innocua, L. ivanovii, L. monocytogenes, L. seeligeriand*, and *L. welshimeri* (Bubert *et al.*, 1999; Cocolin *et al.*, 2002; Farber and Peterkin, 1991). The classification of listeria is dependent on the somatic (O) and heat-labile flagellar (H) antigens. Accordingly, Listeria species have been divided into different serotypes (Table I) (Hitchins, 1998; Pearson and Marth, 1990). Among all the serotypes, the three most predominant serotypes are: 1/2a, 1/2b and 4b.

Listeria can be present in feces, milk and milk based products, soil, water, silage, sewage and plants, they are a part of the normal flora of the intestinal tract of healthy people (Seeliger and Finger, 1976). The optimum growth temperature for Listeria ranges between 25°C to 37°C. In addition, they are still able to grow at lower temperatures but at a slower rate. They are halophiles and can tolerate salt concentrations ranging from 10% to 20% of NaCl. They are also pH tolerant and can grow at pH values ranging from 4.0 to 9.5 (Liu *et al.*, 2003; Pearson and Marth, 1990).

Table I. Serotypes of Listeria species

Listeria species	Serotypes
L. innocua	4ab, 6a, 6b
L. ivanovii	5
L. monocytogenes	1/2a, 1/2b, 1/2c, 3a, 3b, 3c, 4a, 4ab, 4b, 4c, 4d, 4e, 7
L. seeligeri	1/2b, 4c, 4d, 6b
L. welshimeri	6a, 6b

Source: (Holko *et al.*, 2002).

Members of Listeriae are aerobic to micro-aerophilic. They require certain amino acids for their growth such as thiamine, biotin, riboflavin and thioctic acid are considered essential for their growth (Pearson and Marth, 1990). All Listeria species exhibit similar morphologically and physiologically characteristics (Facinelli *et al.*, 1993).

Listeria monocytogenes is considered the most important species in the genus Listeria. It was first described by Murray *et al.* (1926) and named as *"Bacterium monocytogenes"*. It was called by Pirir in 1927, as *"Listerella hepato*lytica". Nyfeldt was the first to confirm its isolation from humans in 1929 (Farber and Peterkin, 1991). In 1940, it was named "Listeria" in honor of the pioneer bacteriologist Lord Lister and was given the suffix "monocytogenes" relating to the presence of a large number of monocytes in the blood of infected animals (Farber and Peterkin, 1991).

Listeria monocytogenes measures around 1.0-2.0 μm by 0.5 μm. It is a non-capsulated microaerophilic bacterium. The ability of *L. monocytogenes* to tolerate a various environmental conditions gave it access to our food products and was reported to exist throughout the various stages involved in food production, processing, manufacturing and distribution (Solano-Lopez and Hernandez-Sanchez, 2000).

L. monocytogenes is a mesophile and can optimally grow at temperatures ranging from 30 to 37°C. It can also tolerate temperatures between -0.4°C to 50°C (Farber and Peterkin, 1991; Singh *et al.*, 2003). Listeria species was isolated from 64% of house refrigerators according to a study conducted by the Center for Disease Control and Prevention (CDC) (Edward *et al.*, 2002). It can also withstand different pH's ranging from 5.0 to 9.6, with optimum growth occurring at neutral to slightly alkaline pH (Farber and Peterkin, 1991).

Listeriosis which is, primarily caused by *L. monocytogenes* is a zoonotic disease affecting both humans and animals (Vela *et al.*, 2001). Listeriosis is directly contracted by humans by occupational exposure through contact with infected animals, or indirectly, by the consumption of their contaminated products like milk and/or dairy based products (Pearson and Marth, 1990). As with most bacterial diseases, cross-contamination plays an important role in the transmission of Listeria to food products (Singh *et al.*, 2003). Listeria is transmitted to humans by the oral, ocular, cutaneous, respiratory (via inhalation) and urogenital routes (Pearson and Marth, 1990). Congenital infections may also occur. Transmission from Person-to-person is possible but extremely rare (Pearson and Marth, 1990).

This review offers an up-to-date synopsis of Listeria infections, epidemiology, pathogenesis and treatment.

Epidemiology

Listeriosis is a major food-borne disease and accounts annually for around 28% of food-borne deaths in the USA alone (Mead *et al.*, 1999; Todar, 2003). Listeria is as an "emerging" bacterium that lately has become more involved in food-borne outbreaks (NIAID, 2005).

The presence Listeria in food is indicative of microbial contamination (Gilot and Content, 2002). Outbreaks of Listeriosis are mainly reported in the developed countries, where most outbreaks are associated with consumption of manufactured foods and are usually reported to the right agencies and documented. In the developing world, such as in Africa, Asia and

South America, most outbreaks are not recognized and are, therefore, not reported. This is because people in those countries do not often seek medical advice upon sickness. Governmental agencies as well do not keep proper surveillance records and doctors do not always report cases to the right agencies (Rocourt *et al.*, 2003).

Listeria monocytogenes has been involved in several outbreaks and sporadic cases of food-borne illnesses associated with the consumption of various foods contaminated with the bacteria especially milk, cheeses made from unpasteurized milk and other dairy based food products in the USA and Europe (Makino *et al.*, 2005). *Listeria monocytogenes* has been isolated from raw milk with a prevalence rate between 1-45%, with an overall incidence rate of around 4% (Farber *et al.*, 1988; Kells and Gilmour, 2004; Swaminathan and Gerner-Smidt, 2007).

The first outbreak that documented an indirect transmission of *L. monocytogenes* from animals to humans was in Canada's Maritime Provinces in 1983. Consumption of cabbage which was stored in the cold during the winter season and was contaminated with the bacteria from infected sheep manure was the source for that outbreak. Another outbreak in California in 1985 further emphasized the role of food as the vehicle for the spread of Listeriosis. Since then, Listeria has been implicated in many outbreaks of food-borne illness especially resulting from consumption of deli meats and turkey, pâté, hot dogs, seafood and fish (Bortolussi, 2008). The most important *L. monocytogenes* food-borne outbreaks that occurred in Canada, USA, Switzerland and Japan are shown in Table II.

Table II includes the different foods involved in food-borne Listeriosis outbreaks. The consumption of cheese made from either pasteurized or non-pasteurized milk was the causative agent in many outbreaks. In investigating one of the cases, it was found that there was a fault in the processing of the cheese caused by inadequate heat treatment during pasteurization, mixing with raw milk post pasteurization, or later by cross-contamination during further processing and distribution of the dairy products (IFST, 1996).

Listeria is present in many dairy-based foods and constitutes a major problem for the food industry.

Table II. Outbreaks of human food-borne Listeriosis caused by *L. monocytogenes*

Country	Year	Food vehicle	Total number of cases
Canada	1981	Coleslaw	41
USA	1983	Pasteurized whole milk	49
USA	1985	Mexican-style soft cheese	142
Switzerland	1983-1987	Soft cheese	122
USA	1994	Chocolate milk	45
Italy	1997	Corn salad	2189
USA	1998-1999	Hot dogs	50
USA	2000	Turkey meat	30
USA	2000-2001	Mexican-style soft cheese	12
Japan	2001	Domestic cheeses	86

Source: (Alwan, N. 2005).

Cheese and milk are the most intensively examined since most Listeriosis outbreaks have been associated with the consumption of contaminated cheese and/or milk. Listeria has the ability to survive all manufacturing and ripening stages of cheese. It can tolerate the low pH and high salt concentration in various foods especially cheeses. It is mostly concentrated in the curd and only small numbers appearing in the whey (Faleiro *et al.*, 2003).

Many types of cheeses especially soft cheeses have been implicated in with human Listeriosis suggesting that this type of food may be a suitable vehicle for infection with *L. monocytogenes*. Surveys, including hundreds of samples, indicate that 1-15% of cheeses are contaminated with the organism (Low and Donache, 1997). The incidences of *L. monocytogenes* in cheeses from various countries were: 17.4% in Italy, 9.2% in Germany, 10% in Austria and 3.3% in France (Rudol and Scherer, 2001). Although pasteurization should be sufficient to prevent Listeriosis, however, the failure to reach to the desired temperature in large packages may allow the organism to survive. Listeria can also be spread by contact with contaminated hands, counter tops and equipment (Bortolussi, 2008).

A study on the presence of Listeria in a Lebanese cheese-based pastry called Halawet El-Jibn was conducted in 2004. The investigators reported the presence of Listeria species from the start up product, which is Baladi cheese to the final product, which is Halawet El-Jibn (Najjar, 2004). In another study conducted by us, using commonly consumed Lebanese dairy products (Baladi cheese, Kishkand Shankleesh) demonstrated the presence of *L. monocytogenes*. Out of one hundred sixty-four dairy samples tested, 30 *L. monocytogenes* isolates were identified.Those isolates showed high levels of antimicrobial resistance to different antimicrobials used (Harakeh *et al.*, 2009).

In Europe, 2065 cases of Listeriosis related to outbreaks were reported between 1991 and 2001 (Rebagliati *et al.*, 2009). In 2006, Listeriosis was reported in 23 European Union Member States and ranked fifth among the most common cause of zoonotic infection in Europe after Campylobacter, Salmonella, Yersinia and Verotoxin-Producing *Escherichia coli* (VTEC) infections(Rebagliati *et al.*, 2009).

In 2006, 290 cases of human Listeriosis were reported in France, 508 cases in Germany and 208 in the United Kingdom. In this study, *L. monocytogenes* occurred in 3.9% of pork meat, 2.4% of bovine meat, 2.7% of poultry, 2.7% of other or unspecified meats, 12.6% of fishery products and 1.3% of cheese (Denny and McLauchlin, 2008).

In 2008, a major *L. monocytogenes* outbreak occurred in Quebec, Canada involving a strain of *L. monocytogenes* (LM P93). The outbreak was associated with the consumption of pasteurized milk cheese. Between June and December 2008, 38 confirmed cases of LM P93 were reported, including 16 maternal-neonatal cases (14 pregnant women and two babies born to asymptomatic mothers). Testing a variety of cheese brands showed that some have tested positive for LM P93, leading to two cheese plants contaminated by *L. monocytogenes* strains. Pulsed field gel electrophoresis (PFGE) profiles confirmed that a single plant was associated with the outbreak. Products from these two plants were distributed to more than 300 retailers in the province, leading to a wide cross-contamination of retail stock (Gaulin *et al.*, 2012).

In 2009, 524 cases of Listeriosis were reported in the USA. Out of those, 99 cases were associated with pregnancy and the rest were not. The pregnancy status of four cases was unknown. The serotype 4b was the most commonly identified in 48% of the isolates. In addition to the death of 19% of the non-pregnancy-associated cases, 13% of the pregnancy-associated cases have led to fetal death and 7% of the infants born with Listeriosis have died (CDC, 2009). The 2011 report included 146 reported cases of Listeriosis among 28 states.

Most of the infected people were over 60 years old. Thirty death cases were reported, in which the age of the deceased ranged from 48 to 96 years old. Seven of the illnesses were related to pregnancy; four were diagnosed in pregnant women and three in newborns. One miscarriage was reported (CDC, 2011).

Pathogenesis

Listeriosis is an emerging public health hazard. It occurs most frequently in immuno-compromised individuals including the elderly, pregnant women, newborns and people with impaired immune systems (Jones, 1990; Munoz et al., 2012).

The case fatality rate of Listeriosis worldwide is about 30-36% (Denny and McLauchlin, 2008; Volokhov et al., 2002). It ranges from 40% to 58% in developing countries and around 10% in the developed ones (Furyk et al., 2011). There are approximately 2,500 cases with 500 deaths caused by Listeriosis each year in the USA (Anon, 1999; White et al., 2002).

Of the six recognized species of the genus Listeria, only L. monocytogenes is an important human and animal pathogen. It is the most commonly encountered species in food-borne outbreaks of Listeriosis. It is a facultative intracellular parasite that is common in temperate regions. It is one of the main causes of acute community-acquired meningitis among adults in the US (Chan et al., 2001).

Other Listeria species such as L. ivanovii, L. seeligeri, and L. welshimeri have rarely been involved in human infections (Cocolin et al., 2002).

In humans, L. monocytogenes causes a variety of manifestations ranging from asymptomatic intestinal carriage and gastroenteritis to invasive and disseminated severe illnesses. Meningoencephalitis, septicemia and infection of the fetus in pregnant women are the most serious clinical features of Listeriosis (Stavru et al., 2011).

In pregnant women, Listeria infects the amniotic fluid causing spontaneous abortion late in the third trimester of pregnancy though several cases of Listeriosis have been found in both the first and second trimesters (Farber and Peterkin, 1991; Hassan et al., 2001). Pregnant women rarely contract symptoms such as mild fever, headache, nausea, vomiting, aches and pains in joints and muscles. They may also suffer from a mild cough or cold. Pregnant women may be carriers of L. monocytogenes and still give birth to healthy infants (Farber and Peterkin, 1991; Rebagliati et al., 2009).

Neonates may present clinically with early-onset (< 7 days) or late-onset forms of infection (≥ 7 days). Those with the early-onset form are often diagnosed in the first 24 hours of life or with sepsis. Early-onset Listeriosis is usually acquired through the mother by transplacental transmission. Late-onset neonatal Listeriosis is less common than the early-onset one. Clinical symptoms may include irritability, fever and loss of appetite. The mode of acquisition of late-onset Listeriosis is still poorly understood but acquisition of the organism after birth is implicated, since such cases are not accompanied by maternal infection. The organism is not spread through breast-feeding (Bortolussi, 2008). In neonates, and within 2-3 days after birth, Listeria causes mononucleosis and pneumonia during the early-onset of the disease (Hassan et al., 2001; Pearson and Marth, 1990). In utero infection with Listeriosis, a disease known as "granulomatosis infantisepticum" occurs. It is characterized by lesions in the liver and placenta. Meningitis may also occur in the late stages of infant Listeriosis.

Vomiting, rash and cramps are other manifestations that may be encountered in infants infected with the disease (Farber and Peterkin, 1991; Hassan *et al.*, 2001).

In immuno-compromised individuals, including the elderly, cancer patients undergoing chemotherapy, AIDS and organ transplant patients, meningitis or bacteremia/septicemia are the most common clinical features of Listeriosis. Other clinical syndromes associated with adult Listeriosis include endocarditis, localized abscesses, cutaneous lesions, conjunctivitis, urethritis and gastroenteritis (Liu *et al.*, 2003; Pearson and Marth, 1990).

The intestinal tract is the major portal of entry for *L. monocytogenes*. Bacteria might penetrate the mucosal tissue either directly, via invasion of enterocytes, or indirectly, via active penetration of the Peyer's patches (Barbuddhe and Chakraborty, 2009). The pathogenicity of *L. monocytogenes* is not fully understood and likely to depend on its ability to grow intracellularly and to secrete hemolysins. Virulence of *L. monocytogenes* is related to the production of two toxins: hemolysin (Listeriolysin) and cytotonic toxins. The hemolysin is a cytolysin that lyses tissue and red blood cells while the cytotonic toxin (similar to cholera toxin) stimulates cAMP production, causing watery diarrhea. All serotypes of *L. monocytogenes* possess a monocytosis activity enabling the pathogen to survive and multiply in white blood cells (Pearson and Marth, 1990).

Previously, it was thought that the essential virulence factors involved in *L. monocytogenes* pathogenesis are protein p60 and listeriolysin O (hemolysin) only. Protein p60 promotes adhesion and penetration of the bacteria into mammalian cells by inducing phagocytosis. Inside the phagocytes, listeriolysin O lyses the membrane-bound phagocytic vacuole (a process essential for survival and multiplication). Once released into the cell cytoplasm, *L. monocytogenes* reacts with the host-cell microfilaments and becomes enveloped in a thick coat of F-actin, which facilitates its penetration into adjacent cells where listeriolysin O lyses the membrane-bound phagocytic vacuole. This aids with the spread of the organism by bypassing the humoral immune system of the host. Non-hemolytic mutants of *L. monocytogenes* demonstrate virtually no intracellular spread, thus stressing the importance of hemolysin for intracellular growth (Farber and Peterkin, 1991; Jones, 1990).

Nowadays species-specific strategies for *L. monocytogenes* intestinal entry are being studied and these strategies involve different virulent proteins including internalin (InlK) (Barbuddhe and Chakraborty, 2009). Under normal conditions, the cytosol is protected against bacterial infection by autophagy which is a cell-autonomous mechanism of innate immunity. Invasive bacteria, such as *L. monocytogenes*, have evolved strategies to counteract autophagy. ActA is a surface protein produced by *L. monocytogenes* to polymerize actin and mediate intra- and intercellular movements, which plays an important role in autophagy escape. Recently, most studies have focused on investigatingthe role of an important *L. monocytogenes* surface protein called InlK.

Studies proved that in the cytosol of infected cells, InlK interacts with the Major Vault Protein (MVP), the main component of cytoplasmic ribonucleoprotein particles named vaults. Although MVP is involved in a variety of key cellular processes, its role remains indefinable. It was demonstrated that *L. monocytogenes* is able, via InlK, to cap its surface with MVP in order to escape autophagic recognition. The process of actin polymerization previously described and the InlK-MVP interactions are two processes that favor the *L. monocytogenes* infection in the same way. *Listeria monocytogenes* uses this camouflage strategy to efficiently survive inside the infected cells (Dortet *et al.*, 2011; Dortet *et al.*, 2012).

Treatment

Ampicillin is the drug of choice for the treatment of Listeriosis caused by *L. monocytogenes* infections. Several other antibiotics have, also, been effective and are used as second-line agents (Temple and Nahata, 2000). *In vivo*, *L. monocytogenes* is highly susceptible to Meropenem. Data on the efficacy of Meropenem in the treatment of clinical cases of Listeriosis are limited. In 2004, Stepanovic*et al.*described the case of a child with aplastic anemia who had acquired nosocomial Listeriosisand failed to respond to the initial Meropenem therapy. The patient's condition began to improve only after Ampicillin was introduced to the treatment protocol (Stepanovic *et al.*, 2004).

Pregnant women with signs of fever or sepsis should have blood and urine culture tests to determine whether their symptoms are caused by listeriosis. In such a case empiric therapy, including using Ampicillin, should be initiated as a treatment for infection with Listeria. For infants born to mothers suspected of having Listeriosis, blood cultures should be taken and antibiotic therapy should be followed (Bortolussi, 2008).

In addition to Ampicillin, Gentamicin should be administered to patients with sepsis. Listeriosis treatment with antibiotics should be accompanied with agents that penetrate, distribute and remain stable within the host cells. An extended treatment with high doses of Ampicillin has a significant outcome in infected neonates (Lamont *et al.*, 2011). In summary, the current treatment of Listeriosis is made of supportive therapy in parallel with the use of intravenous antibiotics (Lungu *et al.*, 2011).

When meningitis occurs upon Listeria infection, the treatment of choice is Ampicillin in synergy with Gentamicin for three weeks or more depending on the case. An alternative option for people allergic to Ampicillin would be Trimethoprim-sulfamethoxazole. In the case of bacteremia, Ampicillin and Gentamicin should also be used for two weeks. When *L. monocytogenes* infection causes brain abscess, treatment with Ampicillin and Gentamicin are used for a period between four to six weeks. Listeriosis-linked gastroenteritis is usually self-limiting but in extreme cases Amoxicillin or Trimethoprim-sulfamethoxazole may be used (Johns Hopkins medicine, 2012).

Ampicillin is allegedly bacteriostatic to Listeria and this is the reason why it is advisable to add an aminoglycoside to the treatment. Some other antimicrobials have been tried in treating Listeriosis, among these is Vancomycin that showed some clinical success as Listeriosis treatment. However, some patients have developed Listeria meningitis while receiving Vancomycin. Rifampinis an effective antimicrobial, *in vitro*, against Listeria, but very limited clinical experience has been conducted on it and therefore it is dangerous for monotherapy of any infection (Johns Hopkins medicine, 2012). Future research may contribute more to the eventual treatment from Listeria infections.

Conclusion

Infections by Listeria monocytogenes cause listeriosis. Listeriosis is caused by the ingestion of foods that are contaminated with the causative agent or by transplacental passage of the bacterium from the mother to the neonate. In case of those who are considered as high-risk individuals, listeriosis may result in diseases as meningoencephalitis and/or septicemia.

The signs and symptoms of the associated diseases can include headache, fever, nausea, vomiting and signs of irritation of the meningeal. In the case of neonatal infections, they can manifest themselves as pneumonia, septicemia and meningitis. Detection of listeria can be accomplished in the laboratory by culturing blood, cerebrospinal fluid, amniotic fluid or other tissues suspected in containing the organism. Persons who are considered as high risk should avoid the consumption of certain foods that are likely to transmit listeriosis. Such foods include soft cheeses and other dairy based foods especially those made from raw or unpasteurized milk. In addition to avoiding deli meats, cold salads, foods that are improperly reheated and ready-to-eat foods may be contaminated too. The use of antimicrobials in the treatment has resulted in emergence of resistance against commonly used agents. Individuals who are considered immunocompromised should avoid contaminated foods with this pathogen, especially when drugs become ineffective in clearing an infection in a host that lost the appropriate potential of his/her immune system.

References

Alwan, N. 2005. Isolation, molecular characterization, and antimicrobial resistance of Brucella and Listeria Species in representative Lebanese foods. American University of Beirut. Lebanon.

Anon, JB. Update: multistate outbreak of Listeriosis-United States, 1998-1999. *MMWR Morb. Mortal Wkly. Rep.* 1999; 47:1117-1118.

Barbuddhe, S.B. and Chakraborty, T. Listeria as an enteroinvasive gastrointestinal pathogen. *Curr. Top. Microbiol. Immunol.* 2009; 337: 173-195.

Bortolussi, R. Listeriosis: a primer. *CMAJ.* 2008; 179 (8):795-797.

Bubert, A., Hein, I., Rauch, M., Lehner, A., Yoon, B., Goebel, W. and Wagner, M. Detection and differentiation of Listeria spp. by a single reaction based on multiplex PCR. *Appl. Environ. Microbiol.* 1999; 65(10): 4688-4692.

CDC. National Enteric Disease Surveillance: Listeria Annual Summary. 2009. Available at http://www.cdc.gov/nationalsurveillance/listeria_surveillance.html.

CDC. Outbreak Highlights, December 8, 2011. Available at: http://www.cdc.gov/listeria/outbreaks/cantaloupes-jensen-farms/index.html.

Chan, Y.C., Ho, K.H., Tambyah, P.A., Lee, K.H. and Ong, B.L. *Listeria* meningoencephalitis: Two cases and a review of the literature. *Ann. Acad. Med. Singapore.*2001; 30: 659-663.

Cocolin, L., Rantsiou, K., Iacumin, L., Cantoni, C. and Comi, G. Direct identification in food samples of Listeria spp. and *Listeria monocytogenes* by molecular methods. *Appl. Environ. Microbiol.* 2002; 68(12):6273-6282.

Denny, J. and McLauchlin, J. Human *Listeria monocytogenes* Infections in Europe – an opportunity for improved European surveillance. *Euro Surveill.*2008; 13(13):pii: 8082.

Dortet, L., Mostowy, S. and Cossart, P. Listeria and autophagy escape, Involvement of InlK, an internalin-like protein. *Autophagy.*2012; 8(1):132-134.

Dortet, L., Mostowy, S., Louaka, A.S., Gouin, E., Nahori, M.A., Wiemer, E., Dussurget, O. and Cossart, P. Recruitment of the Major Vault Protein by InlK: A *Listeria monocytogenes* Strategy to Avoid Autophagy. *PLoS Path.* 2011; 7(8):e1002168.

Edward, J., Wingand Stephen, H. Gregory. *Listeria monocytogenes*: Clinical and Experimental Update. *J. of. Infect. Dis.* 2002; 185(1): 18-24.

Facinelli, B., Roberts, M., Giovanetti, E., Casolari, C., Fabio, U. and Varaldo, P. Genetic basis of tetracycline resistance in food-borne isolates of *Listeria innocua.Appl. Environ. Microbiol.*1993; 59(2): 614-616.

Faleiro, M., Andrew, P. and Power, D. Stress response of *Listeria monocytogenes* isolated from cheese and other foods. *Inter. J. of Food Microbiol.* 2003; 84: 207-216.

Farber, J.M. and Peterkin, P.I. *Listeria monocytogenes*, a food-borne pathogen. *Microbiol. Rev.* 1991;55(3): 476-531.

Farber, J.M., Sanders, J.W. and Malcolm, S.A.The presence of *Listeria* spp. in raw milk in Ontario.*Can. J. Microbiol.*1988;34: 95.

Furyk, J. S., Swann, O. and Molyneux, E. Systematic review: neonatal meningitis in the developing world. *Tropical Med .Int. Health.*2011; 16(6): 672-679.

Gaulin C, Ramsay D. andBekal S.Widespread listeriosis outbreak attributable to pasteurized cheese, which led to extensive cross-contamination affecting cheese retailers, Quebec, Canada, 2008. *J. Food Prot.*2012; 75(1):71-78.

Gilot, P. and Content, J. Specific identification of *Listeria welshimeri*and *Listeria monocytogenes*by PCR assays targeting a gene encoding a fibronectin-binding protein. *J. Clin. Microbiol.*2002;40(2): 698-703.

Graves, L., Hunter, S., Ong, A., Scoonmaker-Bopp, D., Hise, K., Korstein, L.,DeWitt, W., Hayes, P., Dunne, E., Mead, P. and Swaminatham, B. Microbiological aspects of the investigation that traced the 1998 outbreak of Listeriosis in the United States to contaminated hotdogs and establishment of molecular subtyping-based surveillance for *Listeria monocytogenes*in the PulseNet network. *J. Clin. Microbiol.*2005; 43(5): 2350-2355.

Harakeh, S., Saleh, I., Zouhairi, O., Baydoun, E., Barbour, E. and Alwan, N. Antimicrobial resistance of *Listeria monocytogenes* isolated from dairy-based food products. *Sc. of Total Environ.* 2009; 407: 4022-4027.

Hassan, L., Mohammed, H. and McDonough, P.Farm-management and milking practices associated with the presence of *Listeria monocytogenes*in New York state dairy herds. *Preventive Vet. Med.* 2001; 51: 65-73.

Holko, I., Urbanov, J., Kantikova, M., Pastorova, L. and Kme, V.PCRdetection of *Listeria monocytogenes* in milk and milk products anddiffertiation of suspect isolates.*Acta.Vet. BRNO.* 2002; 71: 125-131.

IFST.1996. Food safety and cheese. Available at: http://www.ifst.org/hottopls.html.

Johns Hopkins medicine. 2012. Available at:www.hopkinsguide.com.

Jones, D. Food-borne Listeriosis. *The Lancet.*1990; 336(4):1171.

Kells, J. and Gilmour, A. Incidence of *Listeria monocytogenes* in two milk processing environments and assessment of *Listeria monocytogenes* blood agar for isolation. *Int. J. Food Microbiol.*2004; 91:167– 174.

Lamont, R.F., Sobel, J., Mazaki-Tovi, S., Kusanovic, J.P., Vaisbuch, E., Kim, S.K., Uldbjerg, N. andRomero, R. Listeriosis in human pregnancy: a systematic review. *J. Perinat. Med.* 2011; 39(3): 227-236.

Liu, D., Ainsworth, A., Austin, F. and Lawrence, M.Identification of *Listeria innocua*by PCR targeting a putative transcriptional regulator gene. *FEMS Microbiol. Lett.*2003; 223: 205-210.

Low, JC and Donache, W. A review of *Listeria monocytogenes*and Listeriosis. *The Vetr. J.* 1997; 153: 9-29.

Lungu, B., O'Bryan, C.A., Muthaiyan, A., Milillo, S.R., Johnson, M.G., Crandall, P.G. andRicke, S.C.*Listeria monocytogenes*: antibiotic resistance in food production. *Foodborne Pathog. Dis.*2011; 8(5):569-578.

Makino, S., Kawamoto, K., Takeshi, K., Okada, Y., Yamasaki, M., Yamamoto, S and Igimi, S. An outbreak of food-borne Listeriosis due to cheese in Japan, during 2001. *Inter. J. of Food Microbiol.* 2005; 104(2):189-96.

McLauchlin, J., Mitchell, R., Smerdon, W. and Jewell, K. *Listeria monocytogenes*and Listeriosis: a review of hazard characterization for use in microbiological risk assessment of foods. *Int. J. of Food Microbiol.* 2004;92:15-33.

Mead, P.S., Slutsker, L., Dietz , V., McCaig, LF., Bresee, J.S., Shapiro et al. Food-related illness and death in the United States. *Emerg. Infect. Dis.* 1999; 5607-5625.

Munoz, P., Rojas, L., Bunsow, E., Saez, E., Sanchez-Cambronero, L., Alcala, L., Rodriguez-Creixems ,M. andBouza, E. Listeriosis: An emerging public health problem especially among the elderly. *J. Infect.* 2012; 64(1):19-33.

Murray, D., Webb., R. and Swann, M. A disease of rabbits characterised by alarge mononuclear leukocytes, caused by a hitherto undescribed Bacillus Bacterium monocytogenes (n.sp.). *J. Pathol. Bacteriol.* 1926; 29: 407– 439.

Najjar, M. 2004. Development of a Hazard Analysis Critical Control Points (HACCP) plan for Halawet El Jibn (a Lebanese cheese derived pastry).American University of Beirut, Lebanon.

Olsen, S., Patrick, M. and Hunter, S.Multistate outbreak of *Listeria monocytogenes*infection linked to delicatessen turkey meat. *Clin. Infect. Dis.* 2005; 40(7): 962-967.

Pearson, L.J. and Marth, E.H. *Listeria monocytogenes* - threat to a safe food supply: A review. *J. of Dairy Sc.* 1990; 73(4): 912-928.

Rebagliati V., Philippi R., Rossi M., Troncoso A. Prevention of foodborne listeriosis. *Indian J. Pathol. Microbiol.*2009; 52:145-149.

Rocourt, J., BenEmbarek, P., Toyofuku, H. and Schlundt, J. Quantitative risk assessment of *Listeria monocytogenes*in ready-to-eat foods: the FAO/WHO approach. *FEMS Immunology and Medical Microbiol.*2003; 35: 263-267.

Rudol, M and Scherer, S.High incidence of *Listeria monocytogenes* in European red smear cheese. *Int J. Food Microbiol.* 2001; 63(1-2): 91-98.

Seeliger, H.P.R. and Finger, H. Listeriosis. The W.B. Saunders Co. *Philadelphia.*1976; 333-365.

Singh, A., Singh, R.K., Bhunia, A.K. and Singh, N.Efficacy of plant essential oils as antimicrobial agents against *Listeria monocytogenes* in hotdogs. *Lebensum-Wiss.U.-Technol.* 2003; 36:787-794.

Solano-Lopez, C. and Hernandez-Sanchez, H.Behavior of *Listeria monocytogenes* during the manufacture and ripening of Manchego Chihuahua Mexican cheeses. *Int. J. of Food Microbiol.*2000; 62: 149-153.

Stavru, F., Archambaud, C.andCossart, P.Cell biology and immunology of *Listeria monocytogenes* infections: novel insights. *Immunol. Rev.* 2011; 240(1): 160-184.

Stepanovic, S., Lazarevic, G.,Jesic, M. and Kos, R. Meropenem therapy failure in *Listeria monocytogenes* infection. *Europ. J. Clin. Microbiol. Infect. Dis.* 2004; 23(6):484-486.

Swaminathan B. andGerner-Smidt P.The epidemiology of human listeriosis. *Microbes Infect.* 2007; 9(10):1236-1243.

Temple, M.E. and Nahata, M.C. Treatment of listeriosis. *Ann   Pharmacother.*2000; 34(5):656-661.

Todar, K. 2003. *Listeria monocytogenes* and Listeriosis.Todar's Online Textbook of Bacteriology. Available at: http://www.Textbookofbacteriology.Net.

Troxler, R., Von Graevenitz, A., Funke, G., Wiedemann, B. and Stock, I. Natural antibiotic susceptibility of Listeria species: *L. grayi, L. innocua, L. ivanovii, L. monocytogenes, L. seeligeri*and *L. welshimeri* strains. *Clin. Microbiol. Infect.* 2000; 6(10): 525-535.

Vela, A., Fernandez-GarayzaBal, J., Latre, M, Rodriguez, A. Dominguez, L. and Moreno, M. Antimicrobial   susceptibility   of   *Listeria   monocytogenes*   isolatedfrom meningoencephalitis in sheep. *Inter. J. of Antimicrob.* Agents. 2001; 17: 215-220.

Volokhov, D., Rasooly, A., Chumakov, K. and Chizhikov, V. Identification of *Listeria* species by microarray-based assay. *J. Clini. Microbiol.*2002; 40(12): 4720-4728.

Wagner, M. and Allerberger, F. Characterization of *Listeria monocytogenes*recovered from 41 cases of sporadic listeriosis in Austria by serotyping and pulsed filed gel electrophoresis. *FEMS Immun. Med. Microbiol.* 2003;35: 227-234.

White, D., Zhao, S., Simjee, S., Wagner, D. and Mcdermott, P. Antimicrobial resistance of food-borne pathogens. *Microbes Infect.* 2002;4: 405-412.

In: Listeria Infections
Editors: A. Romano and C. F. Giordano

ISBN: 978-1-62081-639-4
© 2012 Nova Science Publishers, Inc.

Chapter IX

Listeria in Wildlife of Russia

I. Yegorova[1], Ju. Selyaninov[1], and V. Fertickov[2]

[1]National Research Institute for Veterinary Virology and
Microbiology of Russia (NRIVVaMR),
Russian Academy of Agricultural Science (RAAS), Pokrov,
Vladimir region, Russia
[2]Nationl Park "Zavidovo", Tver region, Russia

Abstract

Based on long-term monitoring studies carried out among wild ungulates and aquatic organisms living in woodland and hunting areas and freshwater basins of Russia, we determined a carrier state for both pathogenic and nonpathogenic Listeria species of sika deer, red deer, wild boar, as well as herbivorous and carnivorous fish species. Among the eight currently known listeria species, only two ones, namely Listeria innocua and Listeria monocytogenes have been found in hot- and cold-blooded representatives of the fauna, with Listeria innocua being most often isolated from the samples tested. The prevalence rates among aquatic organisms were 0.8% for L. monocytogenes and 5.2% for L. innocua, while in wild cloven-hoofed species the rates were 2.2 to 12% and 1.5 to 29%, respectively. For wild cloven-hoofed animals, listeria in most cases were found in feces, and only in two cases the agent was found in brain and lymph node of a hunted sika deer, and in the liver of a died wild boar. The carriage state levels among cloven-hoofed species significantly depended on the forms of economic activities and compliance with sanitation requirements. Among fish, the carrier state for listeria was determined in both herbivorous and carnivorous fish species. L. monocytogenes was mainly found in bream, carp, white bream and perch, while L. innocua in bream, pike, white bream, rudd, crucian carp and perch. Listeria of both pathogenic and nonpathogenic species were most frequently found in fish skin and gill tissues.

The carried out investigations also indicated that the soil in feeding grounds and rotting plant residues are natural reservoirs for listeria, with the immigration of juvenile fish not checked for listeria carrier state and carcasses of drowned listeria-carrying wildlife being another source of listeria introduction into aquatic fauna of freshwater basins, beside the known ones.

In order to identify phylogenetic relationships among the identified isolates, a pulse-electrophoresis of a restricted chromosomal DNA (REA-PFGE) was carried out. The results of the investigations into genetic variability among the isolates collected from wild cloven-hoofed animals using REA-PFGE revealed a variety of pulse electrotypes, suggesting multiple sources of infection. In freshwater fish populations a circulation of three L. monocytogenes clonal variants was found, with the pulse-electrotype isolates as found in different fish species, caught in the waters of the same river, having 100% coincidence. In addition, the pulse electrotype of a perch isolate was identical to a restriction profile of an isolate from sika deer feces found in the same region.

Introduction

At present the Russian Federation contains eight administrative- territorial federal districts, the Central Federal District (CFD) being the largest of them, its total area is 652.8 km^2 and the population is 37,121,812 people. Within the territory of the Russian Central Federal District there are 8 national parks, 17 federal nature reserves and over 20 large water storage reservoirs. The RF CDF wildlife population structure is represented by more than 40 mammal species, primarily ungulates and fur-bearing animals, and also fowl. The most prevalent species among the wild ungulates are the European elk (*Alces alces L.*), the wild boar (*Sus scrofa L.*), the red deer (*Cervus elaphus L.*), the sika deer (*Cervus nippon Temm.*), the roe deer (*Capreolus capreolus L.*) and the Siberian deer (*Cervus elapus sibiricus S.*).

In the Russian Central Federal District the Ivankovskoye Water Storage Reservoir (or the Moscow Sea), which has commercial fishing, transport, energy and recreational destination, is located [N.E. Salnickov and L.M. Sappo, 2005]. The Ivankovskoye Water Storage Reservoir is inhabited by some 34 fish species of fish. A significant proportion of the fish catches here (i.e., 78.7 to 89.9%) falls on commercial species like the bream, the silver bream, the carp and the rudd. The percent of carnivorous species like the pike, the walleye or the perch is rather low, making only about 5% [V.I. Fertickov, 1998]. Fish and meat products from wild game animals are a part of the diet of the human population living in the Central Federal District of Russia, and taking into account that wild animals are a natural reservoir of *Listeria*, they create a threat of foodborne listeriosis in humans. The listeriosis occurrence among wild cloven-hoofed animals were at different times reported by Lemenes et al. (1983), L. Eriksen et al. (1988), D.O. Trainer, J.B. Hale (1964), M. Cranfield et al. (1985), M.T. Butt et al. (1991), and others. The data on listeria prevalence in Russian wildlife were not available, which necessitated carrying out the research works reported here.

Spread of Listeria in Cloven-Hoofed Wildlife Populations

To study the spread of Listeria, in the period of 2006 to 2009 we carried out monitoring for listeria in the wildlife of the Moscow, the Kaluga, the Tver and the Vladimir regions being most densely populated populations of wild cloven-hoofed species. Totally, some 845 samples of various objects were examined for listerial contamination and carriage (see Table 1).

Table 1. Geographical locations of samples collected in the period of 2006 to 2009

No	Sampling site (region and/or name of economic entity)	The material type	Number of samples collected
1.	Kaluga region	Environmental objects	285
		Biological materials	51
2.	Moscow and Tver regions	Environmental objects	382
		Biological materials	41
3.	Vladimir region	Environmental objects	86
		Biological materials	0

The research of wildlife feces showed that the wild artiodactyls inhabiting the areas of Moscow, the Tver, the Kaluga and the Vladimir regions are gastrointestinal carriers of two of the eight currently known listerial species, namely *Listeria monocytogenes* and *Listeria innocua,* the listerial carrier levels for wild artiodactyls in various areas apparently depending on the forms of anthropogenic activities and veterinary service development rates there. Thus, in the grounds of the Federal Reserve and the National Park located in the Moscow, the Tver and the Kaluga regions, where all the appropriate preventive measures are taken, listeria carrier rates were 5.5 and 8.7% for the sika deer, 6.6 and 7.8% for the wild boar, and 0 and 6.0% for the Siberian deer, respectively. For the wildlife species inhabiting the grounds of the Vladimir region, where the opportunities for taking full-scale veterinary and sanitary and hunting arrangement measures are rather poor, the above indices were 34.5 and 24.0%, respectively.

The percentage indices of *L. monocytogenes* carriers among wild cloven-hoofed animals ranged from 1.7% to 12% of the population, while for *L. innocua* the figures were 1.1 to 29%, respectively. In our opinion, identification of listerial carriers among wild cloven-hoofed animals within all the year seasons suggests that some part of their population represents chronic gastrointestinal listeria carriers. These data correlate with the opinion of Dr. J.G. Chernukha (1988) that zoonoses in wildlife generally proceed chronically, promoting the pathogen preservation in the Nature for indefinitely long periods.

To identify the natural reservoirs of listeria, the samples of soil from feeding grounds, decaying plant residues, and feeds (like silage and/or forage mixtures) contaminated with rodent feces were additionally analyzed. The soil on the feeding grounds and the feeds contaminated by rodent feces were found to be the major natural reservoirs and sources of listeria intake into the cloven-hoofed wildlife organism (see Table 2).

It should be noted that some undestroyed remnants of the previous year's feeds (e.g., rotting hay or haylage) which are usually stockpiled at the edge of feeding grounds, serve as a man-made reservoir of listeria in the Nature. Thus, for the 13 samples of decaying plant residues examined, listeria were found in three of them, including one case with *L. monocytogenes.*

Of all the biological/pathological materials sampled from wild cloven-hoofed animals, only in three of them *Listeria* cultures were isolated. In one case a *L. monocytogenes* culture was isolated from lung and liver of a dead boar that had lived in the National Park "Zavidovo." A single culture of *L. innocua* was isolated from the stomach contents of a drowned sika deer. In addition, a culture of listeria which takes an intermediate position between *L. monocytogenes* and *L. innocua*, was isolated from the brain of a sika deer found in the Kaluga region hunting grounds.

Table 2. Results of *Listeria monocytogenes* and *Listeria innocua* isolation in the samples of environmental objects collected in the period from 2006 to 2009

Sampling region	Types of the objects examined	Amounts of isolated *L. monocytogenes* cultures	Amounts of isolated *L. innocua* cultures	% of the total amount of samples
Kaluga region	Ground	1	7	25.8
	Plant residues and feeds	3	0	42.8
Moscow and Tver regions	Ground	1	17	19.6
	Plant residues and feeds	1	2	33.3
Vladimir region	Ground	0	2	50

Prevalence of *Listeria* in the Waters of the Ivankovskoye Storage Reservoir

Some 19 fish species inhabiting the waters of the reservoir were examined for listeria carriage state. The major part of the investigated fish accounts for the commercial species such as the bream (33.3%), the river perch (15.9%), the rudd (15.2%), the crucian carp (10.2%) and the white bream (7.4%). Totally, as many as 52 listerial cultures were isolated from fish within the entire observation period, 7 of them belonging to the species *L. monocytogenes*, and 45 to *L. innocua*. The frequency of *Listeria* isolation among the total amounts of samples analyzed was 6.0%, of which the ones for *L. monocytogenes* covered 0.8% of the total amount of cases.

Listeria of the two above species were isolated both from carnivorous and herbivorous fish, as well as from some fish species of a mixed nutrition type. No any dependence of *Listeria* isolation frequencies on fish species or age was determined. The listeria were isolated from fish of any age group ranging from the age of 1 to 9 years (that is the maximal age of the fish studied).

L. monocytogenes cultures were mainly isolated from fish species like the bream, the crucian carp, the white bream and the perch, while *L. innocua* from the bream, the pike, the white bream, the rudd, the crucian carp, and the perch.

The highest numbers of isolates (namely, 30 cultures) belonging to both pathogenic and nonpathogenic *Listeria* species were isolated from fish caught in the waters of the river, on the banks of which a poultry farm and sewage treatment works are located. The *Listeria* cultures of both pathogenic and non-pathogenic species were most often isolated from fish skin (50% of cases for *L. monocytogenes* and 47.0% for *L. innocua*), then from gill filaments (37.0 and 39%) and from bloodstream and intestinal organs (13.0 and 14.5%), respectively.

In 3 cases, *L. monocytogenes* were isolated from bloodstream organs (namely, liver and/or spleen), and in 2 cases, *L. innocua* from intestine.

From roe, milt or *Ligula intestinalis* homogenates no any pathogenic or non-pathogenic *Listeria* species were isolated. We failed to reveal any patterns or regularities in the seasonality of listerial carriage state in fish. Listeria carriers could be found in every season. However, we note that most carriers of pathogenic or nonpathogenic Listeria species were detected in fish caught in summer periods (40% of all the positive cases), which is probably due to the seasonal conditions being most optimal for *Listeria* reproduction and spread in that period.

In order to determine some additional sources of *Listeria* entry into the aquafauna and their carriers, the young fish to be settled into the waters of the storage reservoir were preliminarily examined. As a result of the investigation carried out, the "invaders" were found to be carriers of the non-pathogenic listerial species *L. innocua*. Some non-pathogenic listeria species were detected in 5 of the 6 young bighead samples and in 100% specimens of young carp (8 fish specimens).

We also collected and analyzed as many as 104 various samples including biological materials from wild migratory fowl, semi-aquatic mammals belonging to rodents (e.g., muskrat), mollusks (mussels and snails), arthropods (crayfish), river bottom sediments, aquatic vegetation, surface layers of river waters and carcasses of drowned sika deer. No any listeria were isolated from the samples of river bottom grounds, water plants represented by a range of different algae and emergent plant species, and nor in surface layers of river water, arthropods or molluscs, biological materials collected from wild migratory fowl or semi-aquatic mammals.

In the course of making the analyses of some pathological materials (like the crura of diaphragm, liver and/or spleen fragments or stomach contents) collected from 34 carcasses of drowned sika deer, listeria or their genetic materials were found in two episodes only. In one case, a PCR of 20% suspension prepared from the crura of diaphragm taken from the carcass of a drowned sika deer identified some specific fragments of *L. monocytogenes* genome (*hly*-gene), while in the subsequent bacteriological studies we failed to isolate the agent culture. In the second case a culture of *L. innocua* was isolated from of the stomach contents of a drowned sika deer carcass.

Biological Characteristics of *L. monocytogenes* Isolates Found in Wildlife

When investigating the principal characteristics of *L. monocytogenes* isolates, we determined that the populations of all the examined *Listeria* cultures were represented by rod-shaped and nonspore-forming cells. The cultural and morphological features of all the tested isolates corresponded to a typical representative of *L. monocytogenes*. Following the serological structure adopted in the Russian Federation, 33 of the 35 found *L. monocytogenes* isolates belonged to serological group I, and only two cultures to serogroup II. From their ability to produce oxidase, H2S, indole, catalase, to oxidize and ferment glucose, the absence of any citrate reduction on Simmons medium, the urea digestion on Christensen's agar, and the recovery of nitrates to nitrites, all the isolates examined did not vary.

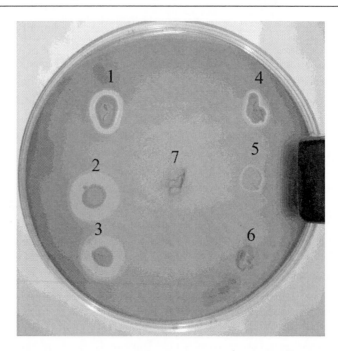

Figure. 1. A two-layer blood agar after 48-hour incubation at 37 °C of a number of strain cultures of the following Listeria species: 1 - L. monocytogenes No 766; 2 - L. monocytogenes No 9-72; 3 - L. monocytogenes No 9-127; 4 - L. monocytogenes No 634, 5 - L. seeligery; 6 - L. welshimeri; 7 - L. innocua.

The analysis of carbohydrates and polyatomic alcohols fermentation by the isolates also failed to reveal any significant differences among them, though a number of the isolates additionally fermented sucrose, sorbite, and galactose.

The potential of listerial pathogenic species to raise lysis of animal erythrocytes and to fermentation or some fractions of chicken egg yolk is known to be the principal feature which allows their differentiation from the non-pathogenic ones.

In the course of our investigations we examined the capability of the isolates tested to produce hemolysins applying a two-phase medium we had developed (RF patent for the invention No 2318022), which surpassed a single-layer medium for sensitivity and allowed studying the populations heterogeneity for this feature, making clonal analyses, etc. (see Figure 1).

The studies into hemolytic (*hly*) and phospholipatic (*plcC*) activities of the isolates showed that, except for the two cultures isolated from a spotted deer brain and from hay, all the *L. monocytogenes* cultures evoked β-type lysis of erythrocytes and digested phosphatidylcholine inositol. At the same time the amplification of PCR products conforming to the calculated *hly*-gene values was observed on the DNA templates of all the tested *L. monocytogenes* isolates, without any exception.

The pathogenicity of the cultures isolated was confirmed by a keratoconjunctival bioassay with guinea pigs. All the cultures (except for 2 isolates only) induced a purulent keratoconjunctivitis in guinea pigs on day 2 or 3 post the pathogen inoculation. The cultures isolated from a spotted deer brain and from silage were an exception, for they did not cause conjunctivitis in guinea pigs and/or death of white outbred mice when administered intraperitoneally to the latter ones at an amount of 10^9 cells.

Genetic Characterization of *L. monocytogenes* Isolates

In addition to their monomorphic phenotypic features, some similar clonal variations of *L. monocytogenes* should possess a genetic identity as well. Therefore, in the next stage of our work some genetic characteristics of the isolates were analyzed with REA PFGE method using restriction enzymes SmaI and ApaI.

On the whole, the obtained results of the cultures genotyping for the both restriction enzymes were completely identical. The degree of the genetic relationship was assessed through a Dice's similarity coefficient calculation (D_{sc}).

Some three *L. monocytogenes* clonal variations were determined to circulate within the fresh water fish population inhabiting the Ivankovskoye Water Storage Reservoir. The first clonal variation was represented by identical isolates found in the bream and the white bream, while the second one by identical isolates found in crucian carp yearlings, and the third clonal variation by isolates taken from 2-year-old perch. The first and the third clonal variations exhibited a high relationship degree ($D_{sc} = 0.09$, see Figure 2).

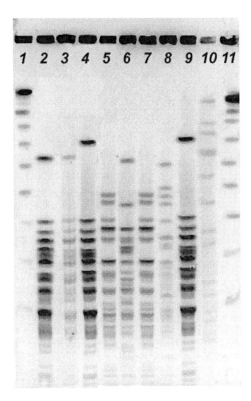

Figure 2. Pulsed-field separation electrophoregram for Sma I DNA fragments of L. monocytogenes isolates. Lanes: 1.11 – marker; 2 - perch (Tver region); 3 - spotted deer (Tver region); 4 – crucian carp (Tver region); 5 – white bream (Tver region); 6 - wild boar (Kaluga region); 7 - bream (Tver region); 8 – soils from feeding grounds (Kaluga region); 9 – crucian carp (Tver region); 10 - S. aureus.

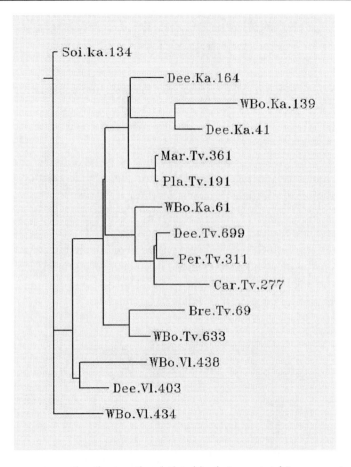

Figure 3. Dendrogram representing the genetic relationships between total L. monocytogenes isolates based on pulsed-field separation of Sma I DNA fragments. (Tv - Tver region; Ka - Kaluga region; Vl - Vladimir region; Soi – Soils from feeding grounds; Dee – Sika deer; Mar – Siberian deer; WBo - Wild boar; Car -crucian carp; Bre – white bream; Per - river perch; Pla - decaying plant residues).

In the course of analyzing the isolates as found in the cloven-hoofed wildlife, we identified a genetic diversity of the circulating variations. In general, the *L. monocytogenes* isolates as found in the wild cloven-hoofed animals inhabiting the same geographic area comprised some separate groups.

The analysis of phylogenetic relationships allowed to determine the identity (for the both of the above restriction enzymes) of the isolates from the feces of the sika deer inhabiting the Kaluga region hunting grounds, and the cultures isolated from plant residues and the feces of the Siberian deer sampled in the Tver region. In our view, the detection of the genetically identical isolates found in decaying plant residues in 2008 and in the Siberian deer feces in 2009 in the same hunting ground is of interest. This suggests a long-term circulation of the same *L. monocytogenes* clonal variation in wildlife. In addition, the analysis of accounting records on wildlife movements in the period of 1997-1999 there has shown that there was an intensive exchange of animals between the hunting grounds then. For example, as many as 158 wild boars taken from the Kaluga region were released into the areas of the Tver region, while in the Kaluga region some 192 sika deer animals having taken from the Tver region were released.

We also found genetic similarity high levels (D_{sc} = 0.05 to 0.14) between the isolates found in aquatic organisms (namely, perch and carp) and some wild cloven-hoofed animals (like deer and wild boar) inhabiting the Tver region, indicating that there is an exchange of *L. monocytogenes* cultures between cold- and warm-blooded animals.

Phylogenetic relationships of *L. monocytogenes* isolates are shown in Figure 3.

Conclusion

On the basis of the long-term monitoring studies we have carried out, a wide prevalence of both pathogenic and nonpathogenic *Listeria* species among the wildlife of the Central Federal District of Russia was determined. A number of cloven-hoofed wildlife populations were shown to be *L. monocytogenes* gastrointestinal chronic carriers and consequently they promote the listeriosis natural foci maintenance. Freshwater aquatic organisms are also natural biological reservoirs of *Listeria* and may serve as indicators of anthropogenic pollution of water bodies. We also determined that the *Listeria* prevalence over aquatic ecosystems was influenced by human economic activities, for example, the release of juvenile fish infected.

The study of some biological and, in particular, genetic features of the obtained isolates revealed the circulation of the same clonal variations both among warm- and cold-blooded wildlife suggesting there is an exchange of isolates between them.

Based on the data obtained, we developed some adequate measures to prevent listeriosis in cloven-hoofed wildlife species, which include carrying out monitoring studies at least 2 times a year, obligatory quarantine institution for animals to be acclimatized or reacclimatized together with their examination for listeria carriage state, feeds checking up for listerial contamination, carrying out deratization and disinsection procedures in feeds storage places, and/or sanitation of soils on feeding grounds using biocides produced from tertiary ammonium compounds and innocuous for animals.

References

D.O. Trainer and J.B. Hale (1964). Wildlife disease report from Wisconsin. *Bulletin of the Wildlife Disease Association*, 1, P.P. 4-5.

F. Lemenes, R. Glavits, E. Ivanics, G. Kovacs, and A. Vanyi (1983). Listeriosis in roedeer in Hungary. *Zentralblatt fur Veterinarmedicin*, 30, P.P.258-265.

Ju.G. Chernukha (1988). Natural focality of bacterial and protozoal infections. Abstracts of the All-Union Conf. "The problems of pathology and ecological relationships of warm-blooded wildlife and livestock diseases" (in Russian), P.P. 11-12.

L. Eriksen, H.E. Larsen, T. Christiansen T., M.M. Jensen, and B. Eriksen B. (1988). An outbreak of meningo-encephalitis in fallow deer caused by Listeria monocytogenes. *Veterinary Record*, 122, P.P. 274-276.

M. Cranfield, M.A. Eckhaus, B.A. Valentine, and J.D. Strandberg (1985). Listeriosis in Angolan giraffes. *Journal of the American Veterinary Medical Association*, 187, P.P. 1238 - 1240.

M.T. Butt, A. Weldon, D. Step, A. DeLahunta, C.R. Huxtable (1991). Encephalitic listeriosis in two adult llamas (*Lama glama*): Clinical presentations, lesions and immunofluorescence of Listeria monocytogenes in brain stem lesions. *Cornell Veterinarian*, 81, P.P. 251-258.

N.E. Salnickov (2005). Some features of hydrochemical regime formation and water quality in the Ivankovskoye water storage reservoir in 1996-2000. *Gidrobiologicheskiy jurnal.* 41, 2, P.P. 73-84.

V.I. Fertickov. The National Park Zavidovo / edited by V.I. Fertickov. - Moscow: Triada-X, 1998.

Index

C

commercial, 16, 17, 19, 20, 21, 22, 23, 24, 30, 34, 77, 124, 135, 144, 168, 170
communication, 124, 125
community(ies), 142, 150, 152, 160
comparative analysis, 70
complement, 72, 73, 119
complexity, 11
compliance, vii, xi, 1, 33, 142, 167
composition, 14, 15, 18, 20, 21, 29, 31, 32, 33, 34, 82, 102, 104, 110
compost, 109
compounds, 7, 30, 31, 79, 82, 83, 97, 103, 104, 175
computer, 46
concordance, 38, 47, 49
condensation, 133
conflict, 152
conflict of interest, 152
conjunctivitis, 117, 161, 172
consensus, 112
conservation, 63, 70
consumer education, 135
consumers, ix, 27, 69, 100, 119, 122, 133, 151
consumption, viii, ix, x, 3, 14, 36, 37, 39, 40, 41, 42, 43, 59, 61, 62, 67, 100, 115, 119, 122, 130, 131, 132, 134, 150, 152, 154, 157, 158, 159, 163
containers, 6, 18, 20, 21, 82, 104
contaminant, 11, 12, 13, 16, 17, 20, 21, 23, 24, 27
contaminated food, viii, 36, 47, 67, 71, 122, 150, 151, 163
contamination, 3, 10, 11, 15, 17, 20, 21, 24, 25, 26, 27, 30, 32, 33, 39, 50, 56, 68, 69, 79, 81, 86, 87, 101, 102, 109, 111, 112, 114, 121, 122, 131, 132, 133, 134, 135, 136, 137, 139, 140, 150, 157, 158, 159, 164, 168, 175
control measures, 27, 101, 109
controversial, 82
cooking, 17, 68, 79, 133, 134
cooling, 21, 100
correlation, 46, 47, 48
correlations, 55
corticosteroid therapy, 147, 148
cost, 36, 58
Costa Rica, 69
cough, 160
covering, 142
crop, 121
crystals, 9
culture, 9, 10, 14, 16, 17, 20, 22, 27, 30, 33, 75, 78, 88, 91, 112, 162, 169, 171
culture media, 91
culture medium, 112
cycles, 102
cytometry, 107

cytoplasm, xi, 73, 118, 156, 161
cytosine, 39
cytoskeleton, 72, 112, 113
Czech Republic, 37

D

dairy industry, 27
damages, 94
database, 37
death rate, 16
deaths, x, 36, 37, 39, 40, 41, 42, 69, 130, 147, 148, 151, 155, 157, 160
decomposition, 80
decontamination, 112
deficiencies, 119
degradation, 73, 85, 118
denaturation, 79
Denmark, 36, 128, 150
Department of Agriculture, 140
depth, 109
detectable, 11
detection, 15, 29, 33, 37, 38, 40, 43, 44, 46, 47, 51, 54, 57, 62, 64, 69, 70, 75, 76, 77, 78, 81, 84, 92, 93, 94, 97, 122, 123, 135, 144, 151, 153, 174
developed countries, 69, 142, 157
developing countries, 160
diabetes, 68, 100, 117, 143, 147, 148, 149
dialysis, 100
diaphragm, 171
diarrhea, 116, 161
diet, 168
digestion, 39, 54, 171
directives, 69
discomfort, 116
discrimination, 47, 50, 63, 151
disease rate, 143
diseases, ix, xi, 28, 38, 59, 122, 129, 140, 142, 147, 148, 153, 156, 157, 162, 175
disinfection, 101
distribution, 16, 18, 21, 38, 43, 57, 60, 123, 148, 149, 150, 154, 157, 158
divergence, 48
diversification, 53, 62
diversity, 54, 55, 62
DNA, viii, xi, 35, 39, 44, 45, 46, 48, 50, 61, 63, 78, 125, 135, 140, 168, 172, 173, 174
DNA polymerase, 50
doctors, 158
dogs, 36, 40, 58, 69, 158
draft, 52, 70, 110
drainage, 8
drugs, 163

T

U